Robert Harris

Robert Harris

(1849 - 1919)

by Moncrieff Williamson
Director,
Confederation Art Gallery and Museum

An exhibition circulated by
the Extension Services of
The National Gallery of Canada,
Ottawa, 1973–1974

par Moncrieff Williamson
directeur de la
Confederation Art Gallery and Museum

Une exposition itinérante organisée par les
Services extérieurs de la
Galerie nationale du Canada
Ottawa, 1973–1974

©The National Gallery of Canada
for the Corporation of the National Museums of
Canada, Ottawa, 1973

ISBN 0-88884-245-7

PRINTED IN CANADA

©Galerie nationale du Canada
pour la Corporation des musées nationaux du Canada
Ottawa, 1973

ISBN 0-88884-245-7

IMPRIMÉ AU CANADA

Preface

Préface

To celebrate the entry of Prince Edward Island into Confederation one hundred years ago nothing could be more appropriate than an exhibition by the Islander painter who stamped a solemn image of the Fathers of Confederation on the Canadian conscience for all time. Although the final canvas was lost in the fire which destroyed the Parliament Buildings in 1916, we have grown up with those serious faces in that formal arrangement recorded in photographs, preliminary drawings, and postage stamps. Harris painted the Quebec Conference of 1864 on that occasion; but that conference led into Confederation in 1867 and finally to the entry of Prince Edward Island in 1873.

Robert Harris was not born in Prince Edward Island but was, nevertheless, very much an Islander – as Moncrieff Williamson has shown in his biography, *Robert Harris, 1849–1919: An Unconventional Biography*. The Island always drew him back – even from such places with seductive preachers (for he was a gourmet of sermons) as London, Boston, and Montreal. Happily his widow bequeathed the works she inherited from her husband to Charlottetown, so that in the capital of the Island there are drawings, oil sketches, photographs, and documents that are essential to study the work of this artist who was President of the Royal Canadian Academy from 1893 to 1906.

Prince Edward Island had another piece of good fortune which this exhibition shares. A Scot, Moncrieff Williamson, became the director of the Confederation Art Gallery and Museum in 1964 and immediately appreciated the possibilities of the material Harris's widow had bequeathed. He advertised for information about other works by Harris. The first stage in his study of this important nineteenth-century Canadian painter's work was the biography which McClelland and Stewart published in 1970. The second stage is this exhibition and catalogue which concentrate upon Harris as portrait-painter. The National Gallery of Canada feels very fortunate that it has been able to collaborate with the Confederation Art Gallery and Museum and its Director on this project which makes an important contribution to the study of Canadian

Pour commémorer le centenaire de l'entrée de l'Île-du-Prince-Édouard dans la Confédération canadienne, rien ne semble aussi approprié qu'une exposition réunissant les œuvres du peintre insulaire qui a empreint à jamais dans la conscience nationale l'image solennelle des pères de la Confédération. Bien que l'œuvre originale, une huile sur toile, ait été détruite au cours de l'incendie des édifices du parlement, à Ottawa en 1916, nous avons tous, un jour ou l'autre, vu des photographies, des dessins préliminaires ou des timbres-poste représentant ces personnages au visage grave, réunis en assemblée. Harris a également représenté la conférence de Québec de 1864, conférence qui entraîna, en 1867, la fondation de la Confédération, à laquelle l'Île-du-Prince-Édouard devait enfin adhérer en 1873.

Bien que Robert Harris ne fût pas originaire de l'Île-du-Prince-Édouard, il devint, par la suite, parfaitement intégré aux «gens de l'Île», comme l'a bien montré Moncrieff Williamson dans son livre *Robert Harris, 1849–1919. An Unconventional Biography*. Très attaché à l'Île-du-Prince-Édouard, il y revenait toujours, même (car il était friand de sermons) d'endroits riches en brillants prédicateurs tels que Londres, Boston et Montréal. Par bonheur, sa veuve a légué à Charlottetown les œuvres qu'il lui avait laissées; ainsi, dans la capitale de l'Île, se trouvent actuellement des dessins, des esquisses à l'huile, des photographies et d'autres documents essentiels à l'étude de l'œuvre de cet artiste qui fut président de l'Académie royale des arts du Canada de 1893 à 1896.

La chance a souri une seconde fois à l'Île-du-Prince-Édouard (et nous avons tout lieu de nous en réjouir) lorsqu'un Écossais, Moncrieff Williamson, devint directeur de la Confederation Art Gallery and Museum en 1964. Il vit immédiatement les ressources de la documentation laissée par la veuve de Harris et, par voie d'annonce, se mit en quête d'autres œuvres de Harris. Une biographie, publiée par McClelland and Stewart en 1970, couronna la première étape de ses travaux sur ce grand peintre canadien du XIXe siècle. La présente exposition et son catalogue, consacrés à Harris en tant que portraitiste, parachèvent la deuxième. La Galerie nationale du Canada se félicite d'avoir pu collaborer avec la Confedera-

art and so appropriately celebrates the entrance of Prince Edward Island into Confederation.

Jean Sutherland Boggs
Director,
The National Gallery of Canada

tion Art Gallery and Museum et son directeur à cette réalisation qui constitue un apport important à l'étude de l'art canadien et commémore si bien l'entrée de l'Île-du-Prince-Édouard dans la Confédération.

La directrice de la Galerie nationale du Canada
Jean Sutherland Boggs

Lenders

Agnes Etherington Art Centre, Queen's University at Kingston

The Art Gallery of Hamilton

Art Gallery of Ontario

Assemblée nationale du Québec

The Bank of Nova Scotia

Barristers' Society of New Brunswick, Fredericton

Beaverbrook Art Gallery, Fredericton

Bishop's University, Lennoxville

Canada, Department of Public Works, Ottawa

The Church of St. James the Apostle, Montreal

The Church Society, Diocese of Quebec

Confederation Art Gallery and Museum, Charlottetown

The Corporation of Trinity College, Toronto

The E.B. Eddy Company, Hull

Government House, Ottawa

McCord Museum, Montreal

McGill University, Montreal

The Montreal General Hospital

The Montreal Museum of Fine Arts

The Mount Royal Club, Montreal

The National Gallery of Canada, Ottawa

New Brunswick Museum, Saint John

O'Neill Collegiate and Vocational Institute, Ontario County Board of Education, Oshawa

The Presbyterian College, Montreal

Prince Street School, Charlottetown

Province of New Brunswick, Department of Supply and Services, Fredericton

Province of Ontario, Toronto

Royal Victoria Hospital, Montreal

Sun Life Assurance Company of Canada, Montreal

Prêteurs

Agnes Etherington Art Centre, Queen's University at Kingston

The Art Gallery of Hamilton

Art Gallery of Ontario, Toronto

Assemblée nationale du Québec, Québec

La banque de Nouvelle-Écosse, Halifax

Barristers' Society of New Brunswick, Fredericton

Beaverbrook Art Gallery, Fredericton

Bishop's University, Lennoxville (Québec)

The Church of St. James the Apostle, Montréal

The Church Society, Diocese of Quebec

Compagnie E.B. Eddy, Ottawa-Hull

Confederation Art Gallery and Museum, Charlottetown

The Corporation of Trinity College, Toronto

Galerie nationale du Canada, Ottawa

Hôpital général de Montréal

Hôpital Royal Victoria, Montréal

Ministère fédéral des travaux publics, Ottawa

The Mount Royal Club, Montréal

Musée des beaux-arts de Montréal

Musée McCord, Montréal

The New Brunswick Museum, Saint-Jean

O'Neill Collegiate and Vocational Institute, Ontario County Board of Education, Oshawa (Ontario)

The Presbyterian College, Montréal

Prince Street School, Charlottetown

Province d'Ontario, Toronto

Province du Nouveau-Brunswick, Ministère des approvisionnements et services, Fredericton

Résidence du gouverneur général, Ottawa

Sun Life du Canada, Compagnie d'assurance-vie, Montréal

Université McGill, Montréal

Mrs. H.R.C. Avison, Montreal

Mr. and Mrs. P. deJong, St. Catharines

Dr. T.G. Fyshe, Hamilton

Mrs. R.J. Currie Gardner, Toronto

Miss Mary Beth Harris, Charlottetown

Dr. Charlotte M. Horner, Coburg

Mr. J.M.M. Kirkland, Islington, Ontario

Katharine Hammond Krug, Waterloo

Lieutenant Colonel H.C.T. MacDougall, Montreal

Hugh McLennan, Vancouver

The Countess of Minto, London, England

David R. Morrice, Montreal

Mrs. Donald J. Oland, Halifax

Maurice Régnier, Outremont, Quebec

Mrs. H.Y. Russel, Pierrefonds, Quebec

Miss June M. Smith, Thetford Mines, Quebec

A.J.R. Stethem, Montreal

Norman Stretch, Long Creek, P.E.I.

The Reverend and Mrs. E.L. Tuck, Charlottetown

Canon Robert Critchlow Tuck, Summerside, P.E.I.

Mme H.R.C. Avison, Montréal

M. et Mme P. deJong, St. Catharines (Ontario)

Dr T.G. Fyshe, Hamilton (Ontario)

Mme R.J. Currie Gardner, Toronto

Mlle Mary Beth Harris, Charlottetown

Dr Charlotte M. Horner, Cobourg (Ontario)

M. J.M.M. Kirkland, Islington (Ontario)

Katharine Hammond Krug, Waterloo (Ontario)

Lieutenant-colonel H.C.T. MacDougall, Montréal

Hugh McLennan, Vancouver

La comtesse de Minto, O.B.E., Londres

David R. Morrice, Montréal

Mme Donald J. Oland, Halifax

Maurice Régnier, Outremont (Québec)

Mme H.Y. Russell, Pierrefonds (Québec)

Mlle June M. Smith, Thetford Mines (Québec)

A.J.R. Stethem, Montréal

Norman Stretch, Long Creek (Î.-P.-É.)

Le révérend et Mme E.L. Tuck, Charlottetown

Le chanoine Robert Critchlow Tuck, Summerside (Î.-P.-É.)

Acknowledgements

The cooperation and encouragement I received from all quarters in the search for portraits by Robert Harris, and biographical documentation about the subjects themselves, made the work of compiling this catalogue both absorbing and rewarding. Numerous persons were kind enough to offer to lend portraits from their own collections, but I had to exclude them because of the overriding factors of space and substantial costs in transportation.

To the various individuals and institutions who loaned works to this exhibition, I extend my personal thanks and appreciation. In addition, there are certain other individuals who were of particular help and I list their names as follows: The Reverend M. Awcock, Mrs. Frances K. Smith, Mr. H.P. Roddick, Mr. W.L. Tomkins, Miss Ruth Jackson, Miss Barbara Whitley, Mrs. R.L. Grout, Dr. E.H. Bensley, Mrs. Harriet Campbell, Colonel A.J.R. Stethem, Mr. William D. Post, Colonel H.C.T. MacDougall, Mr. A.O. Mackay, Mrs. H.Y. Russel, Dr. Hugh McLennan, Professor John Bland, Mr. Alison McKim, Mr. J.L. Harries, Mr. John C.L. Andreassen, Miss Sandra Guillaume, Mr. Claude Minotto of the Public Archives, and Mr. Stanley Triggs, Notman Archives.

A very special word of thanks and appreciation to Miss Diana St. B. Harrison, McGill University Fine Arts Committee; Mr. Nicholas DeJong, Provincial Archivist, Prince Edward Island; Mrs. Margaret Armitage, Head Librarian, Confederation Centre Library and Mrs. Eleanor Vass and other members of her staff.

To the staff of my own Gallery, to Miss Patricia Stunden who did much of the photography, and to my personal secretary and assistant, Mrs. Janet MacGregor, who has had the daily task of creating order out of confusion as the catalogue changed course.

And finally my thanks to Dr. Jean Sutherland Boggs who made this exhibition a reality, to Mrs. Alice Armstrong, Sherrill Moseley, and Peter Smith of the National Gallery, and to those several other individuals whose assistance is most readily acknowledged.　　　　M.W.

Remerciements

Mes recherches en vue de découvrir des portraits peints par Robert Harris et d'accumuler de la documentation sur la biographie de ses modèles, nécessaires à la rédaction de ce catalogue, furent certes astreignantes, mais également satisfaisantes, puisque tous m'ont accordé leur collaboration et leur encouragement. Plusieurs personnes m'ont aimablement offert de prêter des portraits provenant de leur collection personnelle, mais j'ai dû refuser en raison d'importants facteurs comme le manque d'espace et le coût élevé du transport.

Je tiens à remercier les particuliers et les institutions qui ont si gracieusement accepté de prêter des œuvres pour cette exposition. Je suis en outre reconnaissant envers les personnes suivantes pour l'aide particulière qu'elles m'ont apportée: le révérend M. Awcock, Mme Frances K. Smith, M. H.P. Roddick, M. W.L. Tomkins, Mlle Ruth Jackson, Mlle Barbara Whitley, Mme R.L. Grout, M. le docteur E.H. Bensley, Mme Harriet Campbell, M. le colonel A.J.R. Stethem, M. William D. Post, M. le lieutenant-colonel H.C.T. MacDougall, M. A.O. Mackay, Mme H.Y. Russel, M. le docteur Hugh McLennan, M. le professeur John Bland, M. Alison McKim, M. J.L. Harries, M. John C.L. Andreassen, Mlle Sandra Guillaume, M. Claude Minotto des Archives publiques et M. Stanley Triggs des archives Notman.

Je veux adresser des remerciements particuliers à Mlle Diana St. B. Harrison, du Comité des beaux-arts de l'université McGill, à M. Nicholas deJong, archiviste de la province de l'Île-du-Prince-Édouard, à Mme Margaret Armitage, bibliothécaire en chef de la Confederation Centre Library, ainsi qu'à Mme Eleanor Vass et aux autres membres de son personnel.

Mes remerciements vont également au personnel de ma galerie et à ma secrétaire, Mme Janet MacGregor, qui a dû quotidiennement rétablir l'ordre dans la composition changeante du catalogue.

J'exprime enfin ma reconnaissance à Mlle Jean Sutherland Boggs qui a rendu possible la tenue de cette exposition, à Mme Alice Armstrong, à Sherrill Moseley et à Peter Smith de la Galerie nationale du Canada, ainsi qu'aux diverses autres personnes qui m'ont accordé leur aimable collaboration.　　　　M.W.

Itinerary

Confederation Art Gallery and Museum
Charlottetown, Prince Edward Island

The National Gallery of Canada
Ottawa, Ontario

Sir George Williams University
Montreal, Quebec

Norman Mackenzie Art Gallery, University of
Saskatchewan
Regina, Saskatchewan

Winnipeg Art Gallery
Winnipeg, Manitoba

Edmonton Art Gallery
Edmonton, Alberta

Itinéraire

Confederation Art Gallery and Museum
Charlottetown (Île-du-Prince-Édouard)

Galerie nationale du Canada
Ottawa (Ontario)

Université Sir George Williams
Montréal (Québec)

Norman Mackenzie Art Gallery, University
of Saskatchewan
Regina (Saskatchewan)

Winnipeg Art Gallery
Winnipeg (Manitoba)

Edmonton Art Gallery
Edmonton (Alberta)

Table of Contents

Table des matières

Robert Harris

The Making of a Portrait-Painter

"There is no freakish art in the Academy, no Cubists, no Futurists, and what Impressionists we have are not fanatic; we have no Cazennes [sic], nor Leon [sic] Dabos; all our art is sane, healthy, worthy, and inspiring. . . ."
– *R.F. Fleming*[1]

In this exhibition of the portraits of Robert Harris, despite Fleming's remark, we meet the unfamiliar – both in appearance and social attitude. These people not only looked different from us but moved in a closely-knit society which has not survived two world wars intact. They represent ideals and traditions which, if we are to believe the scoffers, are no longer relevant to the 1970s. In a few instances they represent a Canada of over a hundred years ago; in the majority of portraits, however, the Canadian background is the period 1880–1916, two years before the Armistice at the end of the Great War, "the war to end wars," and three years before Robert Harris died, on 27 February 1919.

Material opulence, a jealousy of power, the driving ambition of humble origin; hard work, thrift, the strength derived from Faith in the Almighty (both Deity and Dollar, in that order) – these shine through those eyes that Harris painted with such skill. Pride, snobbery, humility, and courage (especially courage) – a list to which we could add a full spectrum of moral frailties, yet also moral wisdom. However varied our reactions to those eyes watching us from the Gallery walls, we may be united and positive in one response: these sitters contributed mightily to Canada's emergence as an independent Dominion in a now-defunct, but at one time brilliantly-adventurous Empire.

There exists in several of these canvases the aura of an inner conviction of the rightness and fitness of "place" that makes arrival there so eminently proper to the sitter, so definitely predestined. A purple cloud of self-righteousness, of sins forgiven oneself, seems at times to loom above the group as a whole – with fortunate and delightful exceptions. In this respect society has not

---

1. Fleming, "Royal Canadian Academy of Art," p. 209.

Robert Harris

La naissance d'un portraitiste

«Notre académie fait peu de place à la fantaisie: pas de cubisme, pas de futurisme, et nos impressionnistes eux-mêmes ne sont pas fanatiques; nous ne comptons pas de Cazennes [sic], ni de Leon [sic] Dabos; tout notre art est sensé, sain, valable et inspirant . . .»
R.F. Fleming[1]

Dans cette exposition de portraits de Robert Harris, contrairement à cette citation de Fleming, l'insolite se manifeste et ceci aussi bien dans les modèles que dans les attitudes sociales. Non seulement ces personnes se vêtaient-elles différemment de nous, mais encore évoluaient-elles dans une société qui n'est certainement pas sortie indemne de deux guerres mondiales. Elles représentent des idéaux et des traditions qui, si l'on en croit les railleurs, ne semblent plus s'appliquer à notre époque. Quelques-uns des modèles témoignent du Canada d'il y a plus de cent ans. La plupart, toutefois, y ont vécu durant la période allant de 1880 à 1916, soit deux ans avant l'armistice qui marqua la fin de la Grande guerre, «la dernière des guerres», et trois ans avant le décès de Harris, le 27 février 1919.

La richesse, la volonté de réussir, l'ardente ambition qu'inspire une origine modeste, le travail acharné, l'économie, la force émanant de la foi dans le Tout-Puissant (Dieu et le Dollar, dans l'ordre cité et non l'inverse), tout cela luit dans ces yeux que Harris a peints avec tant d'adresse. Y brillent également la fierté, l'affectation, l'humilité et, surtout, le courage; on pourrait ajouter à cette énumération toute une gamme de faiblesses morales, mais aussi de la sagesse. Quelle que soit notre réaction face à ces yeux qui nous regardent des murs de ce musée, un même sentiment nous anime: ces modèles ont grandement contribué à la naissance d'un dominion canadien indépendant, au sein d'un empire maintenant défunt, mais qui illumina son époque de ses hauts faits.

Il émane de plusieurs de ces toiles une conviction intime de la justesse de la «place» d'un être dans la société qui fait de son accession à cette place un événement tout à fait convenable et nettement prédestiné. Une ombre inquiétante

---

1. Fleming: *Royal Canadian Academy of Art*, p. 209.

really changed; and we could at this point quote the words of Peter Quennell:

> Let no one doubt that – both from the humanitarian and from the utilitarian point of view – the Victorians were wide awake to the necessity of doing something to alleviate the condition of the lower classes; but the problem was so huge that philanthropy, even the most enlightened, made exceedingly slow progress. . . ."[2]

Many of the sitters in the Harris portraits would have applauded such a realistic appraisal of a dilemma they knew only too well.

We see before us great educators and disciplinarians (and self-disciplinarians); clerics, scientists, professors of medicine and law, industrial "barons," bankers, railway promoters, and visionaries. Pawky Scots' humour blends with Presbyterian pedagogy – neither of which went unobserved by Harris, the Welsh Anglican. And our halls of fame would echo dull and empty indeed unless those enshrined were inspirited with warmth and love. Harris captured all these varied characteristics.

Nor can it be forgotten that these sitters lived in a period of poor plumbing as well as high ideals. Disease was rampant. Childbed fever, cholera, tuberculosis, typhoid fever, and rat-breeding sewage disrupted daily life to an appalling degree. Through their very survival, these men and women seem to have gained an extra dimension.

Robert Harris was born one of seven children at Cydd, Brymn-a-In, North Wales, on 17 September 1849. In 1856, he emigrated, along with the rest of his family, to Charlottetown, Prince Edward Island, then a Crown Colony – celebrating his seventh birthday at sea. His earliest drawing, lovingly preserved by his family, was of a deer and was part of a letter to his maternal grandmother back in Liverpool, written at the age of eight. The drawing was not exceptional, nor were any of the other drawings preserved from his adolescence. There is, however, one notable feature common to all; while other boys might well have selected buildings, animals, landscapes, and (in a town such as Charlottetown) boats and ships – and he did portray a full range of such subjects – Harris preferred people. The people are sometimes seen in caricature; but for the most part, they occasioned simple studies in pose and movement. From an early age, Harris's bent for portraiture is clear.

For the rest of his life Harris was to fill sketch-

de pharisaïsme et de pardon que l'on accorde à ses offenses semble parfois flotter au-dessus du groupe pris dans son ensemble, à quelques heureuses exceptions près. À cet égard, la société n'a pas changé, ce qui rappelle ces mots de Peter Quennell:

> «Il n'y a pas de doute que, des points de vue humanitaire aussi bien qu'utilitaire, les Victoriens étaient pleinement conscients de la nécessité d'alléger la misère des classes inférieures; mais le problème était si vaste que la philanthropie, si éclairée soit-elle, ne progressait que très lentement[2] . . .»

Bon nombre des modèles de Harris auraient applaudi à une appréciation aussi réaliste d'une situation qu'ils ne connaissaient que trop bien.

Nous avons devant les yeux de grands éducateurs, des partisans de la forte discipline (née de leur maîtrise de soi), des ecclésiastiques, des hommes de science, des professeurs de médecine et de droit, des magnats de l'industrie, des banquiers, des pionniers du chemin de fer et des visionnaires. L'humour écossais se mêle à la pédagogie presbytérienne, car rien n'échappe à Harris, l'anglican gallois. Nos temples de la Renommée ne sauraient certes pas retentir si ceux que nous y vénérons ne possédaient pas les qualités intérieures de chaleur et d'amour. Harris a bien su capter ces diverses caractéristiques.

Il faut aussi se rappeler que ces modèles vivaient à une époque de haut idéal mais de piètre technique. La maladie sévissait. La fièvre puerpérale, le choléra, la tuberculose, la fièvre typhoïde et les égouts fourmillants de rats perturbaient terriblement la vie quotidienne. Le fait que les hommes et les femmes de ces portraits aient survécu leur confère une dimension particulière.

Robert Harris est né dans une famille de sept enfants, le 17 septembre 1849, à Cydd (Brymn-a-In, Galles du Nord). Il émigra, en 1856, avec sa famille à Charlottetown, dans l'Île-du-Prince-Édouard qui était alors une colonie de la Couronne. Il célébra son septième anniversaire en mer. Son premier dessin, affectueusement conservé par sa famille, représentait un cerf et faisait partie d'une lettre, écrite à l'âge de huit ans, à sa grand-mère maternelle restée à Liverpool. Ce dessin n'était pas exceptionnel, pas plus que les autres dessins connus de Harris adolescent. Ils ont toutefois un trait commun remarquable: alors que les autres garçons auraient vraisemblablement choisi comme sujets des édifices, des animaux, des paysages et, dans une ville comme

---

2. Quennell, *Victorian Panorama*, p. 21.

2. Quennell: *Victorian Panorama*, p. 21.

1. The Countess of Minto

1. La comtesse de Minto

book after sketchbook with persons observed; and, as his powers of delineation increased, as his natural talent matured, he bequeathed to us, in his sketches alone, a panoramic survey not only of Islanders and other Canadians, but of those citizens in the numerous countries through which he travelled. Hair styles, ladies hats or bonnets, and other niceties of female fashion seem to have been of special interest to his roving and observant eye, and it is interesting to note that in his portraits women are always immaculately groomed – even the "peasants" (see cat. no. 38) and professional models.

Prior to his first visit to England at the age of eighteen, in 1867, Harris completed two early portrait sketches, those of his sister Sarah and of himself (cat. nos. 1, 2). In these sketches we see – especially in the natural pose of the girl – a maturing in his approach, a passing beyond the previous casualness of his "spot sketches" or *pochades*, as he liked to call them.

Then there was Harris's sense of humour – apparently developed at a very early age. Though he might have been, on occasion, as irascible as the rest of us, his nephews and nieces recall his expansive sense of fun and good humour. It was humour, fortunately, rather than ridicule that controlled his hand. When this quality in Harris was allied with an understanding of human foibles, the end effect could be quite delightful, whether in the early, posed portrait *W.C. Des-Brisay* (cat. no. 3) or in the hastily-scrawled notations of the *Caricature of the Reverend Canon Jacob Ellegood* (cat. no. 87) and the *Caricatures of the Reverend Father Benson* (cat. nos. 7–10). Harris could well have made a reputation as a caricaturist and popular illustrator. In verse he was at home with the lampoon, and in drawing, with the cartoon. His humorous drawings are to be found scattered throughout various issues of the Toronto magazine *Grip*, in his personal correspondence, and on menu cards specially drawn up for the Pen and Pencil Club in Montreal. (The majority of these caricatures and cartoons are, regrettably, in too poor a condition for display – many of them faded or smudged through careless handling. Out of their context, they would have little relevance in an exhibition concerned with portraiture.)

Again, Robert Harris would also have made a good journalist. If Gordon Brown of the Toronto *Globe* (brother of George Brown, and his successor as managing editor) and other editors (of the Montreal *Witness* and *Harper's Magazine* in particular) used his services from time to time as illustrator, it was surely because of their

Charlottetown, des bateaux et des navires (et il ne manqua pas d'en dessiner toute une gamme), il préférait dessiner des personnes. Ce sont parfois des caricatures, mais, la plupart du temps, de simples études d'équilibre et de mouvement. L'inclination de Harris pour le portrait est donc clairement apparue dès son jeune âge.

Toute sa vie, Harris remplit ses carnets de croquis de personnes observées et, la puissance de son trait augmentant avec la maturation de son talent, il nous a légué, même dans ses croquis, tout un panorama de gens de l'Île et d'autres Canadiens, de même que de citoyens des nombreux pays qu'il a parcourus. Les coiffures et les chapeaux ou bonnets et autres parures féminines semblent avoir particulièrement attiré son regard vagabond et observateur et il est intéressant de noter que les femmes de ses portraits sont toujours impeccables, même les «paysannes» (voir n° 38) et les modèles professionnels.

Avant son premier voyage en Angleterre, en 1867, à l'âge de dix-huit ans, Harris termine deux esquisses de portraits, le sien et celui de sa sœur Sarah (n°s 1 et 2), dans lesquels nous constatons, particulièrement dans la pose naturelle de la jeune fille, une maturation de son art, une rigueur que n'avaient pas ses «croquis mouchetés» antérieurs, ou «pochades», comme il aimait les appeler.

Quant au sens de l'humour de Harris, il semble s'être manifesté dès son plus jeune âge. Bien qu'il ait été irascible à l'occasion, comme le commun des mortels, ses neveux et ses nièces se rappellent son grand sens de la plaisanterie et sa bonne humeur. C'était, heureusement, l'humour plutôt que la raillerie qui dirigeait son crayon et cette qualité, alliée à la compréhension des faiblesses humaines, produit parfois de ravissants résultats, tels le portrait de W.C. DesBrisay, un de ses premiers (n° 3), ou les croquis rapides pour la *Caricature du révérend chanoine Jacob Ellegood* (n° 87) et pour la *Caricature du révérend père Benson* (n°s 7–10).

Harris aurait bien pu faire carrière de caricaturiste ou d'illustrateur populaire. Il était à l'aise dans la poésie satirique et dans la caricature. On trouve de ses dessins humoristiques dans divers numéros du magazine torontois *Grip*, dans sa correspondance personnelle et sur des menus qu'il a exécutés spécialement pour le Pen and Pencil Club de Montréal. (La majorité de ces caricatures et de ces dessins humoristiques sont malheureusement trop abîmés pour être exposés, nombre d'entre eux étant jaunis ou maculés par suite de négligence. Hors contexte, ils cadreraient peu dans une exposition de portraits de Harris).

Robert Harris aurait aussi été bon journaliste.

Cat. no. 45   *Bessie in her Wedding Gown*   1885   Cat. nº 45   *Bessie dans sa robe de mariée*   1885

awareness of Harris's appreciation of what was newsworthy and topical and because of his knack for depicting the essence of what would be of interest to the reader. In 1880, for example, Harris was commissioned by Brown to visit the site of the Donnelly murders at Lucan, Ontario, to record the scene of the crime, and later to draw portraits of the accused in jail.

Harris's decision to become a portrait-painter was, however, dictated to him by his Island circumstances, circumstances which may be briefly summarized: lack of money and boredom. Although Harris would eventually leave a fortune of just under $150,000, money was for him a means and not an end. The allure of a career as a portrait-painter must have seemed irresistible to the young Harris when he read the illustrated magazines and newspapers that arrived with each ship in to Charlottetown from England. While in eighteenth-century France the history painters were the élite, the aristocrats of painting, in England portrait-painters such as Reynolds, Lawrence, Gainsborough, or, in Scotland, Raeburn and Ramsay, were the artists whose paintings set standards that in the following century would be emulated by such autocratic Victorians as Lord Leighton. Leighton was the ranking aristocrat in an art that by now catered not only to nobility and landed gentry, but also to those whose wealth had been spawned by the Industrial Revolution.

It is not surprising that we find in Harris's letters, written years later, an intention to visit Leighton at one of the studio "at-homes" in Holland Park. In Harris's notebooks and letters, in fact, there is ample evidence that long before he made his first visit to England, he had already acquired an extensive knowledge of the styles and personalities of those he had previously admired vicariously. He was well prepared for, and not disappointed by, the galleries and exhibitions in his homeland. In Canada there was nothing to compare with the Manchester Institute or London's Royal Academy. What little portrait-painting there was in nineteenth-century Canada at the time when Harris was a student was naturally influenced directly by European tradition. Those itinerant limners who travelled the Maritimes and Upper Canada from New York and the New England States were still not entirely free of the Puritan tradition – edicts against the vanity of portrait-painting preached by the Pilgrim Fathers. In style, the majority of the latter portraits were wooden and scarcely human. What a relief Harris must have felt when he first saw portrait-painting proper in

Si Gordon Brown (frère de George Brown, et son successeur au poste de rédacteur en chef du *Globe* de Toronto), et d'autres directeurs eurent, de temps à autre, recours à ses services comme illustrateur (pour le *Witness* et *Harper's Magazine*, entre autres), c'est certainement parce qu'ils connaissaient l'aptitude de Harris à discerner les événements d'actualité dignes d'être publiés et son art de décrire précisément ce qui intéressait le lecteur. Par exemple, Brown délégua en 1880 Harris sur le lieu des meurtres Donnelly, à Lucan (Ontario), pour peindre la scène du crime et, plus tard, pour faire des portraits de l'accusé en prison.

Sa décision de devenir portraitiste lui fut dictée par sa situation dans l'Île et répondait, en somme, à deux besoins: gagner de l'argent et fuir l'ennui. Bien qu'il ait, par la suite, laissé une fortune de près de $150 000, l'argent était pour lui un moyen et non une fin. La carrière de portraitiste dut exercer un attrait irrésistible sur le jeune Harris lorsqu'il lisait les magazines et journaux illustrés qu'apportaient à Charlottetown les bateaux venus d'Angleterre. Tandis que dans la France du XVIIIe siècle, les peintres d'histoire constituaient l'élite de cet art, ce sont des portraitistes tels que Reynolds, Lawrence et Gainsborough en Angleterre, ou Raeburn et Ramsay en Écosse, qui formaient l'aristocratie de la peinture chez eux. Leurs portraits furent des modèles que devaient imiter, au cours du siècle suivant, des Victoriens aussi éminents que Lord Leighton. Leighton était le principal représentant d'un art qui servait alors non seulement la noblesse et l'aristocratie terrienne, mais aussi la nouvelle bourgeoisie issue de la révolution industrielle.

Il n'est pas étonnant de découvrir, dans la correspondance de Harris, rédigée beaucoup plus tard, qu'il avait l'intention de visiter Leighton dans un de ses «ateliers-maisons» de Holland Park. Il appert de ses carnets de notes et de ses lettres que, longtemps avant son premier voyage en Angleterre, Harris connaissait déjà à fond les styles et les noms de ceux qu'il avait autrefois intuitivement admirés. Il était bien préparé à voir les galeries et les expositions dans sa mère patrie; il n'en fut pas déçu. Rien au Canada n'était comparable au Manchester Institute ou à la Royal Academy de Londres. Les rares portraitistes du XIXe siècle au Canada, lorsque Harris était étudiant, subissaient naturellement l'influence directe de la tradition européenne. Les peintres itinérants qui parcouraient les Maritimes et le Haut-Canada, à partir de New York et de la Nouvelle-Angleterre, n'étaient pas encore tout à fait libérés de la tradition puritaine et des

2.   Robert Harris at the age of seven   2.   Robert Harris à sept ans

England's National Gallery. Imagine his joy when, as a young man in Boston, he saw the portraits of John Singleton Copley and realized that in the Commonwealth of Massachusetts, at least, the Puritans had been routed!

What Harris saw in Prince Edward Island was a void waiting to be filled. He was sufficiently realistic, however, to know that even were he to attempt to fill that void himself with portraits at the rates he set ($25 for strangers, free for friends), there would never be enough money on the Island to make him independent of his family and, at the same time, able to support them.

The family, obeying the custom so frequently followed by so many upper-middle-class immigrants, endeavoured to "keep up appearances" and live the life they were accustomed to in the "old country." They succeeded admirably in this – though at considerable sacrifice. Politically Conservative, and part of the Protestant minority in the Island's predominantly Roman Catholic community, the Harrises were happy, affectionately devoted to each other, and at the same time hard-working and self-sacrificing.

Even the father, Critchlow Harris, a man apparently not renowned either for stability of character or the ability to contribute to the family coffers, found the Island in every way ideal, both for landscape and friendship. Farmers, fishermen, shipbuilders, and merchants were one's neighbours. There was also a garrison stationed in Charlottetown, a militia, a Government House and House of Assembly. Lectures, plays, concerts, dances – a stimulating social life made existence very pleasant indeed unless one were one of the unfortunates, including several families of negroes (who were called "Boggies" because they lived down by the Government Pond in a district known as The Bogs). Trade by sea with England, America, and Canada was frequent and profitable. For artists, however, there seemed to be little or no place at all.

William Valentine, George Thresher, S.W. Martin, and other painters whose names are now generally unfamiliar included Prince Edward Island in their wanderings. For a short period Thresher – together with his wife and son – even lived in Charlottetown, where Eliza Thresher taught painting; but that was in 1829, twenty years before Robert Harris was born. In the 1840s, S.W. Martin operated a gallery and studio at the corner of Grafton and Queen. Art supplies, brushes, paint, canvas were, if not entirely unobtainable, of necessity to be imported to the Island from Liverpool, Boston, or Halifax – at considerable cost. In a family with six children

édits des pèlerins contre la vanité du portrait. Du point de vue du style, la plupart de ces portraits étaient inexpressifs et à peine humains. Quel soulagement pour Harris de voir pour la première fois des portraits dignes de ce nom à la National Gallery d'Angleterre et quelle joie de constater, lorsque, jeune homme à Boston, il vit les portraits de John Singleton Copley, qu'au moins dans le Commonwealth du Massachusetts, les puritains avaient été défaits!

Harris voyait à l'Île-du-Prince-Édouard un vide à combler. Il était toutefois suffisamment réaliste pour se rendre compte que, eut-il tenté de combler à lui seul ce vide avec des portraits au prix forfaitaire qu'il avait lui-même fixé (vingt-cinq dollars pour les inconnus, gratuits pour les amis), il n'y aurait jamais assez d'argent dans l'Île pour lui assurer l'indépendance vis-à-vis de sa famille et lui permettre d'aider les siens.

La famille de Harris, suivant la coutume de tant d'immigrants de la haute bourgeoisie, s'efforçait de «sauver les apparences» et de garder le train de vie auquel elle était habituée dans la mère patrie. Elle y parvint admirablement, mais au prix de grands sacrifices. Conservateurs et protestants dans une Île à majorité catholique, les Harris étaient heureux et unis, laborieux et dévoués.

Même le père, Critchlow Harris, qui n'était pas, semble-t-il, toujours conciliant ni apte à remplir le coffre familial, trouvait l'Île en tous points idéale, tant par son paysage que par sa vie sociale. Les voisins étaient des agriculteurs, des pêcheurs, des constructeurs de navires et des marchands. Il y avait également à Charlottetown une garnison, une milice, l'Hôtel du gouvernement et la Chambre d'assemblée. Des conférences, du théâtre, des concerts, des bals et des activités sociales variées contribuaient à rendre la vie vraiment très agréable, à moins d'être parmi les infortunés, dont plusieurs familles de noirs, qui habitaient près du Government Pond, dans un quartier appelé «Bogs», d'où le nom de «Boggies» qu'on donnait à ses habitants. Le commerce maritime avec l'Angleterre, les États-Unis et le Canada était fréquent et lucratif. Il semblait toutefois n'y avoir que peu ou pas de place pour les artistes.

William Valentine, George Thresher, S.W. Martin et d'autres peintres à peu près inconnus aujourd'hui visitèrent l'Île-du-Prince-Édouard. Thresher, sa femme et son fils vécurent même un certain temps à Charlottetown où Eliza Thresher enseigna la peinture; mais c'était en 1829, soit exactement vingt ans avant la naissance de Robert Harris. Vers les années 1840, S.W. Martin tint

Cat. no. 50 *Harmony* 1886   Cat. n° 50 *Harmonie* 1886

to be educated (the youngest had died soon after coming to the Island), the only money available for art supplies was what young Harris could manage to save for himself (having deducted his share for the family) from an annual salary of never more than £ 100.

A further matter which surely had some bearing on his decision in 1871 to leave the Island and seek professional training in Boston art schools was his increasing concern for his eyesight, a threat of blindness imminent since he was fifteen. In Boston there were specialists who might be able to cure him. (Years later, long after he had been assured by a London ophthalmologist that his trouble was long-sightedness and could be easily corrected, the fear of total blindness never left him). His confidence in his own ability to pursue a successful career as a portrait-painter was impaired by only this nagging concern about his eyes. (There are indications that in times of stress, or during his many bouts of depression, faulty vision undoubtedly prevented him from correcting errors in drawing which otherwise would not have escaped his attention.)

We have spent some time with Harris' early background because it enables us to appreciate all the more his dedication. As a young man, of course, he was encouraged by his family and friends, and he was undoubtedly treated as different from the other children. After he returned from England in 1867, it was inevitable that one day he would return to London to enroll in the Slade Fine Art Course at University College (though, in fact, when finally he did so, he could only afford the fees for one term). In order to achieve a standard of drawing and painting experience that would make him eligible for admission to the Slade, he would go first to Boston. This decision was seconded by the Harris family.

In Charlottetown he found work, first as a surveyor with Henry Cundall (cat. no. 5), and later as a clerk-bookkeeper with Mr. E. Hodgson, a lawyer and, later, a judge. After trying his skill at portraits based on photographs, Harris received his first official commission from the Government. A letter from the Executive Council of Prince Edward Island, signed by W.C. DesBrisay (cat. no. 3), stated:

> "The Government will accept your offer to paint the portraits of the Speakers of the House of Assembly at the rate of Five Pounds each provided that the first portrait is approved."[3]

une galerie et un atelier à l'intersection des rues Grafton et Queen. Le matériel d'art, les pinceaux, les couleurs et la toile, presque introuvables dans l'Île, étaient importés de Liverpool, de Boston ou d'Halifax à des prix très élevés. Dans une famille de six enfants (le benjamin était mort peu après l'arrivée dans l'Île), le jeune Harris ne pouvait compter pour l'achat de fournitures d'art que sur ses économies personnelles (une fois retranchée la pension qu'il donnait à sa famille), et sur son salaire annuel qui ne faisait d'ailleurs jamais plus de cent livres.

L'inquiétude que lui suscitait sa vue (la menace imminente de cécité dès l'âge de quinze ans) influença sans doute sa décision de quitter, en 1871, l'Île, pour acquérir une formation professionnelle dans les écoles de beaux-arts de Boston. Se trouvaient là des spécialistes qui pourraient peut-être le guérir. (La crainte de la cécité totale ne le quittera d'ailleurs jamais, même longtemps après qu'un ophtalmologiste de Londres aura diagnostiqué une presbytie facilement curable.) Il ne douta jamais, sauf lorsqu'il s'inquiétait de sa vue, de son aptitude à faire une brillante carrière de portraitiste. (Tout porte à croire que, dans ses moments de tension ou durant ses nombreux accès de découragement, sa vue déficiente l'empêcha de corriger des erreurs de dessin qui ne lui auraient pas autrement échappé.)

Nous nous sommes attardés aux premiers antécédents de Harris afin de mieux faire voir combien il s'est véritablement consacré à son art. Dans sa jeunesse, il fut encouragé par sa famille et ses amis et fut sans doute traité différemment des autres enfants. À son retour d'Angleterre en 1867, il était entendu qu'il retournerait un jour à Londres et s'inscrirait au Slade Fine Art Course de l'University College (quoique lorsqu'il put enfin réaliser ce rêve, il ne put acquitter que les frais de scolarité d'un trimestre). Dans le but d'acquérir l'expérience en dessin et en peinture qui le rendraient admissible à Slade, il décida d'aller d'abord à Boston, ce que sa famille accepta également.

Il trouva du travail à Charlottetown. En premier lieu, il devint arpenteur-géomètre chez Henry Cundall (nº 5) et, ensuite, commis chargé de la tenue des livres de comptes chez M. E. Hodgson, un avocat qui devint, plus tard, juge. Après avoir exercé ses talents en peignant des portraits d'après des photographies, il reçut sa première commande officielle du gouvernement. Le conseil exécutif de l'Île-du-Prince-Édouard lui fit en effet parvenir une lettre, signée par W.C. DesBrisay (nº 3), lui faisant part de la décision suivante:

---

3. Harris Papers, Letter from W.C. DesBrisay to Harris, dated 21 September 1871.

Voting in Charlottetown, Peter McGill taking then — figure with dark face Ron Fitzgerald, many of the others are portraits

3. *Voting in Charlottetown*
Graphite and ink
11 x 17-3/4 in. (28 x 45.1 cm)
INSCRIPTION: *Voting in Charlottetown, Peter McGill taking then* [talking them?] – *figure with dark face Ron Fitzgerald, many of the others are portraits*

3. *Scrutin à Charlottetown*
Mine de plomb et encre
11 x 17-3/4 po (28 x 45.1 cm)
INSCRIPTION (trad.): Scrutin à *Charlottetown, Peter McGill taking then* [leur parlant (?)] – la personne au teint foncé, *Ron Fitzgerald*, plusieurs parmi les autres sont des *portraits*

It was in 1871 that Robert Harris had written in an old writing book, apparently being prepared for reading to a debating club: "I have certainly to decide on a very important matter. If I have any ambition to get on in the world, that is to say, make money and be of some little importance, now is the capital time to begin."[4] At £ 5 per portrait (approximately $25 at today's rate of exchange), he had a long way to go, though he was even then "of some little importance."

Painting the Assemblymen was, apparently, to occupy Harris for the next two years; the portraits were painted in his spare time, either when he was working with Hodgson the lawyer or after he had saved enough to move to Boston and attend life classes at the Lowell Institute. It was a good enough seeding for any portrait-painter. Painting from a distance as it were, using photographs and descriptions of the sitters written by his mother, his brother Willie, and others who may or may not have known the Assemblymen personally, Harris gave full play to his imagination. Only when back on the Island was he able to obtain sittings as such – something he often regretted. During one of the periods when he was absent from the Island, for example, he wrote:

> "I am going on with my portraits pretty well, but I should like it ever so much better if I could do them from life. After I finish them I am as dissatisfied as when I began. As for the likeness alone, *that is easy*, but all other parts are ever so much more difficult to get".[5]

He had good reason to be dissatisfied, for the results in most cases were dull, lifeless, wooden images devoid of almost all merit. The portraits were not unlike those done by the itinerant painters in the early part of the century. The latter would arrive on one's doorstep with several canvases pre-painted with men's suits or ladies' dresses, and merely add a head and face to them.

However, Harris's portraits were acceptable to the Government and, in 1876, when he once again set sail for England, the Colonial Secretary asked him to purchase some good-quality but inexpensive frames, so that the portraits could be hung in the Provincial Building. And Harris was learning other things: for example, the necessity of keeping a detailed record of each transaction, however insignificant. While people were eager to have their portraits painted, many of them, even

«Le gouvernement accepte votre offre de peindre les portraits des orateurs de la Chambre d'assemblée, au prix de cinq livres pièce, à la condition que le premier portrait soit approuvé[3].»

En 1871, Robert Harris écrivait dans un vieux journal personnel, apparemment afin de le présenter à une société de conférences contradictoires: «J'ai assurément une décision très importante à prendre. Si j'ai la moindre ambition d'arriver, c'est-à-dire de faire de l'argent et d'acquérir une certaine notoriété, c'est le moment ou jamais de commencer[4].» À cinq livres le tableau (environ vingt-cinq dollars au cours actuel), Harris avait beaucoup de chemin à faire, quoiqu'il eut déjà «une certaine notoriété».

Il semble que les portraits des membres de l'Assemblée le tinrent occupé les deux années suivantes; il les exécutait durant ses loisirs, lorsqu'il travaillait chez l'avocat Hodgson ou lorsqu'il eut suffisamment économisé pour se rendre à Boston et suivre les cours de peinture d'après nature du Lowell Institute. C'était un assez bon début pour un portraitiste. Il donna libre cours à son imagination pour exécuter les portraits à distance, d'après des photographies et des descriptions des modèles que lui envoyaient sa mère, son frère Willie et d'autres personnes qui pouvaient, ou non, avoir connu personnellement les membres de l'Assemblée. Ce n'est que de retour à l'Île qu'il obtenait des séances privées de pose, ce qu'il regretta, d'ailleurs, souvent. Il écrira, au cours d'un séjour à l'extérieur de l'Île:

> «Mes portraits avancent assez bien, mais j'aimerais tellement mieux les exécuter d'après nature. Lorsqu'ils sont terminés, je suis aussi mécontent que lorsque je les ai commencés. *Il est facile* de rendre la ressemblance, mais tous les autres aspects sont tellement difficiles à obtenir[5].»

Il avait raison d'être mécontent, car la plupart des portraits étaient ternes et froids, des images inexpressives et médiocres. Ces œuvres ne différaient pas tellement de celles des peintres itinérants du début du siècle qui se présentaient chez les gens avec plusieurs toiles représentant déjà des costumes masculins ou féminins et auxquels ils ajoutaient simplement la tête et le visage du client.

Le gouvernement accepta toutefois les portraits et, lorsque Harris retourna en Angleterre

---

4. Quoted in the anonymous *Some Pages in an Artist's Life*, p. 11.
5. Harris Papers, Letter from Harris to his mother, undated.

3. W.C. DesBrisay: lettre à Harris, 21 septembre 1871, Documents Harris.
4. Cité dans *Some Pages from an Artist's Life*, p. 11.
5. Harris: lettre à sa mère, s.d., Documents Harris.

Cat. no. 51 *Sarah Harris* 1886   Cat. nº 51 *Sarah Harris* 1886

Assemblymen, could be remarkably slow in paying.

The crucial years in Harris' stylistic development were between 1881 and 1884. Prior to 1877 and his enrollment at the Slade (where he studied under Alphonse Legros), his portraits are remarkably devoid of individual style. By 1878, however, following his first exposure in Paris to the teaching methods of Léon Bonnat (for whose studio, see cat. no. 35), Harris surged forward, as is apparent in his portraits of Henry Cundall (cat. no. 5) and the somewhat mysterious Miss Fowle of Charlottetown (cat. no. 6) – the latter extremely French, somewhat in the manner of Manet.

Though still low-keyed, and confined to earth colours, his painting shows a new vigour in the brushstrokes, a lightening of touch, and an evident confidence in execution. By 1881 Harris was already a past Vice-President and Treasurer of the Ontario Society of Artists, and a founding member of the Royal Canadian Academy of Arts (nominated by the Marquess of Lorne). His stay in Toronto from 1879 to 1881 had produced such conversation pieces as *The Stethem Children* (cat. no. 19) and *The Burnside Children* (see cat. nos. 28–33). In 1879 he did the enchanting study *The Newsboy*, which was followed in 1880 by his R.C.A. Diploma picture, *The Chorister* (cat. no. 12), deposited in the National Gallery of Canada, which manages to avoid the sentimentality of so much of Harris's later work.

At this time, also, with his life-size portrait *Provost The Reverend George Whitaker* (cat. no. 24), we feel that Harris has fully justified the words of Lucius O'Brien, who had encouraged him to come to Toronto in the first place:

> "... your work would be among the best, if not better than anything we have, and you would have a fair chance with the others. Success in portrait painting seems to be very much a matter of push and business attack, and in your capacity in this way, I cannot judge."[6]

The generally good state of preservation of Harris's portraits was not due to accident, but due to Harris's sound craftsmanship and a practical knowledge of chemistry. For the most part he ground his own colours. He would never commit the error so common in nineteenth-century painting of using undiluted bitumen. While he may have favoured earth colours, he did not subscribe to the theory of the British painter Ben-

---

6. Harris Papers, Letter from Lucius O'Brien to Harris, undated.

en 1876, le ministre des Colonies lui demanda d'acheter des encadrements de bonne qualité, mais peu coûteux, afin que les toiles puissent être suspendues dans l'édifice du Parlement provincial. C'est également à cette époque que Harris comprit la nécessité de tenir une comptabilité de chaque marché, quel qu'en soit le montant. Il avait en effet appris que, pressés de faire peindre leur portrait, de nombreux clients, même les membres de l'Assemblée, étaient singulièrement lents à en payer le prix.

Du point de vue du style, les années allant de 1881 à 1884 furent décisives pour Harris. Avant 1877 et son inscription à Slade, où il étudia sous la direction d'Alphonse Legros, ses portraits étaient particulièrement dénués d'originalité. Vers 1878, cependant, à la suite d'une première expérience des méthodes d'enseignement de Léon Bonnat à Paris (voir son atelier, n° 35), l'évolution de Harris fait un bond en avant, comme en témoignent ses portraits de Henry Jones Cundall (n° 5) et de la mystérieuse Mlle Fowle de Charlottetown, (n° 6), ce dernier étant de facture extrêmement française, très proche de celle de Manet.

Quoique ses œuvres soient encore sobres et limitées aux ocres, les coups de pinceau sont plus énergiques, la touche, plus légère, et l'exécution révèle une assurance indéniable. Vers 1881, Harris était déjà ex-vice-président et trésorier de l'Ontario Society of Artists et (sur une proposition du marquis de Lorne) membre fondateur de l'Académie royale des arts du Canada. Son séjour à Toronto de 1879 à 1881, nous a valu des tableaux de genre tels que *Les enfants Stethem* (n° 19) et *Les enfants Burnside* (voir les n°s 28–33). En 1879, il exécuta la ravissante étude intitulée *Le camelot* qui fut suivie, en 1880, de son morceau de réception à l'Académie, *Le choriste* (n° 12), déposé à la Galerie nationale du Canada et heureusement dénué de la sentimentalité dont sont empreintes un grand nombre de ses dernières œuvres.

C'est également dans une toile de cette époque, le portrait grandeur nature du *Révérend George Whitaker, principal* (n° 24), que nous sentons toute la justesse des mots de Lucius O'Brien qui avait incité Harris à venir d'abord à Toronto et qui lui avait écrit:

> «... votre œuvre y serait parmi les meilleures, sinon la meilleure de toutes, et vous remporteriez un certain succès avec les autres. La réussite dans le genre du portrait semble être grandement une question de hardiesse et d'audace en affaires, qualités

4. Robert Harris as a young man

4. Robert Harris, jeune homme

jamin Robert Haydon that a good painting, like a good violin, should be brown. Indeed, Robert Harris was an excellent colourist and often experimented freely in the higher keys and tones of the Impressionists (see cat. no. 57).

When he did purchase manufactured oil paints, his choice was for the products of Messrs. Winsor and Newton. A copy of an invoice[7] from that firm records a transaction while he was passing through London on his way back to Canada. The order includes three tubes of Rose Madder, one pale Cadmium yellow, and two tubes of Flake White – as well as three Fitch brushes and one each of numbers 2 and 9 Round Oil Sables. It is a happy speculation that these paints and brushes would be used later in 1883 in his painting *The Fathers of Confederation* (see cat. nos. 40–42) which was commissioned soon after his return. An examination of the fresh and vigorously-painted compositional model (cat. no. 41) for this huge painting shows us that these colours were very much in evidence.

An example of the detailed studies of other artists' palettes which Harris made throughout his life is taken from a sketchbook, dated 1884, in which he records the palette used by Rubens and Sir Joshua Reynolds:

"Rubens used colours as follows: white lead, yellow ochre, madder lake, ultramarine, bitumen assisted in some parts by a clear and opaque yellow and vermillion and black. The clear yellow being composed of oxide of lead and oxide of antimony called Naples or [cadmium?] Yellow. The first five colours were used to produce the tones and shades produced by the former colours."[8]

Rubens used a drying paste mixed with colour previous to its use, Harris notes:

"I think it was as follows, 5 parts drying oil, 1 part mastic to which while still warm five parts of white wax were added. The whole having been heated to the boiling point, then removed from the fire and set to cool. The drying oil employed in the preparation of the paste [was] made by adding 1 part lithopone to 2 parts of linseed oil or other oil, heating the mixture in a bath carefully avoiding to raise it to boiling temperature, and storing the whole well until the combination of oil and lithopone takes place. The paste was probably employed in preparing the bitumen

dont je ne peux juger en ce qui vous concerne[6]. »

Le bon état général des portraits de Harris n'est pas le fait du hasard, mais repose sur une technique sûre et une solide connaissance de la chimie appliquée. La plupart du temps, il broyait lui-même ses couleurs. Il ne commit jamais l'erreur, si répandue chez les artistes du XIXe siècle, d'employer du bitume non dilué. Quoiqu'il eût préféré les ocres, il n'adhéra pas à la théorie du peintre britannique Benjamin Robert Haydon, selon laquelle un bon tableau, comme un bon violon, devrait être brun. Robert Harris fut en fait un excellent coloriste et il expérimenta abondamment les tons les plus clairs des impressionnistes (voir le no 57).

Lorsqu'il achetait effectivement des couleurs préparées, Harris préférait les produits de MM. Winsor et Newton. Une copie de facture[7] de cette maison témoigne d'un achat que Harris y aurait fait lors de son passage à Londres, en route pour le Canada. La commande comprenait trois tubes de rouge garance, un jaune de cadmium pâle et deux tubes de blanc de céruse, ainsi que trois pinceaux en putois et deux pinceaux en poil de martre à bout arrondi, numéros 2 et 9. (Tout porte à croire que, plus tard en 1883, Harris aurait utilisé ces couleurs et ces pinceaux pour son tableau *Les pères de la Confédération* (voir nos 40–42) qui lui fut commandé peu après son retour. Un examen de la fraîche et vigoureuse étude préliminaire (no 41) de cette œuvre colossale atteste l'emploi manifeste de ces couleurs.

Toute sa vie, Harris a fait des études approfondies des palettes d'autres artistes; dans un carnet de croquis, daté de 1884, par exemple, il décrit la palette de Rubens et celle de Sir Joshua Reynolds:

«Rubens se servait des couleurs suivantes: le blanc de plomb, l'ocre jaune, le rouge garance, l'outremer, le bitume accompagné parfois d'un jaune clair et opaque, de vermillon et de noir. Le jaune clair étant composé d'oxyde de plomb et d'oxyde d'antimoine appelé jaune de Naples ou [cadmium?]. Les cinq premières couleurs étaient utilisées pour rendre les tons et les nuances des autres couleurs[8]. »

---

7. Copy of an invoice found among the Harris Papers, dated 5 March 1883.
8. Harris Papers, unnumbered sketchbook, dated 1884.

---

6. Lucius O'Brien: lettre à Harris, s.d., Documents Harris.
7. Copie d'une facture, 5 mars 1883, Documents Harris.
8. Cahier de croquis de Harris, non numéroté, 1884, Documents Harris.

Cat. no. 112 *Portrait of a French Canadian* 1899   Cat. nº 112 *Portrait d'un Canadien français* 1899

for use; [for] other colours, pure oil with about one fourth of the paste."[9]

It is of interest to note that the lithopone in the first recipe originated in England in 1874, only eleven years before Harris made his notes and two hundred and forty-four years after the death of Rubens![10]

While Harris would build up his colours in a series of glazes, restorers have reported an occasional hardness of surface, usually resistant to the weaker solvents used in cleaning. Presumably, having noted certain techniques used by others, Harris would use them in his own compositions. Such techniques, however, can make conservation difficult.

Another of Harris's recipes is in fact worth including here because it may well have been connected with his murals for All Souls Chapel, St. Peter's Cathedral, Charlottetown:

"Med[ium] for Gambier [?] paintings spirit fresco.

Melt 2 oz by weight of elemi resin with 2 oz by measure of spirit of turpentine and strain through muslin. To this add 4 oz melted white wax. While all is still warm add 20 oz by measure of finest picture copal [resin or the varnish] and boil together to a white foam stirring thoroughly then remove the vessel from the fire. This done the mixture is boiled again a 5 oz by measure of oil of spike added just before the vessel is finally removed – any portion of the paint's surface that has become quite hard to be moistened with spike oil before retouching – colour to be ground in medium.

1/4 elem (i) gum elemi, a soft, natural (tree) resin
1/4 turp
1/2 wax
2 1/2 copal (al) a hard dark natural (tree) resin (fossil)
5/8 spike (oil of spike) – distilled extract from the lavender flower."[11]

Mr. Mervyn Ruggles, head of the Restoration and Conservation Laboratory at the National Gallery of Canada, was kind enough to interpret this recipe and observes that the mixture resembles a wax-resin adhesive used for lining paintings many years ago in Europe (Holland

9. *Ibid.*
10. Kay, *The Painter's Guide to Studio Methods and Materials*, pp. 24, 40.
11. Written on an undated sheet of letterhead of the Art Association of Montreal found among the Harris Papers.

Harris note que Rubens utilisait un mélange de pâte siccative et de couleur avant de les appliquer:

«Je pense que la pâte se composait comme suit: 5 parties d'huile siccative, une partie de mastic auquel s'ajoutaient, pendant qu'il était encore chaud, cinq parties de cire blanche. Le mélange était amené au point d'ébullition, puis retiré du feu et mis à refroidir. L'huile siccative employée dans la préparation de la pâte [était] produite en ajoutant une partie de lithopone à deux parties d'huile de lin ou autre, en chauffant au bain-marie le mélange ainsi obtenu, sans toutefois le faire bouillir, et en laissant reposer le tout jusqu'à ce que l'huile et le lithopone soient bien mêlés. La pâte servait probablement à apprêter le bitume; [quant aux] autres couleurs, de l'huile pure et environ un quart de la pâte était utilisés[9].»

Il est en outre intéressant de constater que le lithopone mentionné dans la première recette fut découvert en Angleterre en 1874, soit onze ans avant que Harris prenne ces notes et deux cent quarante-quatre ans après la mort de Rubens[10]!

Étant donné que Harris fixait ses couleurs avec une série de vernis, les restaurateurs ont signalé une dureté occasionnelle de la surface qui résiste habituellement aux faibles solvants utilisés dans le nettoyage des œuvres. Il semble que Harris ait adopté dans ses propres compositions certaines techniques d'autres peintres, tout spécialement lorsqu'elles semblaient rendre l'œuvre plus durable. Ces techniques peuvent, cependant, poser des problèmes de restauration.

Une autre recette vaut la peine d'être mentionnée ici car elle pourrait bien être associée aux murales que Harris a exécutées pour l'All Souls Chapel de la cathédrale St. Peter à Charlottetown:

«Liant pour Gambier [?] et les couleurs de la fresque à l'essence. Fondre 2 onces de résine d'amyris avec 2 onces d'essence de térébenthine et filtrer à travers une mousseline. Ajouter 4 onces de cire blanche fondue. Pendant que le mélange est encore chaud, ajouter 20 onces du plus pur copal à tableau [en résine ou en vernis] et faire bouillir le tout, en remuant bien, jusqu'à ce qu'il se forme une écume blanche, puis retirer du feu. Faire bouillir le mélange à nouveau et ajouter 5 onces d'huile de spic immédiatement avant de retirer une dernière fois du feu – toute

9. *Idem.*
10. Kay: *The Painter's Guide to Studio Methods and Materials*, p. 24 et 40.

5. The Harris family photographed in Charlotte-
town c. 1886
From left to right: Thomas James Harris (the artist's
brother), Charlie (his son), Etta (wife of Thomas),
Elizabeth ("Bessie," wife of the artist), Clare Harris,
Winnifred Cotton, Robert Harris, Sarah Stretch
Harris (the artist's mother), Marion MacNutt, W.L.
Cotton (publisher of the Charlottetown *Examiner*),
Robert Cotton, Margaret Ellin Cotton (the artist's
sister), Margaret Henrietta Cotton, Reverend Edward
Harris (the artist's brother), William Critchlow
Harris, Sr. (the artist's father), Sarah Harris (the
artist's sister), Frank Cotton, Walter Cotton, William
Critchlow Harris, Jr. (the artist's architect brother)

5. La famille Harris, photographiée à Charlotte-
town vers 1886. De gauche à droite: Thomas James
Harris (le frère de l'artiste), Charlie (le fils de
Thomas), Etta (la femme de Thomas), Elizabeth
(«Bessie», la femme de l'artiste), Clare Harris,
Winnifred Cotton, Robert Harris, Sarah Stretch
Harris (la mère de l'artiste), Marion MacNutt,
W.L. Cotton (éditeur de l'*Examiner* de Charlotte-
town), Robert Cotton, Margaret Ellin Cotton (la
sœur de l'artiste), Margaret Henrietta Cotton, le
révérend Edward Harris (le frère de l'artiste),
William Critchlow Harris père (le père de l'artiste),
Sarah Harris (la sœur de l'artiste), Frank Cotton,
Walter Cotton, l'architecte William Critchlow Harris
fils (le frère de l'artiste)

Cat. no. 128   *Lord Strathcona*   1902   Cat. nº 128   *Lord Strathcona*   1902

and England) employing the ordinary hand iron.[12] This medium, he says, could also be used for consolidating paint cleavage, repairing tears in canvas, and applying patches. It would also be employed as a medium with pigments. "It is possible," Mr. Ruggles suggests, "that he [Harris] obtained this recipe in connection with some restoration which he may have undertaken on wall paintings or 'frescoes.' "[13] In this instance, the word fresco can hardly be said to apply. The "murals" in Charlottetown, restored for the Prince Edward Island Centennial celebrations in 1973, are oil paintings on canvas mounted on panels glued to the chapel walls. But here again, the hardening of the paint surface has posed special problems.

In Harris's portraits, yet another chemical curiosity has been encountered, and this is his use of the oil pastels invented by the French artist Jean-François Raffaelli, and introduced by him into Canada in 1895 at a demonstration which Harris attended. In one portrait in the McGill University collection, not included in this exhibition, Harris apparently did the entire painting in this medium.

Except for his use of linen fabric of a fine quality imported from England in his portrait commissions, Harris appears to have been fairly casual in his selection of supports. At times he used a coarse, rough-grained material, somewhat more porous than present-day burlap, and heavily primed. At other times he used prepared canvas-covered panels in a variety of dimensions and makes. He used French-, English-, and American-manufactured stretchers. Frequently he used cardboard which he primed himself, but usually only for landscape sketches and not for portrait commissions (though a few of the models employed by him in Munich were painted on cardboard).

Apparently during his second visit to England, in 1877, Harris acquired a habit of painting on canvas *within* the frame, which was mounted on the easel. After the portrait had been completed in the centre, the frame would be removed and the canvas finished to its outer edges. This was an interesting though not unusual practice, and certainly enabled an artist accurately to centre his composition. It may also account for the many oval portraits that originated from Harris's studio, a gold-leaf oval liner often being used to conceal the unpainted areas of canvas.

portion durcie de la surface peinte doit être humectée d'huile de spic avant de faire les retouches – la couleur doit être broyée dans le liant.»
1/4 de résine d'amyris, résine (d'arbre) molle
1/4 de térébenthine
1/2 de cire
2-1/2 de copal, résine (d'arbre) dure et foncée (fossile)
5/8 de spic (huile de spic) – essence distillée de la fleur de lavande[11].»

M. Mervin Ruggles[12], chef du Laboratoire de restauration et de recherche à la Galerie nationale du Canada, a bien voulu nous expliquer cette recette. Il a fait remarquer que le mélange ressemble à un adhésif de cire et de résine qui servait, avec un fer ordinaire, à entoiler les œuvres, il y a de nombreuses années, en Europe (Pays-Bas et Angleterre). Ce liant, dit-il, pouvait aussi servir à arrêter le clivage de la peinture, tout en permettant de réparer les déchirures dans la toile et de faire des retouches. Il était également employé comme médium pour les pigments. D'après M. Ruggles, «il est possible qu'il [Harris] ait découvert cette recette lors d'un travail de restauration qu'il a peut-être exécuté sur des murales ou des fresques[13].» Dans ce cas-ci, il peut difficilement s'agir d'une fresque. Les «murales» de Charlottetown, restaurées pour les fêtes du Centenaire de l'Île-du-Prince-Édouard, en 1973, sont des huiles sur toile, montées sur bois, qui ont été collées aux murs de la chapelle. Toutefois, ici encore, le durcissement de la surface peinte a posé des problèmes particuliers.

Une autre curiosité chimique a été observée dans les portraits de Harris, à savoir l'utilisation des pastels à l'huile inventés par l'artiste français Jean-François Raffaelli, qui les a introduits au Canada en 1895, lors d'une démonstration à laquelle Harris a assisté. Un portrait de Harris dans la collection de l'université McGill, qui ne fait cependant pas partie de la présente exposition, semble avoir été entièrement exécuté avec ce médium.

Mise à part son utilisation de toile de très belle qualité importée d'Angleterre pour ses commandes de portraits, Harris semble avoir été assez désinvolte dans le choix de supports pour ses œuvres. Il employait parfois un tissu grossier et un peu rude, plus poreux en quelque sorte que

---

12. Mervyn Ruggles in a letter to the author, dated 26 May 1972.
13. *Ibid.*

11. Harris: écrit sur une feuille de papier portant l'en-tête de l'Art Association of Montreal, s.d., Documents Harris.
12. Mervyn Ruggles: lettre à l'auteur, 26 mai 1972.
13. *Idem.*

The oval was a popular shape and went well with the decorative scheme of many a Victorian and Edwardian living-room. A good example of this is the painting *Miss Innocence* (cat. no. 116), in the Art Gallery of Hamilton. Harris wrote that the child's mother, Mrs. George Smithers of Montreal, had specifically requested an "oval, to match the portrait of the other daughter I painted earlier."[14] The final canvas, however, is signed in the lower right of the rectangle, while normally, in an oval, the signature would have been centred and sloped upwards with the oval's outline. In this particular painting, we can, if we study the original photograph through a magnifying glass, trace the outline of the oval liner, which Harris had made before the picture was delivered.

Harris invariably did several pencil or charcoal drawings,[15] principally, of course, to get to know the features of the sitter, and, as well, to establish a suitable pose. The posing drawings, usually three or four in number, were seldom if ever deviated from, unless the sitter requested him to do so – in which case Harris would record the fact in his notes. The final drawing, varying in size, would then he squared for transfer to canvas.

Harris worked at a steady pace, and in the nineties he would be working at two or three portraits during the course of a week. Price, size, and framing (invariably by Scott of Montreal) would have been negotiated well in advance of the first studio visit. The portraits which apparently gave him most trouble were the presentation portraits which had to be ready so that the recipients could be honoured with them at a banquet, convocation, or other splendid occasion. Working steadily, Harris liked nevertheless to take his time and make last-minute changes. Hands seemed to have caused him most trouble and in many portraits we can see repeated alterations to them.

At the periods when he was most in demand – usually after he and Bessie had returned from lengthy tours of Europe or prolonged summer visits to the Island, Maine, Nova Scotia, or the Gaspé Peninsula – his sitter-book would record

l'actuelle toile d'emballage, et abondamment apprêté. D'autres fois, il se servait de panneaux manufacturés déjà couverts de toile, de dimensions et de fabrication diverses. Il utilisait des châssis manufacturés en France, en Angleterre et aux États-Unis. Il se servait fréquemment de carton qu'il apprêtait lui-même, mais sur lequel il ne faisait habituellement que des esquisses de paysages et non des portraits sur commande (quoique certains des modèles qu'il a employés à Munich furent peints sur carton).

C'est au cours de son deuxième voyage en Angleterre, en 1877, que Harris a apparemment acquis l'habitude de peindre de la toile déjà encadrée, l'encadrement étant monté sur le chevalet. Lorsque le portrait était terminé dans le centre, l'encadrement était enlevé et la toile était peinte jusqu'aux bords. Cette pratique intéressante, mais courante, permettait certainement à un artiste de bien centrer sa composition. Elle peut aussi justifier les nombreux portraits ovales qui sortaient de l'atelier de Harris, dans lesquels un cache ovale et doré masquait souvent les parties non peintes de la toile.

La forme ovale était populaire et se mariait bien avec l'arrangement décoratif de nombreux salons sous les règnes de Victoria et d'Édouard VII. La tableau *Mademoiselle Innocence* (nᵒ 116) de l'Art Gallery of Hamilton en est un bon exemple. La mère de l'enfant, Mᵐᵉ George Smithers, de Montréal, avait précisé qu'elle voulait un «ovale qui soit le pendant du portrait de l'autre fille dont j'ai antérieurement fait le portrait[14]», note Harris. Toutefois, le tableau est signé en bas, à droite du rectangle, alors que normalement, dans un portrait «ovale», la signature devrait apparaître au centre et remonter le long du tracé de l'ovale. Dans le cas de cette toile, si nous examinons la photographie originale avec une loupe, nous pouvons déceler le tracé du cache ovale que Harris a fait avant d'exécuter le tableau.

Harris faisait toujours plusieurs dessins[15] au crayon ou au fusain, sans doute afin de se familiariser avec les traits du modèle, mais aussi pour trouver une pose qui convienne. Ensuite, il faisait généralement trois ou quatre dessins de la pose choisie, dont il ne s'écartait jamais, sauf à la de-

14. Harris Papers, Letter from Harris to his mother, undated.
15. With the assistance of funds from the Canada Council, work has been progressing in Charlottetown since 1965 to identify and record the 1,500 drawings by Harris, and to research and collate the contents of sixty-six sketchbooks and other documentary material.

14. Harris: lettre à sa mère, s.d., Documents Harris.
15. Grâce à des crédits consentis par le Conseil des arts du Canada, on travaille à Charlottetown depuis 1965 à l'identification et au classement de 1 500 dessins de Harris ainsi qu'au rassemblement du contenu de 66 cahiers de croquis et d'autres documents le concernant.

6. Sarah Stretch Harris, the artist's mother   6. Sarah Stretch Harris, la mère de l'artiste

several names grouped together as potential clients. Like a successful Harley-Street specialist, he had his waiting list; and while in the majority of cases, though not always, portraits would eventually materialize, sometimes two or three years might elapse between the entering of a person's name in the sitter-book and the final delivery of the portrait. (A true professional, Harris would accept commissions to paint both the quick and the dead, at one time even painting the portrait of a dead baby in its coffin.)

With some artists, the placing of the signature, the colour of paint used, and indeed even the use of full name or simply initials serve as a private code, indicating whether or not in the artist's opinion the painting is finished. Harris appears to have followed no such system, and to have signed his canvases in a variety of ways, even those that obviously required additional work. It is to be noticed that when commissioned to paint portraits of both husband and wife, Harris usually put his signature in the wife's portrait on the left, or distaff side.

In his book *Styles in Painting*, Paul Zucker remarks: "If the portrait is biography, the self-portrait represents autobiography. Like its counterpart in literature, the self-portrait involves a special problem in so far as its subject and its maker are identical."[16] Harris was an untiring self-portrayer, and he certainly saw himself as others saw him, through youth to old age. We have no idea of just how many self-portraits he made, just as we have been unable to arrive at a satisfactory estimate of the number of drawings and paintings he made of his wife. The self-portraits included in this exhibition show the same attention he would give to commissioned portraits; but in the majority of known self-portraits – drawings or otherwise – Robert Harris was perhaps merely keeping his eye in, while on holiday or on slack days between official studio commissions. The purpose of his self-portraits was similar to that of keyboard exercises played by musicians between concerts. They had nothing to do with vanity.

For an art historian concerned with the minutiae of research, Harris had his bad side. He seldom remembered to date his paintings, and he was entirely casual in his spelling of names. Once in a while he made entries in his sitter-book long after the event, so that a commission might be recorded more than once in different years. He was in the habit of making replicas so that, as in

mande du modèle, auquel cas il en prenait note. L'ébauche finale, de dimensions variées, était enfin mise au carreau pour être reportée sur la toile.

Il peignait à un rythme constant et, dans les années 1890, il lui arrivait de travailler à deux ou trois portraits en une même semaine. Le prix, les dimensions et le type d'encadrement (toujours de la maison Scott de Montréal) du tableau étaient fixés bien avant la première visite du modèle à l'atelier. Sa plus grande difficulté semble avoir été de respecter les délais de livraison des portraits à offrir aux intéressés en des occasions bien déterminées: banquet, assemblée ou autre cérémonie d'apparat. Travailleur assidu, Harris aimait néanmoins prendre son temps et apporter des changements de dernière minute. Il semble avoir eu surtout du mal à peindre les mains qui, dans nombre de ses portraits, dénotent des retouches successives.

Dans les périodes où il était le plus en demande, soit habituellement au retour de ses longs voyages en Europe avec Bessie ou de leurs séjours d'été prolongés à l'Île, dans le Maine, en Nouvelle-Écosse ou en Gaspésie, des séries de noms de clients éventuels figuraient dans son journal de travail. Tout comme un vrai spécialiste de Harley Street, il avait sa liste d'attente et, bien que dans la plupart des cas il donnait suite aux commandes qu'il avait reçues, il se passait parfois deux ou trois ans entre la commande et la livraison du portrait. (Professionnel accompli, Harris acceptait de peindre tant les morts que les vivants, allant même jusqu'à faire le portrait d'un bébé dans son cercueil.)

Chez certains artistes, l'emplacement de la signature, la couleur de la peinture utilisée et le fait de signer au long ou d'un parafe, constituent un code personnel qui leur indique si, à leurs yeux, un tableau est réellement terminé. Harris ne semble pas avoir employé un tel système; il signait ses toiles de diverses façons, même celles qui auraient manifestement nécessité des retouches. Il appert que dans ses portraits jumelés du mari et de la femme, il signait habituellement ce dernier à gauche, côté de la femme.

Dans son ouvrage *Styles in Painting*, Paul Zucker fait remarquer: «Si le portrait est une biographie, l'autoportrait est une autobiographie. Tout comme son pendant littéraire, l'autoportrait pose un problème particulier dans la mesure où le modèle et le peintre ne sont qu'une seule et même personne[16].» Harris ne se lassa jamais de faire des autoportraits, qui furent certainement

16. Zucker, *Styles in Painting, a Comparative Study*, p. 162.

16. Zucker: *Styles in Painting. A Comparative Study*, p. 162.

7. Robert Harris in 1885   7. Robert Harris en 1885

the case of *Frederic Nicholls* (cat. no. 120), there might be three almost identical versions of a portrait. In one instance, having listed some commissions by name, and as completed while in Toronto, he comments, "did several other portraits while there but do not remember who."[17] Nor could he ever remember the name of Mr. Stethem, who commissioned what Harris refers to in all his notes as "the Peterborough Group" (cat. no. 19). The compilation of a chronology of Harris portraits is thus as challenging as a double-acrostic.

On the other hand, the documents open windows through which we can see fascinating glimpses of a portrait-painter's life:

> "I have been to paint Mr. John Hope, an old gentleman who is too ill to leave his house, so I have to go up there for sittings, a thing which I don't like as I have to paint in a restricted space sitting and I always like to walk up and down and see my work a long way off...."[18]
>
> "Working on portraits of Mr. Hugh McLennan (replica), Mrs. Stearns' little girl, Mrs. Leonowens and Mrs. Cooke. Sketch Hartland S. McDougall...."[19]
>
> "first sketch for Hon. W. Weir...55″ x 40″ proposed size for canvas."[20]

Harris was a *safe* painter. In any generation, a portrait-painter of his calibre can set his own price, and in exchange for good money he will produce good, straightforward work. Portraits symbolize permanency as well as pride and accomplishment in wealth, social status, or profession. A portrait of a chairman commissioned by fellow-members of a board reflects pride in the commercial achievements of the Company itself, as well as recording the physical appearance of the man at the helm. A distinguished (though humble and self-effacing) faculty-member may be honoured by his university before all trace of his

---

17. Harris Papers, Sitter-book, undated entry.
18. Harris Papers, Letter from Harris to his mother, undated.
19. Harris Papers, Sitter-book, entry dated 14 September 1905.
20. Harris Papers, Sitter-book, entry dated 14 October 1905. Upon receipt of the portrait, Weir replied, in part: "The portrait arrived yesterday and has been prominently placed on an easel in the main corridor near the other portraits of former Speakers. It arrived in perfect condition and has been very much admired. I never had much of an opinion of the other portraits and still less now when I can make the comparison!" (Harris Papers, Letter from the Hon. Mr. Weir to Harris, dated 7 February 1906.)

---

très objectifs, tout au long de sa vie. Nous ignorons totalement combien il en fit au juste, tout comme nous n'avons pu déterminer une somme acceptable des dessins et des portraits à l'huile qu'il fit de sa femme. Les autoportraits qui font partie de la présente exposition dénotent la même application de la part de Harris que les portraits de commande; cependant, en peignant la plupart des autoportraits que nous connaissons, par le dessin ou autrement, Robert Harris ne faisait peut-être que se garder en forme, pendant ses vacances ou les jours creux entre les commandes officielles. Ces autoportraits tendaient au même but que les exercices du pianiste entre les concerts. Ils n'avaient rien à voir avec la vanité!

Pour un historien de l'art soucieux de découvrir les faits, Harris présente quelques difficultés. Il oubliait toujours, par exemple, de dater ses toiles et il épelait les noms de façon très désinvolte. Il n'inscrivait souvent le nom de ses modèles dans son journal de travail que longtemps après avoir peint leur portrait, de sorte que certains d'entre eux étaient enregistrés plus d'une fois, et même au cours d'années différentes. Il avait l'habitude de faire des copies, ce qui fait que, dans le cas du portrait de Frederic Nicholls (nᵒ 120), par exemple, trois versions, presque identiques, existent. Une fois, ayant enregistré quelques commandes qu'il remplit lorsqu'il était à Toronto, il ajoute: «ai peint plusieurs autres portraits là-bas, mais ne me souviens pas de qui[17].» Il ne pouvait jamais non plus se souvenir du nom de M. Stethem, qui commanda l'œuvre que Harris appelle dans toutes ses notes «le groupe de Peterborough» (nᵒ 19). Établir une chronologie des portraits de Harris représente donc un défi comparable à celui que pose le déchiffrage d'un double acrostiche.

Les documents personnels de Harris nous font, par contre, découvrir des aspects fascinants de la vie d'un portraitiste:

> «Je suis allé peindre M. John Hope, un vieux monsieur qui est trop malade pour quitter la maison. Je dois donc me rendre chez lui pour les séances de pose, chose que je n'aime pas faire parce que je dois peindre assis, ne disposant que d'un espace étroit alors que j'aime toujours marcher de long en large et voir mon œuvre de loin[18]...»
>
> «Travaille actuellement aux portraits de M. Hugh McLennan (copie), de la fillette de Mᵐᵉ Stearns, de Mᵐᵉ Leonowens et de Mᵐᵉ

---

17. Journal de travail de Harris, s.d., Documents Harris.
18. Harris: lettre à sa mère, s.d., Documents Harris.

8. "Some notable members of the Royal Canadian Academy," 1903. Left to right, back row: F. McGillivray Knowles, William Brymner, F.M. Bell-Smith; front row: C.J. Way, Homer Watson, Robert Harris (President), A.C. Hutchison, J. Smith (Secretary)

8. «Quelques membres distingués de l'Académie royale des arts du Canada», 1903. De gauche à droite, seconde rangée: F. McGillivray Knowles, William Brymner, F.M. Bell-Smith; première rangée: C.J. Way, Homer Watson, Robert Harris (président), A.C. Hutchison, J. Smith (secrétaire)

appearance vanishes at his retirement. If others wish you to become a permanent object, remembered in perpetuity, they will naturally select the artist most capable of achieving that end without fuss, regardless of expense. The portrait-painter has, as well, to be able to meet his client on equal terms, and must be a strong enough personality in his own right not to be dominated by the sitter. The first confrontation is not unlike that of a patient meeting the surgeon who is going to operate and who must, in the first few minutes, establish pre-operative confidence. To mount the "throne" in an artist's studio might well alarm the timid. It is up to the artist to make the client feel at ease.

The degree of confidence that Harris inspired can be clearly traced in the series of commissions by persons connected with the Canadian Pacific Railway, for the Dominion Wire Company, the Grand Trunk Railway, and the Bank of Nova Scotia. The series of five portraits of Lord Strathcona (for one of which, see cat. no. 128) were in themselves an achievement with which some lesser artist would have been justifiably satisfied. Living so near to McGill, Harris was in close contact with members of the faculty and was their natural selection for many of the portraits found throughout the campus.

Safe and dependable as he was, Robert Harris also enjoyed experimenting, and it is for this reason that the exhibition contains a selection of portrait-studies of paid models. What better example of this experimental work than the two canvases, both titled *Composing his Serenade* (cat. nos. 56, 57), painted in 1887? The latter, with its more intense colour, would, had he put it on display, have been regarded as a gross distortion of nature. Wisely he kept it in his studio rather than risk possible damage to his income-producing activity as a portrait-painter.

This exhibition has brought to light numerous extant portraits, and others which, along with portraits of whole families, cannot be traced. As a rule, portraits, unless by Old Masters, and in public collections, do not have a history of exhibition. Once delivered and placed in a family home or board room they seldom re-appear in public. The search for portraits by Robert Harris led to inquiries in Italy and Scotland, in Dublin and in New York, and from British Columbia to Newfoundland. (In one instance, through the generosity of the owner, an important work by Harris has been returned to Canada and donated to a museum.) Unfortunately, through circumstances entirely beyond the control of the owner, it was found impossible to borrow the great portrait

Cooke. Esquisse le portrait de Hartland S. McDougall[19]. . .»

«. . . première esquisse du portrait de l'honorable W. Weir . . . Dimensions proposées pour la toile: 55 po x 40 po[20].»

Harris était un peintre *prudent*. Quelle que soit l'époque, un portraitiste de son calibre peut fixer son prix et produire en retour un travail honnête. Les portraits symbolisent la permanence de même que la fierté et le succès, qu'il soit financier, social ou professionnel. La société qui commande le portrait de son président montre combien elle est fière de ses réalisations commerciales, tout en préservant l'image physique de celui qui tient la barre. De même, un membre distingué d'une faculté universitaire, mais modeste et effacé, peut être honoré par ses confrères avant de quitter l'université pour prendre sa retraite. Si d'autres veulent vous immortaliser, ils choisiront tout naturellement l'artiste le plus susceptible de le faire en toute simplicité et sans égard au coût. Le portraitiste doit pouvoir traiter d'égal à égal avec son client et avoir une personnalité assez forte pour ne pas se laisser dominer par le modèle. La première entrevue ressemble à celle d'un malade et du chirurgien qui doit établir une certaine confiance dans les quelques minutes précédant l'opération. Monter sur le «trône» dans un atelier d'artiste peut en intimider certains. C'est à l'artiste qu'il incombe de mettre son client à l'aise.

Harris savait inspirer confiance, comme en témoigne nettement la série de commandes passées par des personnes étroitement liées aux compagnies du Canadien Pacifique, de la Dominion Wire, du Grand Tronc ainsi qu'à la Banque de Nouvelle-Écosse. La série des cinq portraits de Lord Strathcona (voir nº 128) était en soi une réussite qui aurait comblé à raison un artiste de moindre talent. Vivant très près de l'université McGill, Harris entretenait des relations étroites avec des universitaires, qui l'ont tout naturellement choisi pour peindre les nombreux portraits que l'on a découverts sur le campus.

19. Journal de travail de Harris, 14 septembre 1905, Documents Harris.

20. Journal de travail de Harris, 14 octobre 1905, Documents Harris. Accusant, plus tard, réception du portrait, Weir écrira: «Le portrait est arrivé hier et a été exposé, bien en vue, sur un chevalet dans le couloir principal, près des autres portraits des anciens orateurs. Le tableau nous est arrivé en excellent état et il a été fort admiré. Je n'ai jamais fait grand cas des autres portraits et j'en ferai encore moins maintenant que je puis les comparer au mien!» (William Weir: lettre à Harris, 7 février 1906, Documents Harris).

9. Robert Harris, The Reverend Edward Harris, Mrs. Edward Harris, and Mrs. Robert Harris at 11 Durocher Street, Montreal, in 1917

9. Robert Harris, le révérend Edward Harris, Mme Edward Harris et Mme Robert Harris au 11, rue Durocher, Montréal, en 1917

group *Mrs. C.E.L. Porteous and Her Children*, the only Canadian painting to represent Canada at the 1900 Paris Exposition.

A vigorous era of discovery and achievement in a growing nation came under Harris's scrutiny. Although the exact figure will probably never be ascertained, Harris is said to have painted over three hundred portraits (as well as numerous landscapes and genre pictures). These Canadians, he seems to tell us, may be ordinary people, but they are also extraordinary. It is our good fortune that Robert Harris lived when he did, and could leave us such an inspiring legacy.

Quoique prudent et digne de confiance, Robert Harris aimait faire des expériences. C'est pourquoi l'exposition comprend une sélection d'études de portraits de modèles qu'il a payés pour poser. Quels merveilleux exemples de ce travail expérimental que les deux toiles intitulées *Composant sa sérénade* (nos 56 et 57), peintes en 1887! Si Harris avait exposé la seconde, aux couleurs plus vives, on l'aurait accusé de déformer grossièrement la réalité. Prudent, il décida de la garder dans son atelier où elle ne risquait pas de compromettre son occupation lucrative de portraitiste.

La présente exposition révèle l'existence de nombreux portraits et l'absence d'autres qui, avec ceux des membres de familles entières, n'ont pu être retrouvés. En règle générale, les portraits ne sont pas continuellement exposés à moins d'être de la main de grands maîtres et de faire partie de collections publiques. Une fois fixés aux murs d'un salon privé ou d'une salle de conseil, ils réapparaissent rarement en public. La recherche de portraits par Harris nous a menés en Italie et en Écosse, à Dublin et à New York, et de la Colombie britannique à Terre-Neuve. (Dans un cas précis, une œuvre importante de Harris a été retournée au Canada par son généreux propriétaire et donnée à un musée.) Des circonstances entièrement indépendantes de la volonté du propriétaire ont malheureusement rendu impossible l'emprunt du grand portrait collectif *Mme C.E.L. Porteous et ses enfants*, le seul tableau canadien qui représenta notre pays à l'Exposition universelle de Paris, en 1900.

Le regard attentif de Robert Harris nous a permis de connaître une période importante, par ses découvertes et ses réalisations, de l'histoire de notre pays. On ne saura probablement jamais le nombre exact de ses portraits, mais on estime qu'il en a peint plus de trois cents, auxquels s'ajoutent de nombreux paysages et tableaux de genre. Ces Canadiens, semble-t-il nous dire, sont des gens comme vous et moi, mais comme ils sont extraordinaires aussi! Il est heureux que Robert Harris ait vécu pour nous léguer un tel héritage d'inspiration.

10. Portrait group, *Mrs. C.E.L. Porteous and Children*, which was exhibited in the Royal Canadian Academy Exhibition, 1889, no. 63, and in the Paris Exposition Universelle, 1900

10. Le portrait de groupe *Mme C.E.L. Porteous et ses enfants*, présenté à l'exposition de l'Académie royale des arts du Canada en 1889 (sous le n° 63) et à l'Exposition universelle de Paris en 1900

Catalogue

by Moncrieff Williamson

Entries are presented in chronological order. Medium is oil on canvas unless otherwise stated. Dimensions are given in inches and centimeters, height preceding width.

par Moncrieff Williamson

Les notices de ce catalogue sont présentées chronologiquement. À moins d'avis contraire, les œuvres décrites sont des huiles sur toile. Les dimensions sont données en pouces et en centimètres; la hauteur précède toujours la largeur.

Abbreviations

Note: Like many portrait painters, especially in his own time, Harris often painted several copies or versions of his own works. It is difficult and, in some cases, probably impossible to determine which copy or version of a work was exhibited in a given show. The fact of its exhibition in some form or other should, however, be noted, if only in hopes of eliciting further information on the subject. Also, as noted in the Introduction, many of the finished portraits, intended to satisfy private demand, have little or no history of public exhibition.

➤ *Montreal Spring Exhibition*
1880– , Montreal, Art Association of Montreal and later (1950–) The Montreal Museum of Fine Arts, [spring exhibition with varying titles] (exhibition catalogues)

➤ *R.C.A.*
1880– , [various Canadian cities], Royal Canadian Academy of Arts, [annual exhibition with varying titles] (exhibition catalogues)

1919 Montreal
1919, Montreal, Art Association of Montreal, *Memorial Exhibition of the Work of the Late Robert Harris, C.M.G., R.C.A.* (exhibition catalogue)

1967 Charlottetown
1967, Charlottetown, Confederation Art Gallery and Museum, *Robert Harris 1849-1919* (exhibition catalogue)

Abréviations

Notes: Comme plusieurs portraitistes, ceux de son époque particulièrement, Harris reproduisait souvent en plusieurs copies (dont certaines avec des variantes) ses œuvres originales. Il est donc difficile, voire, dans certains cas, impossible, de déterminer si, à l'occasion de telle ou telle exposition, l'œuvre originale fut effectivement présentée. On ne peut toutefois pas le passer sous silence, car le fait de mentionner qu'une œuvre fut exposée risque de susciter d'autres renseignements à son sujet. Enfin, comme nous l'avons déjà fait remarquer dans notre introduction, plusieurs de ces portraits, exécutés pour des particuliers, ne furent jamais, ou très peu souvent présentés, dans leur version définitive, publiquement.

➤ *A.R.A.C.*
1880– , [Diverses villes canadiennes], Académie royale des arts du Canada. Exposition annuelle dont le titre varie. Catalogues d'exposition.

➤ *Montréal, Printemps*
1880– , Montréal, Art Association of Montreal et, plus tard (1950–), Musée des beaux-arts de Montréal. Exposition présentée chaque année, au printemps, et dont le titre varie. Catalogues d'exposition.

1919 Montréal
1919, Montréal, Art Association of Montreal, *Memorial Exhibition of the Work of the Late Robert Harris, C.M.G., R.C.A.* Catalogue d'exposition.

1967 Charlottetown
1967, Charlottetown, Confederation Art Gallery and Museum, *Robert Harris, 1849-1919.* Catalogue d'exposition.

1 *Self-portrait* c. 1868
10-1/2 x 8 in. (26.7 x 20.3 cm) (s)
INSCRIPTION: c.r., *R.H./when/a boy.*

Framed with cat. no. 2. For later self-portraits, see cat. nos. 47, 62, 158, 169.
CONFEDERATION ART GALLERY AND MUSEUM, CHARLOTTETOWN

1 *Autoportrait* c. 1868
10-1/2 x 8 po (26.7 x 20.3 cm) (s.v.)
INSCRIPTION: c.d. (trad.): *R.H./alors/un petit garçon.*

Encadré avec le nº 2. Voir également ses autoportraits réalisés ultérieurement (nᵒˢ 47, 62, 158 et 169).
CONFEDERATION ART GALLERY AND MUSEUM, CHARLOTTETOWN

2 *Sarah Harris* 1871
Oil on paper
9-1/2 x 6 in. (24.2 x 15.3 cm) (s)

Framed with cat. no. 1. The artist's sister, who later became Mrs. George E. Robinson. For later portraits, see cat. nos. 51, 161.
CONFEDERATION ART GALLERY AND MUSEUM, CHARLOTTETOWN

2 *Sarah Harris* 1871
Huile sur papier
9-1/2 x 6 po (24.2 x 15.3 cm) (s.v.)

Encadré avec le nº 1. Le modèle était la sœur de l'artiste et devint plus tard Mᵐᵉ George E. Robinson. Voir également ses portraits réalisés ultérieurement (nᵒˢ 51 et 161).
CONFEDERATION ART GALLERY AND MUSEUM, CHARLOTTETOWN

3 *W.C. DesBrisay* c. 1871
Oil on paper
7 x 6-1/2 in. (17.8 x 16.5 cm) (s)
CONFEDERATION ART GALLERY AND MUSEUM, CHARLOTTETOWN

3 *W.C. DesBrisay* c. 1871
Huile sur papier
7 x 6-1/2 po (17.8 x 16.5 cm) (s.v.)
CONFEDERATION ART GALLERY AND MUSEUM, CHARLOTTETOWN

4 *Margaret Ellin Cotton* 1874
25 x 20-1/4 in. (63.5 x 51.2 cm)

One of the artist's sisters in her wedding dress.
PROVENANCE: Gift of the Margaret Cotton Estate, 1966.
EXHIBITION: *1967 Charlottetown*, no. 7 (as *Portrait of the Artist's Sister, Margaret Ellin Harris*).
CONFEDERATION ART GALLERY AND MUSEUM, CHARLOTTETOWN

4 *Margaret Ellin Cotton* 1874
25 x 20-1/4 po (63.5 x 51.2 cm)

Le modèle, représenté ici en robe de mariée, était la sœur de l'artiste.
HISTORIQUE: Don de la succession Margaret Cotton, 1966.
EXPOSITION: *1967 Charlottetown*, nº 7 (*Portrait of the Artist's Sister, Margaret Ellin Harris*).
CONFEDERATION ART GALLERY AND MUSEUM, CHARLOTTETOWN

5 *Henry Cundall* 1878
36-3/4 x 28-1/4 in. (93.4 x 71.8 cm)
HARRIS PAPERS: "You will have heard of Mr. Cundall's death. We hear he left over $50,000 in various legacies among a large number of relatives and friends and $100,000, the bulk of the estate, to found a home for friendless girls. He did what he had to do in his will as in all else, conscientiously." (Sitter-book, entry dated 27 July 1916)

At one point in his sitter-book, Harris lists eighteen portraits completed between the autumn of 1878, when he returned to Charlottetown from Europe, and the autumn of 1879, when he set out for Toronto. One of the entries reads: "H.J. Cundall 1/2 length, he has it." (Indeed, this portrait was still hanging above a steam radiator in the old Cundall home till the summer of 1972.) A few pages back there is another entry: "Wm Cundall, Ch'town, his son has this. I painted it in the bank of P.E.I. of which he was cashier. Head 20 x 24."
It is fitting that Henry Jones Cundall should take his place in this exhibition, for Cundall was both close friend and mentor to the artist. Compared with the majority of Harris portraits at this time, it amply displays the benefits of his exposure to European training.
Cundall was the land-surveyor in whose office Harris served his apprenticeship. He died in 1916.
PROVENANCE: Donated by the H.J. Cundall Trust, June 1972.
CONFEDERATION ART GALLERY AND MUSEUM, CHARLOTTETOWN

5 *Henry Cundall* 1878
36-3/4 x 28-1/4 po (93.4 x 71.8 cm)
DOCUMENTS HARRIS: «Vous avez sûrement appris la mort de M. Cundall. Il aurait laissé plus de $50 000 en donations testamentaires à partager entre un grand nombre de parents et d'amis, et destiné $100 000, le gros du legs, à la fondation d'un refuge pour jeunes filles abandonnées. Il aurait rédigé son testament comme tout ce qu'il a toujours entrepris, consciencieusement.» (Journal de travail de l'artiste, 27 juillet 1916).

Dans son journal de travail, Harris énumère dix-huit portraits terminés entre l'automne de 1878, à son retour d'Europe à Charlottetown, et l'automne de 1879, alors qu'il partit pour Toronto. Sous une des rubriques, on lit: «H.J. Cundall, portrait en buste, livré.» (Effectivement, jusqu'à l'été de 1972, ce portrait était encore accroché au-dessus d'un radiateur dans la maison des Cundall.) Quelques pages plus tôt, on peut lire: «William Cundall, Charlottetown, son fils a ceci. Je l'ai peint à la banque de l'Î.-P.-É., où il était caissier. Tête 20 x 24».
Il est fort approprié que Henry Jones Cundall ait sa place dans cette exposition, car Cundall était un ami intime et le mentor de l'artiste. Si on compare ce portrait à la plupart des œuvres de Harris exécutées à cette époque, il est manifeste que l'artiste a amplement profité de son contact avec la peinture européenne.
Cundall était l'arpenteur-géomètre chez qui le jeune Robert Harris avait fait son apprentissage. Il mourut en 1916.
HISTORIQUE: Don du H.J. Cundall Trust, juin 1972.
CONFEDERATION ART GALLERY AND MUSEUM, CHARLOTTETOWN

6   *?Miss Fowle of Charlottetown*   1879
36 x 28-1/2 in. (91.5 x 72.4 cm)
INSCRIPTION: signed and dated u.l., *R.H./
Sept 1879.*
HARRIS PAPERS: "I had better speak of that
picture of Miss Fowle, as it has always been
forgotten before. I suppose if they want it at
all they would not mind giving $25 for
it. That is about one-eighth of the present
prices [*sic*] of a portrait of mine the same size
here." (Letter from Harris to his mother,
dated 17 December 1891) "You did not say
anything about what I said in regard to the
picture of Miss Fowle, when you wrote."
(Letter from Harris to his mother, dated 3
January 1892)

This canvas was still in the artist's studio
at the time of his death in 1919. (It was restored in 1972.) Who was Miss Fowle? It has
been suggested, though not confirmed, that
this was a misspelling for Ellen Fouldes, a
sister-in-law of Harris' mother, visiting Charlottetown from Ormskirk. A portrait of a
Miss Fowle, from the collection of Mr. and
Mrs. William Cotton, was in the Centennial-
year Harris exhibition. However, the date,
which came to light during cleaning, would
indicate that the work was painted in Charlottetown after Harris had returned from
Paris, and is included here because of its
close affinity with French portraits of that
period.
    The sitter-book notes: "Miss Fowle head
16 x 20''. Miss Fowle (younger) kitcat [*sic*]."
This entry might suggest that Miss Fowle
had an older sister.
EXHIBITION: *1967 Charlottetown*, no. 47.
CONFEDERATION ART GALLERY AND
MUSEUM, CHARLOTTETOWN

6   *Mlle Fowle (?) de Charlottetown*   1879
36 x 28-1/2 po (91.5 x 72.4 cm)
INSCRIPTION: signature et date, h.g.: *R.H./
Sept 1879.*
DOCUMENTS HARRIS: «Je ferais mieux de
parler du tableau de Mlle Fowle, puisqu'il a
été relégué aux oubliettes jusqu'ici. Je pré-
sume que s'ils le veulent, ils donneront
volontiers $25 pour l'avoir. Ce qui représente
environ un huitième du prix actuel de mes
portraits de cette taille-ci» (Lettre de
Harris à sa mère, 17 décembre 1891).
«Vous ne m'avez pas dit, dans votre lettre,
ce que vous pensez de ce que je vous ai dit
au sujet du tableau de Mlle Fowle.» (Lettre
de Harris à sa mère, 3 janvier 1892).

Cette toile se trouvait toujours dans l'atelier de l'artiste à sa mort, en 1919. (Elle fut
restaurée en 1972.) Qui était Mlle Fowle?
Selon une hypothèse non vérifiée, ce serait
Ellen Fouldes, belle-sœur de la mère de
Harris, venue d'Ormskirk en visite à Charlottetown, et dont le nom aurait été mal
orthographié. Un portrait de Mlle Fowle,
appartenant à la collection de M. et Mme
William Cotton, a fait partie de l'exposition
Harris, l'année du centenaire de la Confédération (*1967 Charlottetown*). Cependant, la
date, qui a été découverte lors du nettoyage
du tableau, situe son exécution à Charlottetown, après le retour de Harris de Paris.
Le tableau a été inclus dans la présente exposition en raison de son affinité avec les
portraits français de la même époque.
    Dans le journal de travail de l'artiste, on
trouve: «Mlle Fowle, tête 16 x 20 pouces.
Mlle Fowle (plus jeune), portrait en buste
avec mains.» Cette rubrique semble laisser
entendre que Mlle Fowle avait peut-être une
sœur aînée.
EXPOSITION: *1967 Charlottetown*, n° 47.
CONFEDERATION ART GALLERY AND
MUSEUM, CHARLOTTETOWN

7   *Caricature of the Reverend Father Benson*
c. 1879
Pen and sepia ink
5-1/4 x 5-1/8 in. (13.3 x 13 cm) (s)

Framed with cat. nos. 8, 9, 10. Father Benson, a brother of the novelist E.F. Benson,
belonged to the Community of the Cowley
Fathers ("The Oxford Movement"), Oxfordshire.
Harris here appears to express a conven-
tional dislike of fin-de-siècle converts to Roman Catholicism. His satirical anti-clericism,
however, was hardly restricted to one deno-
mination (see cat. nos. 58, 85, 86, 87, 93, 94).
CONFEDERATION ART GALLERY AND
MUSEUM, CHARLOTTETOWN

7   *Caricature du révérend père Benson*
c. 1879
Plume, sépia
5-1/4 x 5-1/8 po (13.3 x 13 cm) (s.v.)

Encadré avec les n°s 8, 9 et 10. Le révérend
père Benson, frère du romancier E.F. Benson,
appartenait à la communauté des pères
Cowley («*The Oxford Movement*»), dans
l'Oxfordshire.
Harris semble ici partager une aversion,
fort répandue au tournant du siècle dernier,
pour les convertis à la religion catholique
romaine. Son anticléricalisme satirique ne
s'attaquait cependant pas qu'à une seule
confession (voir les n°s 58, 85, 86, 87, 93 et 94).
CONFEDERATION ART GALLERY AND
MUSEUM, CHARLOTTETOWN

8 *Caricature of the Reverend Father Benson*
c. 1879
Pen and sepia ink
4-3/4 x 6 in. (12.1 x 15.3 cm) (s)

Framed with cat. nos. 7, 9, 10.
CONFEDERATION ART GALLERY AND
MUSEUM, CHARLOTTETOWN

8 *Caricature du révérend père Benson*
c. 1879
Plume, sépia
4-3/4 x 6 po (12.1 x 15.3 cm) (s.v.)

Encadré avec les nos 7, 9 et 10.
CONFEDERATION ART GALLERY AND
MUSEUM, CHARLOTTETOWN

9 *Caricature of the Reverend Father Benson*
c. 1879
Pen and sepia ink
4-5/8 x 7-1/2 in. (11.8 x 19.1 cm) (s)

Framed with cat. nos. 7, 8, 10.
CONFEDERATION ART GALLERY AND
MUSEUM, CHARLOTTETOWN

9 *Caricature du révérend père Benson*
c. 1879
Plume, sépia
4-5/8 x 7-1/2 po (11.8 x 19.1 cm) (s.v.)

Encadré avec les nos 7, 8 et 10.
CONFEDERATION ART GALLERY AND
MUSEUM, CHARLOTTETOWN

10 *Caricature of the Reverend Father Benson*
c. 1879
Pen and sepia ink
8-1/4 x 6-1/4 in. (21 x 15.9 cm) (s)

Framed with cat. nos. 7, 8, 9.
CONFEDERATION ART GALLERY AND
MUSEUM, CHARLOTTETOWN

10 *Caricature du révérend père Benson*
c. 1879
Plume, sépia
8-1/4 x 6-1/4 po (21 x 15.9 cm) (s.v.)

Encadré avec les nos 7, 8 et 9.
CONFEDERATION ART GALLERY AND
MUSEUM, CHARLOTTETOWN

11 *The "C.P.R. Syndicate"* 1880
Woodcut
5-7/8 x 10 in. (14.9 x 25.4 cm)
INSCRIPTION: dated and signed u.l., pencil,
Toronto 79 or 80 or 81 RH; top edge, ink,
*When I had a studio in Leader Lane Toronto
Gordon Brown of the Globe/brought photos
of the three men just reported from Montreal as having formed the/Syndicate to build the
C.P.R. and asked me to make drawings on the
block/which could be cut very quickly & effec-
tively for use in the next issue of the paper./They
were the first of the likenesse* [sic] *of the Syndicate put before the public after it was formed/
R. Harris/McIntyre* [Duncan McIntyre] *Stephen* [Lord Mount Stephen] *Angus* [R.B.
Angus].

For portrait and biography of R.B. Angus,
see cat. no. 141.
  The Gordon Brown (1827-96) mentioned
in the inscription was brother of George
Brown of the Toronto *Globe,* who succeeded
his brother as managing editor after the
latter's murder in 1880.
CONFEDERATION ART GALLERY AND
MUSEUM, CHARLOTTETOWN

11 *Syndicat du C.P.* 1880
Gravure sur bois
5-7/8 x 10 po (14.9 x 25.4 cm)
INSCRIPTION: lieu, date et signature, h.g., au
crayon: *Toronto 79 ou 80 ou 81 RH;* inscription, marge h., à l'encre (trad.): Lorsque
j'avais un atelier à *Leader Lane, Toronto,
Gordon Brown* du journal *Globe* apporta les
photos des trois hommes qui, selon les dernières nouvelles en provenance de Montréal,
venaient de former le syndicat qui construi-
rait le chemin de fer du Canadien Pacifique.
Il me demanda de dessiner leur portrait sur
la planche à graver, de manière à ce qu'il
puisse être taillé très rapidement et imprimé
dans la prochaine livraison du journal.
C'était le premier portrait du Syndicat jamais présenté au public depuis sa formation.
R. Harris/[Duncan] *McIntyre/*[Lord Mount]
Stephen/[R.B.] *Angus.*

Voir également le portrait et des notes
biographiques sur R.B. Angus (no 141). Le
Gordon Brown (1827–1896) dont il est question dans l'inscription était le frère de George
Brown du *Globe* de Toronto, qui succéda à
son frère (assassiné en 1880) au poste de
rédacteur en chef.
CONFEDERATION ART GALLERY AND
MUSEUM, CHARLOTTETOWN

12 *The Chorister* 1880
29-1/4 x 24-1/4 in. (74.3 x 61.5 cm)
INSCRIPTION: signed and dated l.r., *R. Harris/ 1880.*
EXHIBITIONS: *1880 Ottawa R.C.A.,* no. 36; *1881 Halifax R.C.A.,* no. 314; ?1887, Liverpool, The Walker Gallery, *Seventeenth Autumn Exhibition of Pictures in Oil and Water-Colours,* no. 215.
THE NATIONAL GALLERY OF CANADA, OTTAWA (117)
ROYAL CANADIAN ACADEMY, DIPLOMA WORK, DEPOSITED C. 1881

12 *Le choriste* 1880
29-1/4 x 24-1/4 po (74.3 x 61.5 cm)
INSCRIPTION: signature et date, b.d.: *R. Harris/1880.*
EXPOSITIONS: *1880 Ottawa, A.R.A.C.,* n° 36; *1881 Halifax, A.R.A.C.,* n° 314; 1887(?), Liverpool, The Walker Gallery, *Seventeenth Autumn Exhibition of Pictures in Oil and Water-Colours,* n° 215.
GALERIE NATIONALE DU CANADA, OTTAWA (117)
MORCEAU DE RÉCEPTION, VERS 1881, ACADÉMIE ROYALE DES ARTS DU CANADA

13 *Study for "The Stethem Children"* 1880
Oil on paper
6-7/8 x 10 in. (17.4 x 25.4 cm)
INSCRIPTION: l. edge, pencil, *Final compson for group for Mr. ... Peterborough.*
CONFEDERATION ART GALLERY AND MUSEUM, CHARLOTTETOWN

13 *Étude pour Les enfants Stethem* 1880
Huile sur papier
6-7/8 x 10 po (17.4 x 25.4 cm)
INSCRIPTION: marge g., au crayon (trad.): *Composition finale pour un groupe pour M. ... Peterborough.*
CONFEDERATION ART GALLERY AND MUSEUM, CHARLOTTETOWN

14 *Study for "The Stethem Children"* 1880
Graphite
10-1/4 x 12-1/4 in. (26 x 31.1 cm)
INSCRIPTION: u.l., *for Peterborough Group.*

Framed with cat. nos. 15, 16.
CONFEDERATION ART GALLERY AND MUSEUM, CHARLOTTETOWN

14 *Étude pour Les enfants Stethem* 1880
Mine de plomb
10-1/4 x 12-1/4 po (26 x 31.1 cm)
INSCRIPTION: h.g. (trad.): pour le groupe de *Peterborough.*

Encadré avec les n°ˢ 15 et 16.
CONFEDERATION ART GALLERY AND MUSEUM, CHARLOTTETOWN

15 *Study for "The Stethem Children": George Stethem* 1880
Graphite
14 x 10-5/8 in. (35.6 x 27 cm)
INSCRIPTION: l.c., *for Peterborough Group.*

Framed with cat. nos. 14, 16.
CONFEDERATION ART GALLERY AND
MUSEUM, CHARLOTTETOWN

15 *Étude pour Les enfants Stethem:
George Stethem* 1880
Mine de plomb
14 x 10-5/8 po (35.6 x 27 cm)
INSCRIPTION: b.c. (trad.): *pour le groupe de
Peterborough.*

Encadré avec les n°s 14 et 16.
CONFEDERATION ART GALLERY AND
MUSEUM, CHARLOTTETOWN

16 *Study for "The Stethem Children": Catherine Stethem* 1880
Graphite
14 x 10-5/8 in. (35.6 x 27 cm)
INSCRIPTION: l.c., *for Peterborough Group.*

Framed with cat. nos. 14, 15.
CONFEDERATION ART GALLERY AND
MUSEUM, CHARLOTTETOWN

16 *Étude pour Les enfants Stethem:
Catherine Stethem* 1880
Mine de plomb
14 x 10-5/8 po (35.6 x 27 cm)
INSCRIPTION: b.c. (trad.): *pour le groupe de
Peterborough.*

Encadré avec les n°s 14 et 15.
CONFEDERATION ART GALLERY AND
MUSEUM, CHARLOTTETOWN

17 *Study for "The Stethem Children":*
Catherine Stethem 1880
Oil on board
12 x 9-1/2 in. (30.5 x 24.1 cm)
INSCRIPTION: l.r., pencil, *study for group*
painted at Peterborough.

Framed with cat. no. 18.
CONFEDERATION ART GALLERY AND
MUSEUM, CHARLOTTETOWN

17 *Étude pour Les enfants Stethem:*
Catherine Stethem 1880
Huile sur panneau
12 x 9-1/2 po (30.5 x 24.1 cm)
INSCRIPTION: b.d., au crayon (trad.): étude
pour le groupe peint à *Peterborough.*

Encadré avec le n° 18.
CONFEDERATION ART GALLERY AND
MUSEUM, CHARLOTTETOWN

18 *Study for "The Stethem Children":*
Winifred Stethem 1880
Oil on board
12 x 9-1/2 in. (30.5 x 24.1 cm)
INSCRIPTION: l.r., pencil, *study for group*
painted/for Mr. – at Peterborough.

Framed with cat. no. 17.
CONFEDERATION ART GALLERY AND
MUSEUM, CHARLOTTETOWN

18 *Étude pour Les enfants Stethem:*
Winifred Stethem 1880
Huile sur panneau
12 x 9-1/2 po (30.5 x 24.1 cm)
INSCRIPTION: b.d., au crayon (trad.): étude
pour le groupe peint/pour M. – à *Peter-*
borough.

Encadré avec le n° 17.
CONFEDERATION ART GALLERY AND
MUSEUM, CHARLOTTETOWN

19 *The Stethem Children* 1880
37 x 49 in. (94 x 124.5 cm) (s)
INSCRIPTION: signed l.r., *R. Harris.*

As noted in the Introduction, Harris had
great difficulty in remembering the name of
the Stethem family of Peterborough. He
tended to label all the preceding studies for
this portrait group "The Peterborough
Group."
EXHIBITION: *1880 Ottawa R.C.A., no. 112 (as*
The unruly guest, Portraits of the children of
G. Stethem, Esq).
A.J.R. STETHEM

19 *Les enfants Stethem* 1880
37 x 49 po (94 x 124.5 cm) (s.v.)
INSCRIPTION: signature, b.d.: *R. Harris.*

Comme nous l'avons déjà fait remarquer
dans notre introduction, Harris semblait
éprouver de la difficulté à se souvenir du
nom de la famille Stethem de Peterborough.
Ainsi, sur chacune des études mentionnées
précédemment (n°s 13–18), il a spontanément
inscrit, pour identifier ce portrait collectif,
«le groupe de Peterborough».
EXPOSITION: *1880 Ottawa, A.R.A.C., n° 112*
(The unruly guest, Portraits of the children of
G. Stethem, Esq.).
A.J.R. STETHEM, MONTRÉAL

20 *Homer Watson* 1880
Pen and sepia ink
4 x 7 in. (9.9 x 17.8 cm)
INSCRIPTION: u.r., pencil, *Homer Watson*; l.r., pencil, *Homer Watson*; dated l.r., pen, *May 26/80*.

Homer Ransford Watson (1855-1936), a landscape painter, became R.C.A. (1882) and P.R.C.A. (1912-22).
EXHIBITION: *1967 Charlottetown*, no. 92, repr.
CONFEDERATION ART GALLERY AND MUSEUM, CHARLOTTETOWN

20 *Homer Watson* 1880
Plume, sépia
4 x 7 po (9.9 x 17.8 cm)
INSCRIPTION: h.d., au crayon: *Homer Watson*; date, b.d., à la plume (trad.): mai *26/80*.

Homer Ransford Watson (1855–1936), un paysagiste, devint membre de l'A.R.A.C. en 1882, société dont il fut le président de 1912 à 1922.
EXPOSITION: *1967 Charlottetown*, n° 92, reprod.
CONFEDERATION ART GALLERY AND MUSEUM, CHARLOTTETOWN

21 *William Weeks* 1880
24 x 20-1/8 in. (61 x 51.1 cm)
INSCRIPTION: signed l.l., *R. Harris*.

Between 1871 and 1875, Harris completed sixty-one portraits (including portraits painted during his student days in Boston), many of them of questionable merit and listed in his sitter-book in no particular order. Among them were: two portraits of James Yeo and, along with the several other Speakers of the Assembly, John Yeo, Judge Edward Palmer, Mr. Haviland, the first Mayor of Charlottetown, two portraits of John Lawson, the City's first recorder, portraits of G.W. DeBlois, the Honourable Joseph Howe, Bishop Birney (of Nova Scotia), William Dodd, John Morris, and often their wives.

There are fascinating side entries in the sitter-book, such as: "Bishop (R.C.) McEachern, a copy from an old portrait by Fraser [?] full length in Bishop's Palace, Ch'town. Bishop MacDonald R.C. full length in soutan[e] in Bishop's Palace, Ch'town. Three priests (can't recall the names) heads or busts life size for Bishop MacDonald. Full length of Daniel O'Connell which was done as a banner and used in the O'Connell celebrations after they placed it as a picture in one of the halls in Ch'town. Mr. Murphy of Havana 24 x 20 Mrs. Murphy, these were taken to Cuba." (Sitter-book, undated entry)

From the fascinating hodge-podge of this period we have selected the portrait of William Alfred Weeks, a prosperous Charlottetown merchant, member of a large and well-known Island family, who, along with the Haslams, have a distinguished record of service in the legal profession, the army, and in commerce. Two extant drawings of the artist's mother have an inscription (*In Weeks' cottage*) which indicates that at one time Weeks was the Harrises' landlord. Although there is a portrait of Mrs. Weeks painted before 1877, the portrait of Weeks was probably painted during the summer be-

21 *William Weeks* 1880
24 x 20-1/8 po (61 x 51.1 cm)
INSCRIPTION: signature, b.g.: *R. Harris*.

Entre 1871 et 1875, Robert Harris a peint divers portraits d'un mérite souvent douteux et dont le nombre total est de soixante-et-un, dûment inscrits, sans ordre précis, dans son journal de travail (dont, bien entendu, des portraits faits au cours de ses études à Boston). On compte, parmi eux, deux portraits de James Yeo et, avec les autres orateurs de l'Assemblée, John Yeo, le juge Edward Palmer, le premier maire de Charlottetown, M. Haviland; deux portraits du premier greffier de la ville, John Lawson, les portraits de G.W. DeBlois, de l'honorable Joseph Howe, de l'évêque Birney (de la Nouvelle-Écosse), de William Dodd, de John Morris et, souvent, de leurs femmes.

Il y a, en outre, dans son journal, des renseignements fascinants tels: «L'évêque McEachern (C.R.), copie du vieux portrait de Fraser [?], portrait en pied, à l'évêché de Charlottetown. L'évêque MacDonald, C.R., portrait en pied, en soutane, à l'évêché de Charlottetown. Trois prêtres (ai oublié leurs noms) têtes ou bustes grandeur nature pour l'évêque MacDonald. Portrait en pied de Daniel O'Connell, en forme de bannière et utilisé dans les célébrations O'Connell, se trouvait par la suite, comme tableau, dans une salle de Charlottetown. M. Murphy, de la Havane, 24 x 20, Mme Murphy, qui furent envoyés à Cuba.» (Journal de travail de l'artiste, s.d.)

Du méli-mélo fascinant de cette période, nous avons extrait le portrait de William Alfred Weeks, marchand prospère de Charlottetown, appartenant à une famille nombreuse, et fort connue de l'île, qui, avec les Haslam, a un long état de service distingué dans la pratique du droit, l'armée et le commerce. Deux dessins de la mère de l'artiste portent une inscription (dans la villa des Weeks) qui semble indiquer qu'à un moment donné, M. Weeks était leur proprié-

fore Harris left for Toronto in 1880. The latter work retains some of the stiffness of Harris's early portraits, while showing the increased stylistic confidence which came from his first exposure to European training.
PROVENANCE: Donated by Mr. and Mrs. M. W. Weeks, 1972.
CONFEDERATION ART GALLERY AND MUSEUM, CHARLOTTETOWN

taire. Bien qu'un portrait, exécuté avant 1877, de Mme Weeks existe, Harris peignit probablement le portrait de M. Weeks au cours de l'été qui a précédé son départ pour Toronto, en 1880. On retrouve dans ce dernier tableau encore un peu de la rigidité des premiers portraits de Harris, mais cette rigidité semble céder graduellement le pas à un style plus délié, né de son premier contact avec la peinture européenne.
HISTORIQUE: Don de M. et Mme M.W. Weeks, 1972.
CONFEDERATION ART GALLERY AND MUSEUM, CHARLOTTETOWN

---

22   *Study for "Provost The Reverend George Whitaker"*   1880
Graphite
11 x 9 in. (27.9 x 22.9 cm)
INSCRIPTION: r. edge, pencil, *Study for background of Dr. Whitaker's portrait/for Trinity Coll.*

Framed with cat. no. 23.
CONFEDERATION ART GALLERY AND MUSEUM, CHARLOTTETOWN

22   *Étude pour Le révérend George Whitaker, principal*   1880
Mine de plomb
11 x 9 po (27.9 x 22.9 cm)
INSCRIPTION: marge d., au crayon (trad.): Étude pour l'arrière-plan du portrait de M. *Whitaker*/pour le *Trinity* College.

Encadré avec le n° 23.
CONFEDERATION ART GALLERY AND MUSEUM, CHARLOTTETOWN

---

23   *Study for "Provost The Reverend George Whitaker"*   1880
Watercolour and graphite
11-1/4 x 9 in. (28.3 x 22.9 cm)
INSCRIPTION: r. edge, *Provost Whitaker for Trinity Coll/sketch for life size full length.*

Framed with cat. no. 22.
CONFEDERATION ART GALLERY AND MUSEUM, CHARLOTTETOWN

23   *Étude pour Le révérend George Whitaker, principal*   1880
Aquarelle et mine de plomb
11-1/4 x 9 po (28.3 x 22.9 cm)
INSCRIPTION: marge d. (trad.): Le principal *Whitaker* pour *Trinity* College/esquisse pour le portrait en pied, grandeur nature.

Encadré avec le n° 22.
CONFEDERATION ART GALLERY AND MUSEUM, CHARLOTTETOWN

24 *Provost The Reverend George Whitaker*
1880
95 x 58-5/8 in. (241.3 x 148.9 cm)
INSCRIPTION: signed and dated l.l., *R. Harris. 1880.*
HARRIS PAPERS: "I got a note from Dr. Whitaker this morning saying he would be ready to sit on Thursday . . . ." (Letter from Harris to his mother, dated July 1880) "I'm quite collapsing with the awfully hot weather here, but shall have to stand it until I get the backbone of the portrait well in, though I don't propose to finish it till Fall. The canvas is 5 feet by 8 feet, so you can see there is a lot of work on it. He is a good sitter and lies up against the back of a chair as solemn as a log of hemlock." (Letter from Harris to his mother, dated 19 July 1880)

The Whitaker portrait was Harris's first major commission in Toronto. George Whitaker was born about 1810 and obtained his B.A. from Queen's College, Cambridge, in 1833. He was Fellow and Classical Lecturer at Queen's College from 1834–40, and was ordained deacon (1837) and priest (1838) in the Church of England.
In 1850, when King's College, Toronto, was secularized as the University of Toronto, Bishop John Strachan set out to establish a Church of England university in Canada West, Trinity College. Whitaker was appointed first Provost of the newly-formed college, and for thirty years combined administrative duties with a professorship in Divinity. He was involved in a long controversy over the content of his teachings in the late 1850s and early 1860s, and opposition from Low-Churchmen prevented his election as Bishop of Toronto in 1866, 1878, and, again, in 1879. Whitaker returned to England, and shortly after becoming rector at Newton Toney, Salisbury, in 1882, he died.
THE CORPORATION OF TRINITY COLLEGE, TORONTO

24 *Le révérend George Whitaker, principal*
1880
95 x 58-5/8 po (241.3 x 148.9 cm)
INSCRIPTION: signature et date, b.g.: *R. Harris. 1880.*
DOCUMENTS HARRIS: «J'ai reçu une lettre de M. Whitaker ce matin m'annonçant qu'il serait prêt à poser jeudi...» (Lettre de Harris à sa mère, juillet 1880).
«Je suffoque sous l'abominable chaleur qui règne ici, mais il faut que je m'en accomode jusqu'à ce que je jette sur la toile les grandes lignes du portrait, même si je ne compte pas le terminer avant l'automne. La toile fait 5 pieds sur 8, vous comprendrez donc le travail que cela représente. Il est un modèle parfait; il se tient, sur son fauteuil, raide comme un échalas.» (Lettre de Harris à sa mère, 19 juillet 1880).

Ce portrait du révérend Whitaker était la première commande importante que Harris recevait à Toronto. Né vers 1810, George Whitaker avait obtenu son baccalauréat au Queen's College (Cambridge) en 1833. De 1834 à 1840, il fut boursier et chargé de cours en études classiques au Queen's College; ordonné diacre en 1837, il fut nommé ministre de l'Église d'Angleterre un an plus tard.
En 1850, lorsque le King's College, à Toronto, se laïcise et devient l'université de Toronto, l'évêque John Strachan décide de fonder une université anglicane dans l'Ouest du Canada: Trinity College. Whitaker est alors nommé premier principal de ce collège nouvellement formé et, pendant les trente années suivantes, allie ses fonctions administratives à l'enseignement de la théologie. Toutefois, une vive controverse éclate au sujet du contenu de son enseignement à la fin des années 1850 et se poursuit au début des années 1860. Par suite de l'opposition du bas clergé, il se voit refuser le siège épiscopal de Toronto en 1866, en 1878 et, de nouveau, en 1879. De retour en Angleterre, Whitaker devient recteur de Newton Toney à Salisbury en 1882, mais meurt peu après.
THE CORPORATION OF TRINITY COLLEGE, TORONTO

25 *Children Playing* c. 1880
Gouache
5-5/8 x 7-7/8 in. (14.3 x 20 cm)
CONFEDERATION ART GALLERY AND MUSEUM, CHARLOTTETOWN

25 *Enfants au jeu* c. 1880
Gouache
5-5/8 x 7-7/8 po (14.3 x 20 cm)
CONFEDERATION ART GALLERY AND MUSEUM, CHARLOTTETOWN

26 *Mrs. William Harris: The Artist's Mother* 1881
Watercolour
11-1/4 x 8-7/8 in. (28.3 x 22.5 cm)
INSCRIPTION: signed and dated l.r., *R.H./ 1881.*

For a photograph of the elder Mrs. Harris, see Introduction, fig. 6.
EXHIBITION: *1967 Charlottetown*, no. 96, repr.
CONFEDERATION ART GALLERY AND MUSEUM, CHARLOTTETOWN

26 *Mᵐᵉ William Harris, mère de l'artiste* 1881
Aquarelle
11-1/4 x 8-7/8 po (28.3 x 22.5 cm)
INSCRIPTION: signature et date, b.d.: *R.H./ 1881.*

Une photographie de Mᵐᵉ Harris, plus âgée, est reproduite dans notre texte d'introduction (fig. 6).
EXPOSITION: *1967 Charlottetown*, n° 96, reprod.
CONFEDERATION ART GALLERY AND MUSEUM, CHARLOTTETOWN

27 *Man in Armour* 1881
21-1/4 x 17-3/4 in. (53.9 x 45.1 cm)
INSCRIPTION: signed and dated l.l., *R. Harris/ 1881.*
EXHIBITIONS: *1967 Charlottetown*, no. 9.
THE NATIONAL GALLERY OF CANADA, OTTAWA (23)

27 *Homme revêtu d'une armure* 1881
21-1/4 x 17-3/4 po (53.9 x 45.1 cm)
INSCRIPTION: signature et date, b.g.: *R. Harris/1881.*
EXPOSITION: *1967 Charlottetown*, n° 9.
GALERIE NATIONALE DU CANADA, OTTAWA (23)

28 *Study for "The Burnside Children"* 1881
Oil on paper
10-1/4 x 12 in. (26 x 30.5 cm)
INSCRIPTION: r. edge, pencil, *compson for group Burnside children – Toronto.*

The finished portrait for this study, and for the ones that follow (cat. nos. 29–33), is not in the exhibition.
CONFEDERATION ART GALLERY AND MUSEUM, CHARLOTTETOWN

28 *Étude pour Les enfants Burnside* 1881
Huile sur papier
10-1/4 x 12 po (26 x 30.5 cm)
INSCRIPTION: marge d., au crayon (trad.): composition pour le groupe des enfants Burnside – Toronto.

Le portrait exécuté à la suite de cette étude et des suivantes (n°ˢ 29–33) n'est pas présenté dans le cadre de cette exposition.
CONFEDERATION ART GALLERY AND MUSEUM, CHARLOTTETOWN

29 *Study for "The Burnside Children":*
Anson Burnside 1881
Graphite
12-1/2 x 9-3/8 in. (31.8 x 23.8 cm) (s)
INSCRIPTION: l.c., *Anson Burnside study for*
group.
CONFEDERATION ART GALLERY AND
MUSEUM, CHARLOTTETOWN

29 *Étude pour Les enfants Burnside: Anson*
Burnside 1881
Mine de plomb
12-1/2 x 9-3/8 po (31.8 x 23.8 cm) (s.v.)
INSCRIPTION: b.c. (trad.): étude d'*Anson*
Burnside pour le groupe.
CONFEDERATION ART GALLERY AND
MUSEUM, CHARLOTTETOWN

30 *Study for "The Burnside Children":*
?Norah Burnside 1881
Graphite
12-1/2 x 9-1/2 in. (31.8 x 24.1 cm)
INSCRIPTION: l.c., *Nor* [?Norah] *for Burnside*
Group.

    Framed with cat. no. 31.
CONFEDERATION ART GALLERY AND
MUSEUM, CHARLOTTETOWN

30 *Étude pour Les enfants Burnside:*
Norah(?) *Burnside* 1881
Mine de plomb
12-1/2 x 9-1/2 po (31.8 x 24.1 cm)
INSCRIPTION: b.c. (trad.): *Nor*[ah?] pour le
groupe des *Burnside.*

    Encadré avec le n° 31.
CONFEDERATION ART GALLERY AND
MUSEUM, CHARLOTTETOWN

31 *Study for "The Burnside Children"*:
?Norah Burnside 1881
Graphite
12-1/2 x 9-1/2 in. (31.8 x 24.1 cm) (s)
INSCRIPTION: l.r., *for Burnside Group*.

    Framed with cat. no. 30.
CONFEDERATION ART GALLERY AND
MUSEUM, CHARLOTTETOWN

31 *Étude pour Les enfants Burnside:*
Norah(?) *Burnside* 1881
Mine de plomb
12-1/2 x 9-1/2 po (31.8 x 24.1 cm) (s.v.)
INSCRIPTION: b.d. (trad.): pour le groupe des
Burnside.

    Encadré avec le nº 30.
CONFEDERATION ART GALLERY AND
MUSEUM, CHARLOTTETOWN

32 *Study for "The Burnside Children"*:
Thrift Burnside 1881
Graphite
12-1/2 x 9-1/4 in. (31.8 x 23.5 cm) (s)
INSCRIPTION: l.c., *Thrift Burnside – Toronto
study for group*.

    Framed with cat. no. 33.
CONFEDERATION ART GALLERY AND
MUSEUM, CHARLOTTETOWN

32 *Étude pour Les enfants Burnside: Thrift
Burnside* 1881
Mine de plomb
12-1/2 x 9-1/4 po (31.8 x 23.5 cm) (s.v.)
INSCRIPTION: b.c. (trad.): *Thrift Burnside –
étude* à *Toronto pour un groupe*.

    Encadré avec le nº 33.
CONFEDERATION ART GALLERY AND
MUSEUM, CHARLOTTETOWN

33 *Study for "The Burnside Children":
Thrift Burnside* 1881
Graphite
12-1/2 x 9-1/4 in. (31.8 x 23.5 cm) (s)
INSCRIPTION: l.c., *Thrift Burnside—study for
group.*

Framed with cat. no. 32.
CONFEDERATION ART GALLERY AND
MUSEUM, CHARLOTTETOWN

33 *Étude pour Les enfants Burnside: Thrift
Burnside* 1881
Mine de plomb
12-1/2 x 9-1/4 po (31.8 x 23.5 cm) (s.v.)
INSCRIPTION: b.c. (trad.): *Thrift Burnside –
étude pour un groupe.*

Encadré avec le n° 32.
CONFEDERATION ART GALLERY AND
MUSEUM, CHARLOTTETOWN

34 *Adversity* 1882
42 x 31-1/2 in. (106.7 x 80 cm)
INSCRIPTION: signed l.l., *Robert Harris.*
EXHIBITIONS: *1886 Montreal Spring Exhibition*, no. 83; *1910, Toronto, Canadian National Exhibition*, [exhibition by the Department of Fine Art], no. 123, repr.; *1919 Montreal*, no. 61; *1967 Charlottetown*, no. 13, repr. in colour.
CONFEDERATION ART GALLERY AND
MUSEUM, CHARLOTTETOWN

34 *Adversité* 1882
42 x 31-1/2 po (106.7 x 80 cm)
INSCRIPTION: signature, b.g.: *Robert Harris.*
EXPOSITIONS: *1886 Montréal, Printemps*, n° 83; *1910, Toronto*, [organisée par le Department of Fine Art], *Canadian National Exhibition*, n° 123, reprod.; *1919 Montréal*, n° 61; *1967 Charlottetown*, n° 13, reprod. en couleurs.
CONFEDERATION ART GALLERY AND
MUSEUM, CHARLOTTETOWN

35 *Anteroom of the Atelier Bonnat, Paris*
1882
Oil on panel
12-1/4 x 15-1/8 in. (31.1 x 38.4 cm)
INSCRIPTION: signed and dated l.r., *R. Harris./
Vestiare* [sic]*/l'atelier Bonnat./Impasse Helene
1882/Paris.*

Harris studied here with such artist-friends as Nicholson (cat. no. 36).
BIBLIOGRAPHY: Williamson, "Charlottetown's Robert Harris, 1849–1919," repr. p. 3.
EXHIBITIONS: *1883 Toronto R.C.A.*, no. 39; *1967 Charlottetown*, no. 12, repr. in colour.
CONFEDERATION ART GALLERY AND
MUSEUM, CHARLOTTETOWN

35 *Antichambre de l'atelier Bonnat, Paris*
1882
Huile sur bois
12-1/4 x 15-1/8 po (31.1 x 38.4 cm)
INSCRIPTION: signature, inscription et date, b.d.: *R. Harris./Vestiare/l'atelier Bonnat./
Impasse Helene 1882/Paris.*

Harris a étudié à l'atelier Bonnat avec des artistes qui étaient également des amis. Nicholson (n° 36) fut l'un de ceux-là.
BIBLIOGRAPHIE: Williamson: *Charlottetown's Robert Harris, 1849–1919*, reprod. p. 3.
EXPOSITIONS: *1883 Toronto, A.R.A.C.*, n° 39; *1967 Charlottetown*, n° 12, reprod. en couleurs.
CONFEDERATION ART GALLERY AND
MUSEUM, CHARLOTTETOWN

36 *?Mr. Nicholson* 1882
18 x 14-1/2 in. (45.7 x 36.8 cm)

Nicholson was a fellow-student of Harris's at the Atelier Bonnat in Paris (cat. no. 35). This lively study, recently cleaned, is especially interesting when compared with the style of Harris's later self-portrait (cat. no. 47).
CONFEDERATION ART GALLERY AND MUSEUM, CHARLOTTETOWN

36 *M. Nicholson (?)* 1882
18 x 14-1/2 po (45.7 x 36.8 cm)

Nicholson était un camarade de Harris à l'atelier Bonnat (n° 35) de Paris. Cette étude pleine de vie, récemment nettoyée, devient particulièrement intéressante lorsqu'on compare son style à celui utilisé par l'artiste dans un autoportrait ultérieur (n° 47).
CONFEDERATION ART GALLERY AND MUSEUM, CHARLOTTETOWN

37 *A Roman Model* c. 1882
Oil on panel
16-1/8 x 12-3/4 in. (40.9 x 32.4 cm)
INSCRIPTION: signed l.l., *R. HARRIS, ROMA*; on reverse, an old label in artist's handwriting, pen, *A Roman model/N° 7 R. Harris.*
PROVENANCE: A. Harvey, Rochdale, Ontario.
EXHIBITION: *1883 Toronto R.C.A.*, no. 102.
DR. CHARLOTTE M. HORNER

37 *Modèle romain* c. 1882
Huile sur bois
16-1/8 x 12-3/4 po (40.9 x 32.4 cm)
INSCRIPTION: signature, b.g.: *R. HARRIS, ROMA;* au verso, sur une ancienne étiquette, une inscription de la main de l'artiste, à la plume (trad.): *Modèle romain/ N° 7 R. Harris.*
HISTORIQUE: A. Harvey, Rochdale (Ontario).
EXPOSITION: *1883 Toronto, A.R.A.C.*, n° 102.
DR CHARLOTTE M. HORNER, COBOURG (ONTARIO)

38 *Romany Girl* c. 1882
20-3/4 x 17-3/16 in. (52.7 x 43.6 cm)
EXHIBITIONS: *1883 Toronto R.C.A.*, no. 42;
1967 Charlottetown, no. 19.
CONFEDERATION ART GALLERY AND
MUSEUM, CHARLOTTETOWN

38 *La jeune bohémienne* c. 1882
20-3/4 x 17-3/16 po (52.7 x 43.6 cm)
EXPOSITIONS: *1883 Toronto, A.R.A.C.*, n° 42;
1967 Charlottetown, n° 19.
CONFEDERATION ART GALLERY AND
MUSEUM, CHARLOTTETOWN

39 *Joseph Stretch* 1883
25-3/4 x 21-5/8 in. (65.4 x 54.9 cm) (s)
INSCRIPTION: signed and dated l.l., *R. Harris 1883.*

The sitter was from Long Creek, P.E.I.
NORMAN STRETCH

39 *Joseph Stretch* 1883
25-3/4 x 21-5/8 po (65.4 x 54.9 cm) (s.v.)
INSCRIPTION: signature et date, b.g.: *R. Harris 1883.*

Le modèle demeurait à Long Creek (Î.-P.-É.).
NORMAN STRETCH, LONG CREEK (Î.-P.-É.)

40 *Study for "The Fathers of Confederation"* 1883
Graphite
13-3/4 x 22-3/4 in. (34.9 x 57.8 cm) (s)
INSCRIPTION: signed on bottom edge, *Preliminary drawing for Fathers of Confederation made before I got all my detailed sketches and materials together. After getting these I made the full-size charcoal drawing which I followed with some changes in painting the picture/R. Harris.*
BIBLIOGRAPHY: Williamson, "Robert Harris and *The Fathers of Confederation*," pp. 8–21, repr. p. 14.
EXHIBITION: 1967, Ottawa, National Gallery of Canada, *Three Hundred Years of Canadian Art*, no. 148, repr.
CONFEDERATION ART GALLERY AND
MUSEUM, CHARLOTTETOWN

40 *Étude pour Les pères de la Confédération* 1883
Mine de plomb
13-3/4 x 22-3/4 po (34.9 x 57.8 cm) (s.v.)
INSCRIPTION: signature, marge b. (trad.): dessin préliminaire pour Les pères de la Confédération exécuté avant de rassembler mes esquisses détaillées et autres documents. Après les avoir rassemblés, j'ai exécuté au fusain un dessin grandeur nature que j'ai suivi, en y incorporant quelques variations, lorsque j'ai peint le tableau. *R. Harris.*
BIBLIOGRAPHIE: Williamson: *Robert Harris and The Fathers of Confederation*, pp. 8–21 et reprod. p. 14.
EXPOSITION: 1967, Ottawa, Galerie nationale du Canada, *Trois cents ans d'art canadien*, n° 148, reprod.
CONFEDERATION ART GALLERY AND
MUSEUM, CHARLOTTETOWN

41 *Study for "The Fathers of Confederation"*
1883
13 x 22-1/2 in. (33 x 57.2 cm)

Original oil sketch from which Harris developed the large portrait group burned in a fire which destroyed the Parliament Buildings in Ottawa in 1916.
BIBLIOGRAPHY: Williamson, "Robert Harris and *The Fathers of Confederation*," pp. 8–21, repr. p. 16.
EXHIBITION: *1967 Charlottetown*, no. 18 (as *Meeting of the Delegates of British North America [to settle Terms of Confederation, Quebec, October 1864]*).
CONFEDERATION ART GALLERY AND MUSEUM, CHARLOTTETOWN

41 *Étude pour Les pères de la Confédération*
1883
13 x 22-1/2 po (33 x 57.2 cm)

Esquisse originale à l'huile dont se servit Harris pour exécuter son grand portrait de groupe détruit au cours de l'incendie des édifices du parlement, à Ottawa en 1916.
BIBLIOGRAPHIE: Williamson: *Robert Harris and The Fathers of Confederation*, pp. 8–21 et reprod. p. 16.
EXPOSITION: *1967 Charlottetown*, nº 18 (*Meeting of the Delegates of British North America [to settle the Terms of Confederation, Quebec, October 1864]*).
CONFEDERATION ART GALLERY AND MUSEUM, CHARLOTTETOWN

42 *Study for "The Fathers of Confederation":
Sir John A. Macdonald* c. 1883
Oil on paper
10-7/8 x 8-1/2 in. (27.6 x 21.6 cm)
INSCRIPTION: signed l.r., *RH.*

John Alexander Macdonald was born in Glasgow, Scotland, in 1815, and at the age of five emigrated with his parents to Canada, settling in Kingston, Upper Canada. Macdonald attended the Royal Grammar School, Kingston, and was called to the Bar of Upper Canada in 1836. Four years later, he was elected to the Legislative Assembly of Canada, representing Kingston.

His political career and splendid sense of statesmanship culminated, through the "Great Coalition" government of 1864, in the confederation of British North America. He played a leading role in the conferences at Charlottetown and Quebec in 1864, and in the London Conference in 1866. The following year, Macdonald became the first Prime Minister of the newly-formed Dominion of Canada and, except for a brief period of five years (1873–78), when he suffered political defeat because of alleged scandals involving the building of the C.P.R., he held that office until his death in 1891.

Macdonald's platform of high tariff-protection, known as the "National Policy," successfully carried his Conservative Party through three general elections. It was not without reason that, on a visit to Government House, Charlottetown, on 9 August 1890, he signed the visitors book "John A. Macdonald, Cabinet Maker."

The oil sketch in the present exhibition was based on the photograph taken by Topley, the Court Photographer in Ottawa, and was used by Harris for the figure of Macdonald in *The Fathers of Confederation* (see cat. nos. 40, 41). Another portrait of Sir John A. Macdonald (water-damaged), also by

42 *Étude pour Les pères de la Confédération:
Sir John A. Macdonald* c. 1883
Huile sur papier
10-7/8 x 8-1/2 po (27.6 x 21.6 cm)
INSCRIPTION: signature, b.d.: *RH.*

Sir John Alexander Macdonald est né à Glasgow (Écosse) en 1815. À cinq ans, il émigra au Canada avec ses parents qui s'installèrent à Kingston, dans le Haut-Canada. Macdonald fréquenta la Royal Grammar School de Kingston, puis, en 1836, fut admis au barreau du Haut-Canada. Quatre ans plus tard, il devenait député de Kingston à l'Assemblée législative du Canada.

La confédération de l'Amérique du Nord britannique, à laquelle ont abouti les efforts du gouvernement de la «Grande coalition» de 1864, fut la consécration de sa carrière politique et de ses qualités d'homme d'État. Il joua un rôle de premier plan aux conférences de Charlottetown et de Québec en 1864, et à la conférence de Londres en 1866. L'année suivante, il devenait le premier chef de gouvernement du nouveau Dominion du Canada et, sauf pendant une brève période de cinq ans (1873–1878), à la suite de prétendus scandales entourant la construction du chemin de fer du Canadien Pacifique, il allait le rester jusqu'à sa mort en 1891.

La politique protectionniste, dite «politique nationale», de Macdonald assura aux Conservateurs trois victoires électorales. Ce n'est donc pas sans raison que, lors d'une visite au Palais du gouvernement à Charlottetown, le 9 août 1890, Macdonald apposa la signature suivante dans le livre des visiteurs: «John A. Macdonald, faiseur de cabinets.»

Le croquis à l'huile de la présente exposition a été fait d'après une photographie prise par Topley, photographe de la cour vice-royale à Ottawa, et utilisé par Harris pour son portrait de John A. Macdonald dans le

Robert Harris, is, at last report, still in a private collection in Toronto.

PRIVATE COLLECTION

tableau *Les pères de la Confédération* (voir n⁰ˢ 40 et 41). Un autre portrait de Sir John A. Macdonald, également de Robert Harris, fut endommagé par l'eau et se trouve aujourd'hui, selon les dernières nouvelles, dans une collection privée à Toronto.

COLLECTION PRIVÉE

43 *Thomas Workman* c. 1884
30 x 23-3/4 in. (76.2 x 60.3 cm)
INSCRIPTION: signed l.r., *Robert Harris.*

One of nine children born in County Antrim, Ireland, Workman emigrated with three other brothers to Canada in the 1820s, to be joined by the rest of the family in 1829. He and his brother, William, later Mayor of Montreal, were merchants in the wholesale hardware firm of John Frothingam. In 1836 they became full partners.

Involved in politics, banking, and the other interests he shared with his brother, Thomas was a most generous benefactor to McGill University. He and Sir William MacDonald (1831-1917), the tobacco baron (native of Prince Edward Island and founder of MacDonald College), endowed McGill's Faculty of Applied Science in 1878.

At about the time that the MacDonald Engineering Building, including the Workman Wing, was endowed, Workman, as a further indication of his appreciation for McGill, made a separate donation of $3,000 with instructions that this sum should be presented to the retired Principal, Dr. Edmund A. Meredith.

MCGILL UNIVERSITY, MONTREAL

43 *Thomas Workman* c. 1884
30 x 23-3/4 po (76.2 x 60.3 cm)
INSCRIPTION: signature, b.d.: *Robert Harris.*

Né dans une famille de neuf enfants du comté d'Antrim, en Irlande, Workman émigra au Canada, avec trois autres frères, au début des années 1820. Le reste de la famille l'y rejoignit neuf ans plus tard. Son frère William, plus tard maire de Montréal, et lui-même furent négociants pour la quincaillerie en gros de John Frothingam avant d'en devenir des associés à part entière, en 1836.

Prenant une part active à la politique, aux finances et à d'autres domaines d'intérêt qu'il partageait avec son frère, Thomas fut un généreux bienfaiteur de l'université McGill. Avec Sir William MacDonald (1831–1917), le fabricant de tabac (né à l'Î.-P.-É. et fondateur du collège MacDonald), il dota, en 1878, la Faculté des sciences appliquées de McGill.

Il dota également l'édifice de génie civil MacDonald, qui comporte une aile Workman, montrant bien son appréciation pour cette université, et il ordonna que $3 000 soient alloués au principal à la retraite, M. Edmund A. Meredith.

UNIVERSITÉ MCGILL, MONTRÉAL

44 *Sir Hugh Allan* 1885
51 x 42 in. (129.6 x 106.7 cm)
INSCRIPTION: signed l.l., *Robert Harris.*

Founder of the Allan Steamship Line, Hugh Allan was born in Ayrshire in 1810, and emigrated to Canada in 1820. After working with William Kerr, merchants, he joined the ship-building firm of John Millar and Co., becoming a partner in 1835. Allan and another partner, Edmonstone, formed their own company and established a line of steamers on the St. Lawrence. (Two of the Allan ships were used as transports during the Crimean War.)

Allan was an original contract-holder for the construction of the C.P.R. But as soon as his large contributions to the party funds for Sir John A. Macdonald (cat. no. 42) became generally known, his contract was nullified. Allan was knighted for his services to Canadian commerce and retired to Edinburgh, where he died in 1882.

Harris was commissioned by Montague

44 *Sir Hugh Allan* 1885
51 x 42 po (129.6 x 106.7 cm)
INSCRIPTION: signature, b.g.: *Robert Harris.*

Né en 1810 dans l'Ayrshire, le fondateur de l'Allan Steamship Line, Hugh Montague Allan, émigra au Canada en 1820. Après avoir travaillé pour le marchand William Kerr, il entre au service d'une entreprise de construction navale, la John Millar and Co., dont il devient associé en 1835. Avec un autre associé, Edmonstone, il forme une nouvelle société et établit une ligne de navires à vapeur qui dessert le Saint-Laurent. (Deux de ses navires servent au transport des troupes lors de la guerre de Crimée.)

Détenteur du contrat pour la construction du Canadien Pacifique, Allan le voit résilié à la suite de la découverte de ses contributions généreuses à la caisse du parti de Sir John A. Macdonald (n⁰ 42). Fait chevalier pour les services rendus au commerce canadien, il se retire à Édimbourg où il meurt en 1882.

Allan (later Sir Montague; for Lady Allan, see cat. no. 101) to paint this portrait of his father in February 1885.

THE NATIONAL GALLERY OF CANADA, OTTAWA (4551)
GIFT OF SIR MONTAGUE ALLAN, C.V.O.

C'est en février 1885 que Sir Hugh Montague Allan (voir également Lady Allan, nᵒ 101) commanda à Harris ce portrait de son père.

GALERIE NATIONALE DU CANADA, OTTAWA (4551)
DON DE SIR MONTAGUE ALLAN, C.V.O.

---

45 *Bessie in her Wedding Gown*   1885
50 x 40 in. (127 x 101.6 cm)
INSCRIPTION: signed l.l., *Robert Harris.*

The artist's wife, Elizabeth. For another portrait, see cat. no. 50.
EXHIBITION: *1967 Charlottetown*, no. 22, repr.
MISS MARY BETH HARRIS, CHARLOTTETOWN

45 *Bessie dans sa robe de mariée*   1885
50 x 40 po (127 x 101.6 cm)
INSCRIPTION: signature, b.g.: *Robert Harris.*

Le modèle était Elizabeth Harris, l'épouse de l'artiste. Voir également son autre portrait (nᵒ 50).
EXPOSITION: *1967 Charlottetown*, nᵒ 22, reprod.
Mᴸᴸᴱ MARY BETH HARRIS, CHARLOTTETOWN

---

46 *Mrs. Lester N. Putman*   1885
Oil on panel
7-5/8 x 6-3/8 in. (19.4 x 16.2 cm) (s)
INSCRIPTION: signed and dated l.r., *R. Harris/ 1885.*

Harris's mother-in-law.
CONFEDERATION ART GALLERY AND MUSEUM, CHARLOTTETOWN

46 *Mᵐᵉ Lester N. Putnam*   1885
Huile sur bois
7-5/8 x 6-3/8 po (19.4 x 16.2 cm) (s.v.)
INSCRIPTION: signature et date, b.d.: *R. Harris/1885.*

Le modèle était la belle-mère de l'artiste.
CONFEDERATION ART GALLERY AND MUSEUM, CHARLOTTETOWN

---

47 *Self-portrait*   1885
50 x 40 in. (127 x 101.6 cm)
INSCRIPTION: dated and signed l.l., *May 1885/Robert Harris.*
EXHIBITION: *1967 Charlottetown*, no. 8.
CONFEDERATION ART GALLERY AND MUSEUM, CHARLOTTETOWN

47 *Autoportrait*   1885
50 x 40 po (127 x 101.6 cm)
INSCRIPTION: date et signature, b.g.: *May 1885/Robert Harris.*
EXPOSITION: *1967 Charlottetown*, nᵒ 8.
CONFEDERATION ART GALLERY AND MUSEUM, CHARLOTTETOWN

48 *A Meeting of the School Trustees* c. 1885
39-1/4 x 48-3/4 in. (99.7 x 123.8 cm)
INSCRIPTION: signed l.r., *Robert Harris;* as if carved into desk at l., *Robert Harris;* as if written on paper on desk, *ROLL/Pine Creek/SCHOOL/Kate Henderson/Teacher.*

This painting will be shown only in Charlottetown and Ottawa.
BIBLIOGRAPHY: Harte, "Canadian Art and Artists," repr. p. 152.
EXHIBITIONS: *1886 Ottawa R.C.A.,* no. 156 (as *Meeting of Trustees of a Back Settlement School, Canada – The Teacher, Talking them Over*); 1886, London, [no further information available]; 1938, London, The Tate Gallery, *A Century of Canadian Art,* no. 84; 1945, Toronto/Montreal/Quebec/Ottawa, The Art Gallery of Toronto/The Art Association of Montreal/Musée de la Province de Québec/ The National Gallery of Canada, *The Development of Painting in Canada, 1665–1945,* no. 73; 1949, Richmond, Virginia, Virginia Museum of Fine Arts, *Exhibition of Canadian Painting 1668–1948,* no. 32; *1967 Charlottetown,* no. 21.
THE NATIONAL GALLERY OF CANADA, OTTAWA (6)

48 *Une rencontre des commissaires d'école*
c. 1885
39-1/4 x 48-3/4 po (99.7 x 123.8 cm)
INSCRIPTION: signature, b.d.: *Robert Harris;* signature gravée, en trompe-l'œil, sur le bureau, g.: *Robert Harris;* inscription, en trompe-l'œil, sur la première feuille du cahier sur le bureau, g. (trad.): *ROLL/Pine Creek/ ÉCOLE/Kate Henderson/Professeur.*

Cette peinture ne sera présentée qu'aux expositions de Charlottetown et d'Ottawa.
BIBLIOGRAPHIE: Harte: *Canadian Art and Artists,* reprod. p. 152.
EXPOSITIONS: 1886 Ottawa, A.R.A.C., n° 156 (*Meeting of Trustees of a Back Settlement School, Canada – The Teacher, Talking them Over*); 1886, Londres, [documentation incomplète]; 1938, Londres, The Tate Gallery, *A Century of Canadian Art,* n° 84; 1945, Toronto/Montréal/Québec/Ottawa, The Art Gallery of Toronto/The Art Association of Montreal/Musée de la province de Québec/ Galerie nationale du Canada, *Le développement de la peinture au Canada, 1665–1945,* n° 73; 1949, Richmond (Virginie), Virginia Museum of Fine Arts, *Exhibition of Canadian Painting 1668–1948,* n° 32; *1967 Charlottetown,* n° 21.
GALERIE NATIONALE DU CANADA, OTTAWA (6)

49 *Mrs. Maurice-Nolan Delisle* c. 1885
46-1/8 x 28-7/8 in. (117.2 x 73 cm)
INSCRIPTION: on reverse before relining, *Madame M. Delisle – Montréal.*

This charming young lady is almost certainly the wife of Maurice-Nolan Delisle, Manager of the Delisle Estate. In Lovell's *Montreal Directory* for 1889–90, Delisle is listed as having offices in the same building, where Harris and Otto Jacobi (cat. nos. 61, 80) had studios. A photograph almost identical to the one held in Madame Delisle's hand is in the Notman Archives, dated 1871. Joint manager of the Estate with Delisle were Alexandre-Maurice Delisle and William Workman, brother of Thomas (cat. no. 43).
MAURICE RÉGNIER, OUTREMONT

49 *Mme Maurice-Nolan Delisle* c. 1885
46-1/8 x 28-7/8 po (117.2 x 73 cm)
INSCRIPTION: au dos de la toile, avant le rentoilage: *Madame M. Delisle – Montréal.*

Cette charmante jeune femme est sans doute la femme de Maurice-Nolan Delisle, administrateur du patrimoine Delisle qui, selon l'annuaire montréalais de Lovell pour l'année 1889–1890, avait des bureaux dans l'édifice où se trouvaient également les ateliers de Harris et d'Otto Jacobi (n°s 61 et 80). Une photographie, presque identique à celle que tient Mme Delisle, fait partie des archives Notman et est datée de 1871. Alexandre Maurice Delisle et William Workman, frère de Thomas (n° 43) partageaient la direction du patrimoine avec Maurice-Nolan Delisle.
MAURICE RÉGNIER, OUTREMONT (QUÉBEC)

50 *Harmony* 1886
Oil on panel
12 x 9-3/4 in. (30.5 x 24.8 cm)
INSCRIPTION: signed l.r., *Robt. Harris.*

This is a portrait of Elizabeth ("Bessie") Harris, the artist's wife, painted in Runswick, Yorkshire, in 1886.
    See also cat. no 45.
PROVENANCE: D. Morrice, Montreal.
EXHIBITIONS: *1888 Montreal Spring Exhibition*, no. 47; *1888 Toronto R.C.A.*, no. 175; 1893, Chicago, World's Columbian Exposition, [exhibition of the Canadian Department of Fine Arts], no. 62; *1893 Montreal R.C.A.*, no. 75; Toronto, Laing Galleries, *One Hundred Years of Canadian Painting: A Loan Exhibition for the Benefit of the Women's Association of the Ontario Heart Foundation*, no. 8, repr.; 1962, Bordeaux, Musée de Bordeaux, *L'Art au Canada*, no. 14.
THE NATIONAL GALLERY OF CANADA, OTTAWA (6757)

50 *Harmonie* 1886
Huile sur bois
12 x 9-3/4 po (30.5 x 24.8 cm)
INSCRIPTION: signature, b.d.: *Robt. Harris.*

Le modèle était Elizabeth («Bessie») Harris, l'épouse de l'artiste. Harris a peint ce portrait à Runswick (Yorkshire) en 1886.
    Voir également le nº 45.
HISTORIQUE: D. Morrice, Montréal.
EXPOSITIONS: *1888 Montréal, Printemps*, nº 47; *1888 Toronto, A.R.A.C.*, nº 175; 1893, Chicago, [exposition du Canadian Department of Fine Arts], *World's Columbian Exposition*, nº 62; *1893 Montréal, A.R.A.C.*, nº 75; 1959, Toronto, Laing Galleries, *One Hundred Years of Canadian Painting. A Loan Exhibition for the Benefit of the Women's Association of the Ontario Heart Foundation*, nº 8, reprod.; 1962, Bordeaux, Musée de Bordeaux, *L'art au Canada*, nº 14.
GALERIE NATIONALE DU CANADA, OTTAWA (6757)

---

51 *Sarah Harris* 1886
39 x 30 in. (99.1 x 76.2 cm) (s)

See also cat. nos. 2, 161.
BIBLIOGRAPHY: Percival, *Museum Memo*, pp. 4–6, repr. p. 5.
THE NEW BRUNSWICK MUSEUM

51 *Sarah Harris* 1886
39 x 30 po (99.1 x 76.2 cm) (s.v.)

Voir également les nᵒˢ 2 et 161.
BIBLIOGRAPHIE: Percival: *Museum Memo*, pp. 4–6 et reprod. p. 5.
THE NEW BRUNSWICK MUSEUM, SAINT-JEAN

---

52 *Jennie Stewart* 1886
Oil on panel
11 x 9 in. (27.9 x 22.8 cm)
INSCRIPTION: signed l.r., *R. Harris.*

According to Harris's sitter-book, this portrait was painted during Harris's stay in Runswick, Yorkshire. One of the two girls in *The Little Gossips* (in Edgehill Girls' School, Windsor, Nova Scotia) closely resembles her, even in such details as clothing.
PROVENANCE: Estate of Mrs. Robert W. Reford, Montreal; Christie's, Toronto, April 1971; Gift of Noranda Mines Limited.
EXHIBITION: 1886, Manchester, [no further information available].

52 *Jennie Stewart* 1886
Huile sur bois
11 x 9 po (27.9 x 22.8 cm)
INSCRIPTION: signature, b.d.: *R. Harris.*

Si l'on se fie au journal de travail de Harris, il aurait exécuté ce portrait au cours de son séjour à Runswick (Yorkshire). Le modèle ressemble beaucoup, même par ses vêtements, à une des deux jeunes filles des *Jeunes causeuses* (Windsor (N.-É.), Edgehill Girls School).
HISTORIQUE: Succession de Mᵐᵉ Robert W. Reford, Montréal; Christie's, Toronto, avril 1971; don de la Noranda Mines Limited.
EXPOSITION: 1886, Manchester, [documentation incomplète].

53 *Indian Squaw and Papoose* c. 1886
31-1/8 x 25 in. (79.0 x 63.5 cm)
INSCRIPTION: signed l.r., *Robert Harris.*
EXHIBITION: *1886 Ottawa R.C.A.*, no. 174.
THE NATIONAL GALLERY OF CANADA,
OTTAWA (15234)

53 *Femme indienne et son enfant* c. 1886
31-1/8 x 25 po (79.0 x 63.5 cm)
INSCRIPTION: signature, b.d.: *Robert Harris.*
EXPOSITION: *1886 Ottawa, A.R.A.C.*, nº 174.
GALERIE NATIONALE DU CANADA,
OTTAWA (15234)

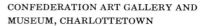

54 *Study of a Man* c. 1886
18 x 15 in. (45.7 x 38.1 cm)
INSCRIPTION: signed u.r., *R. Harris.*
EXHIBITION: *1967 Charlottetown*, no. 34.
THE ART GALLERY OF HAMILTON

54 *Étude d'homme* c. 1886
18 x 15 po (45.7 x 38.1 cm)
INSCRIPTION: signature, h.d.: *R. Harris.*
EXPOSITION: *1967 Charlottetown*, nº 34.
THE ART GALLERY OF HAMILTON

55 *The Young Model* c. 1886
24 x 20 in. (60.9 x 50.8 cm)
INSCRIPTION: signed l.r., *R. Harris.*
MR. AND MRS. P. DEJONG

55 *Le jeune modèle* c. 1886
24 x 20 po (60.9 x 50.8 cm)
INSCRIPTION: signature, b.d.: *R. Harris.*
M. ET Mᴹᴱ P. DEJONG, ST. CATHARINES
(ONTARIO)

56 *Composing his Serenade* 1887
30 x 24 in. (76.2 x 60.9 cm)
INSCRIPTION: signed l.r., *Robert Harris.*
BIBLIOGRAPHY: Harte, "Canadian Art and
Artists," p. 156, repr. (as *An Improvisatore*).
EXHIBITIONS: *1888 Toronto R.C.A.*, no. 107;
1888 Montreal Spring Exhibition, no. 24;
1893, Chicago, World's Columbian Exposition, [exhibition by the Canadian Department of Fine Art], no. 59; *1915 Montreal Spring Exhibition*, no. 163; *1919 Montreal*, no. 60; *1967 Charlottetown*, no. 68 (as *The Man with the Mandolin*).
CONFEDERATION ART GALLERY AND
MUSEUM, CHARLOTTETOWN

56 *Composant sa sérénade* 1887
30 x 24 po (76.2 x 60.9 cm)
INSCRIPTION: signature, b.d.: *Robert Harris.*
BIBLIOGRAPHIE: Harte: *Canadian Art and Artists*, p. 156 et reprod. (*An Improvisatore*).
EXPOSITIONS: *1888 Toronto, A.R.A.C.*, nº 107; *1888 Montréal, Printemps*, nº 24; 1893, Chicago, [exposition du Canadian Department of Fine Art], *World's Columbian Exposition*, nº 59; *1915 Montréal, Printemps*, nº 163; *1919 Montréal*, nº 60; *1967 Charlottetown*, nº 68 (*The Man with the Mandolin*).
CONFEDERATION ART GALLERY AND
MUSEUM, CHARLOTTETOWN

57 *Composing his Serenade* 1887
30 x 24-1/4 in. (76.2 x 61.6 cm)
INSCRIPTION: signed u.r., *Robert Harris.*

This is an extraordinarily free version of the previous work (cat. no. 56). The brightness of colour and lightness of touch seem quite uncharacteristic of Harris. Harris himself seemed to think so; as mentioned in the Introduction, this variation on a theme was never publicly exhibited.
CONFEDERATION ART GALLERY AND
MUSEUM, CHARLOTTETOWN

57 *Composant sa sérénade* 1887
30 x 24-1/4 po (76.2 x 61.6 cm)
INSCRIPTION: signature, h.d.: *Robert Harris.*

Cette toile est une version extrêmement libre de l'œuvre précédente (nº 56). La grande luminosité des couleurs et la légèreté du trait ressemblent peu à la manière habituelle de Harris, ce qu'il ne manquera pas d'ailleurs lui-même de constater. Comme nous l'avons déjà mentionné dans notre introduction, cette variation sur un même sujet n'a jamais été présentée publiquement.
CONFEDERATION ART GALLERY AND
MUSEUM, CHARLOTTETOWN

58 *Caricature of Evangelist Moody* 1887
Pen and ink
6-1/4 x 4 in. (15.9 x 10.2 cm) (s)
INSCRIPTION: dated l.r., pencil, *Evangelist/ Moody/2nd Jan 87.*

A *1* has been inscribed on top of the *2*, and a *6* has been inscribed on top of the *7*. Framed with cat. nos. 85, 86, 87, 93, 94.

Dwight Lyman Moody (1837–99) and Ira David Sankey (1840–1908), American evangelists, were joint authors of enormously popular gospel hymnaries.
EXHIBITION: *1967 Charlottetown*, no. 80 (one of six framed together).
CONFEDERATION ART GALLERY AND
MUSEUM, CHARLOTTETOWN

58 *Caricature de l'évangéliste Moody* 1887
Plume, encre
6-1/4 x 4 po (15.9 x 10.2 cm) (s.v.)
INSCRIPTION: date, b.d., au crayon (trad.): L'évangéliste/*Moody*/2 janvier 87.

Un «1» a été inscrit sur le «2» et un «6», sur le «7». Encadré avec les nᵒˢ 85, 86, 87, 93 et 94.

Dwight Lyman Moody (1837–1899) et Ira David Sankey (1840–1908), sont les évangélistes américains qui composèrent des hymnes évangéliques qui devinrent très populaires.
EXPOSITION: *1967 Charlottetown*, nº 80 (qui comportait également les cinq autres).
CONFEDERATION ART GALLERY AND
MUSEUM, CHARLOTTETOWN

59 *Marion Taylor* 1887
20-1/16 x 15-15/16 in. (51 x 40.5 cm), oval
INSCRIPTION: signed l.l., *Robert Harris.*
HARRIS PAPERS: "I have a little picture in the Suffolk Street Exhibition [in London, England] where Whistler predominates." (Letter from Harris to his mother, dated April 1887) "Domett and Collins (a friend of his) and I are just making portraits of Marion Taylor, D's [Domett's] neice [*sic*]; he got her to sit, she is a great beauty and we are painting her in D's studio." (Letter from Harris to his mother, dated 24 April 1887)
PROVENANCE: Dr. Robert L. Cotton Estate.
EXHIBITION: *1967 Charlottetown*, no. 29.
CONFEDERATION ART GALLERY AND MUSEUM, CHARLOTTETOWN

59 *Marion Taylor* 1887
20-1/16 x 15-15/16 po (51 x 40.5 cm), ovale
INSCRIPTION: signature, b.g.: *Robert Harris.*
DOCUMENTS HARRIS: «J'ai un petit tableau à l'exposition de la rue Suffolk [Londres] où prédomine Whistler.» (Lettre de Harris à sa mère, avril 1887).
«Domett, Collins (un de ses amis) et moi-même sommes justement en train de peindre Marion Taylor, la nièce de D. [Domett]; il lui a demandé de poser, elle est très belle et nous la peignons à l'atelier de D.» (Lettre de Harris à sa mère, 24 avril 1887).
HISTORIQUE: Succession du Dr Robert L. Cotton.
EXPOSITION: *1967 Charlottetown*, no 29.
CONFEDERATION ART GALLERY AND MUSEUM, CHARLOTTETOWN

60 *Henry Botterell* 1888
28-1/2 x 20-1/2 in. (72.4 x 52.1 cm)
INSCRIPTION: signed l.r., *R. Harris;* on reverse, *25-II-89/41.*
MRS. H.R.C. AVISON

60 *Henry Botterell* 1888
28-1/2 x 20-1/2 po (72.4 x 52.1 cm)
INSCRIPTION: signature, b.d.: *R. Harris;* au verso: *25-II-89/41.*
MME H.R.C. AVISON, MONTRÉAL

61 *Study for "Otto Jacobi"* 1888
Graphite
19-1/2 x 9-3/4 in. (49.5 x 24.8 cm)
INSCRIPTION: dated and signed c.r., *19th May 1888/R Harris;* c., *O.R. Jacobi;* l.r., *He sat for this in the studio he had for a winter at the foot of Beaver/Hall hill over the flower shop.*

For biography and finished portrait, see cat. no. 80.
EXHIBITION: *1967 Charlottetown*, no. 107.
CONFEDERATION ART GALLERY AND MUSEUM, CHARLOTTETOWN

61 *Étude pour Otto Jacobi* 1888
Mine de plomb
19-1/2 x 9-3/4 po (49.5 x 24.8 cm)
INSCRIPTION: date et signature, c.d. (trad.): *19 mai 1888/R Harris;* c.: O.R. Jacobi; b.d. (trad.): Il a posé pour ce portrait dans l'atelier qu'il eut, un hiver, au pied de la côte du *Beaver/Hall*, au dessus de la boutique de fleuriste.

Voir également le portrait exécuté à la suite de cette étude et les notes biographiques sur Otto Jacobi (no 80).
EXPOSITION: *1967 Charlottetown*, no 107.
CONFEDERATION ART GALLERY AND MUSEUM, CHARLOTTETOWN

62 *Self-portrait* c.1888
Watercolour
11 x 8-1/2 in. (27.9 x 21.6 cm)
PROVENANCE: Dr. Robert J. Cotton Estate.
CONFEDERATION ART GALLERY AND
MUSEUM, CHARLOTTETOWN

62 *Autoportrait* c.1888
Aquarelle
11 x 8-1/2 po (27.9 x 21.6 cm)
HISTORIQUE: Succession du Dr Robert J.
Cotton.
CONFEDERATION ART GALLERY AND
MUSEUM, CHARLOTTETOWN

63 *Study for "George Allan"* 1889
Charcoal and graphite
6-1/2 x 5-1/4 in. (16.5 x 13.3 cm)
HARRIS PAPERS: "Went up to Toronto to
paint portraits of Hon. G.W. Allan Speaker
of Dominion Senate and Sir Alexander
Campbell, Lt. Gov. of Ontario for Govt.
House. Copies of these both for families.
Paid." (Sitter-book, entry dated June 1889)

Study for a portrait not in the exhibition.
George William Allan was Speaker of the
Senate of Canada from 1888 to 1891. Born
at York (later Toronto), in 1822, he was
educated at Upper Canada College and
called to the Bar in 1846. He was involved in
municipal politics and was elected mayor of
Toronto in 1855. In 1858 he was appointed
to the Legislative Council of Canada.
A member of the Privy Council for
Canada, Senator Allan was Chancellor of
Trinity College from 1877 till his death in
1901. Among the many offices held by him
was presidency of the Ontario Society of
Artists, a position the artists themselves
reserved for businessmen. (Harris himself
was Vice-President and Treasurer of the
O.S.A. in 1881.)
EXHIBITION: *?1889 Ottawa R.C.A.*, no. 53.
CONFEDERATION ART GALLERY AND
MUSEUM, CHARLOTTETOWN

63 *Étude pour George Allan* 1889
Fusain et mine de plomb
6-1/2 x 5-1/4 po (16.5 x 13.3 cm)
DOCUMENTS HARRIS: «Suis allé à Toronto
pour faire les portraits, pour la résidence du
gouverneur général, de l'honorable G.W.
Allan, président du Sénat canadien, et de
Sir Alexander Campbell, lieutenant-gouverneur de l'Ontario. Copies des deux pour leurs
familles. Payés» (Journal de travail de l'artiste, juin 1889).

Le portrait exécuté à la suite de cette étude
n'est pas présenté dans le cadre de cette
exposition.
George William Allan fut orateur du Sénat
canadien de 1888 à 1891. Né à York (qui
deviendra, plus tard, Toronto) en 1822, il fit
ses études au Upper Canada College et entra
au barreau en 1846. S'intéressant aux affaires municipales, il fut élu maire de Toronto en 1855. En 1858, il fut nommé au
Conseil législatif du Canada.
Membre du Conseil privé du Canada, le
sénateur Allan fut chancelier de Trinity
College de 1877 à sa mort, en 1901. Parmi ses
nombreuses fonctions, citons la présidence
de l'Ontario Society of Artists, poste que les
artistes eux-mêmes réservaient aux hommes
d'affaires. (Harris fut lui-même vice-président et trésorier de l'O.S.A. en 1881).
EXPOSITION: (?) *1889 Ottawa, A.R.A.C.*,
no 53.
CONFEDERATION ART GALLERY AND
MUSEUM, CHARLOTTETOWN

64 *Study for "Sir Alexander Campbell"*
1889
Graphite
11-5/8 x 8-1/2 in. (29.5 x 21.6 cm) (s)
INSCRIPTION: l.r., *preliminary sketch/Sir Alex Campbell.*

Framed with cat. nos. 65, 66.
CONFEDERATION ART GALLERY AND
MUSEUM, CHARLOTTETOWN

64 *Étude pour Sir Alexander Campbell*
1889
Mine de plomb
11-5/8 x 8-1/2 po (29.5 x 21.6 cm) (s.v.)
INSCRIPTION: b.d. (trad.): esquisse préliminaire/*Sir Alex Campbell.*

Encadré avec les nos 65 et 66.
CONFEDERATION ART GALLERY AND
MUSEUM, CHARLOTTETOWN

65 *Study for "Sir Alexander Campbell"*
1889
Charcoal
11-5/8 x 9 in. (29.5 x 22.4 cm) (s)
INSCRIPTION: l.r., pencil, *1st sketch for Sir Alex/Campbell port[rait],/Changed pose after.*

Framed with cat. nos. 64, 66.
CONFEDERATION ART GALLERY AND
MUSEUM, CHARLOTTETOWN

65 *Étude pour Sir Alexander Campbell*
1889
Fusain
11-5/8 x 9 po (29.5 x 22.4 cm) (s.v.)
INSCRIPTION: b.d., au crayon (trad.): première esquisse pour le portrait de *Sir Alex/Campbell*/Ai changé ultérieurement la pose.

Encadré avec les nos 64 et 66.
CONFEDERATION ART GALLERY AND
MUSEUM, CHARLOTTETOWN

66 *Study for "Sir Alexander Campbell"*
1889
Charcoal
11-5/8 x 8-3/8 in. (29.5 x 21.3 cm) (s)
INSCRIPTION: l.c., ink, *First drawing for portrait of Sir Alex Campbell painted in Toronto/89./I changed the pose of this very much in carrying it out.*

Framed with cat. nos. 64, 65.
CONFEDERATION ART GALLERY AND
MUSEUM, CHARLOTTETOWN

66 *Étude pour Sir Alexander Campbell*
1889
Fusain
11-5/8 x 8-3/8 po (29.5 x 21.3 cm) (s.v.)
INSCRIPTION: b.c., à l'encre (trad.): premier dessin pour le portrait de *Sir Alex Campbell* peint à *Toronto/89.*/J'ai beaucoup changé la pose en cours de travail.

Encadré avec les nos 64 et 65.
CONFEDERATION ART GALLERY AND
MUSEUM, CHARLOTTETOWN

67 *Sir Alexander Campbell* 1889
50 x 39 in. (127 x 99.1 cm) (s)
INSCRIPTION: l.r., *Robert Harris.*
HARRIS PAPERS: "The Jesuits Bill which made so much stir in Ontario seems to excite very little discussion here, which surprises the Toronto [*sic*] very much. I had lunch with Sir Alexander Campbell here the other day and it seemed to strike him very strange." (Letter from Harris to his mother, dated 31 March 1889) "Went up to Toronto to paint portraits of Hon. G.W. Allan Speaker of Dominion Senate and Sir Alexander Campbell, Lt. Gov. of Ontario for Govt. House. Copies of these both for families. Paid." (Sitter-book, entry dated June 1889)

Sir Alexander Campbell was born at Kingston-upon-Hull in 1822, the year before his father, James Campbell, M.D., emigrated with the family to Canada. Educated at St-Hyacinthe College and Kingston Grammar School, Campbell practised law and entered into partnership with Sir John A. Macdonald (cat. no. 42), with whom he established a life-long friendship. He was created K.C.M.G. in 1879. During his career, Sir Alexander Campbell was successively Minister of the Interior, Receiver-General, Postmaster General, Minister of Militia, Minister of Justice, and, in 1887, Lieutenant-Governor of Ontario. He represented Canada at the Imperial Conference in 1887. He died in Toronto in 1892.

PROVINCE OF ONTARIO, TORONTO

67 *Sir Alexander Campbell* 1889
50 x 39 po (127 x 99.1 cm) (s.v.)
INSCRIPTION: signature, b.d.: *Robert Harris.*
DOCUMENTS HARRIS: «Au grand étonnement de Toronto, le bill des Jésuites, qui a soulevé tant de controverses en Ontario, fait l'objet de très peu de commentaires ici. J'ai déjeuné en compagnie de Sir Alexander Campbell ici l'autre jour et il trouve cela fort bizarre.» (Lettre de Harris à sa mère, 31 mars 1889). «Suis allé à Toronto pour faire les portraits, pour la résidence du gouverneur général, de l'honorable G.W. Allan, président du Sénat canadien, et de Sir Alexander Campbell, lieutenant-gouverneur de l'Ontario. Copies des deux pour leurs familles. Payés.» (Journal de travail de l'artiste, juin 1889).

Sir Alexander Campbell est né à Kingston-upon-Hull en 1822, une année avant que son père, le médecin James Campbell, n'émigre avec sa famille au Canada. Après avoir étudié au collège de Saint-Hyacinthe, puis à l'école secondaire de Kingston, Campbell se dirige vers le droit. Il s'associe avec Sir John A. Macdonald (no 42), avec lequel il se lie d'une amitié qui durera toute sa vie. En 1879, il est fait chevalier commandeur de l'Ordre de Saint-Michel et de Saint-Georges. Durant sa carrière, Sir Alexander Campbell fut tour à tour ministre de l'intérieur, receveur-général, ministre des postes, ministre de la milice, ministre de la justice et, finalement en 1887, lieutenant-gouverneur de l'Ontario. Cette même année, il représenta le Canada à la conférence impériale. Il mourut à Toronto en 1892.

PROVINCE D'ONTARIO, TORONTO

68 *John Carruthers* 1889
30 x 24 in. (76.2 x 60.9 cm) (s)
INSCRIPTION: l.r., *Robert Harris.*
HARRIS PAPERS: "Professor Bovey, Mrs. Bovey (two) Bishop Williams for Lennoxville College, Mr. Carruthers Snr. (Just after this went to Toronto to paint Miss Marjorie Campbell daughter of Sir Alexander also his son and to Kingston to paint Mr. John Carruthers.)" (Sitter-book, undated entry)

John Carruthers was born in Ecclefechan, Dumfriesshire, Scotland, in 1815, and came to Canada in 1838, taking part in the Battle of Windmill Point, near Prescott, Ontario, shortly after his arrival. In 1840 he returned to Scotland and brought his mother and sister to Kingston, where he lived until his death in 1889.

A prominent merchant in Kingston, owning a wholesale grocery business, Carruthers was also a ship-owner and trader on

68 *John Carruthers* 1889
30 x 24 po (76.2 x 60.9 cm) (s.v.)
INSCRIPTION: signature, b.d.: *Robert Harris.*
DOCUMENTS HARRIS: «Le professeur Bovey, Mme Bovey (deux), l'évêque Williams pour le collège de Lennoxville, M. Carruthers père. (Suis allé ensuite à Toronto pour peindre Mlle Marjorie Campbell, fille de Sir Alexander, ainsi que son fils, puis à Kingston pour peindre M. John Carruthers.)» (Journal de travail de l'artiste, s.d.)

John Carruthers est né en 1815 à Ecclefechan (Dumfriesshire), en Écosse, et vint s'établir au Canada en 1838. Peu après son arrivée, il fut mêlé au conflit de Windmill Point, près de Prescott (Ontario). En 1840 il rentre en Écosse chercher sa mère et sa sœur. Il vivra à Kingston jusqu'à sa mort, en 1889.

Négociant à Kingston, où il possédait un commerce en gros de produits alimentaires, Carruthers fut aussi armateur, fit du com-

the Great Lakes and owned considerable property. He was one of the organizers of the local Board of Trade and held the office of President. He was a staunch Presbyterian and a supporter of Kingston's Chalmers Church.

Carruthers was a warm friend of Queen's University in a practical sense: in addition to other gifts, recognizing the need for buildings, he gave $10,000 in 1887 for the erection of a science hall.

His personal characteristics were summed up in an obituary in the Kingston *British Whig* (15 February 1889): "In a representative capacity as a member of the Board of Health or Board of Trade, as a leader in every public movement, he was the uncompromising advocate of the right and the uncompromising censor of the wrong. His language was terse and to the point. He believed that brevity was not only the soul of wit but the essence of common sense."

For sitter's son, see cat. no. 148.

merce sur les Grands Lacs et fut un grand propriétaire foncier. Un des fondateurs de la chambre de commerce locale, il en devint le président. Presbytérien convaincu, il fut membre de l'Église de Chalmers à Kingston.

Grand ami de l'université Queen's, il a contribué à la construction de différents bâtiments et a légué, en 1887, $10 000 pour l'édification d'un immeuble des sciences.

À sa mort, la nécrologie du *British Whig* de Kingston (livraison du 15 février 1889) le décrivait en ces termes: «En tant que membre représentatif du Conseil d'hygiène et de la Chambre de commerce, en tant que chef de tout mouvement public, il était un défenseur inflexible du bien et un censeur intransigeant du mal. Son langage était concis et sans ambages. Il croyait que, tout comme l'esprit, le bon sens réside dans la concision.»

Voir également le fils du modèle de ce portrait (n° 148).

69 *Sir William Dawson*   1889
29-1/2 x 23-1/4 in. (74.9 x 59.1 cm) (s)
INSCRIPTION: signed l.r., *Robert Harris*.
HARRIS PAPERS: "Just now I'm waiting for Sir William Dawson, who is coming to sit in a few minutes, for a portrait [completed 24 June 1889] I am painting of him for the Natural History Society." (Letter from Harris to his mother, dated 10 June 1889)

Sir William Dawson, a Principal of McGill, was born in Pictou County, Nova Scotia, in 1820, the son of Scottish immigrants. He was educated at Pictou and at Edinburgh University, where he earned an M.A. in Geology.

Natural History and Practical Chemistry had been his main interests at Edinburgh, and after his return to Canada, Dawson accompanied the great English scientist Sir Charles Lyell in his geological exploration of Nova Scotia. In 1850, Dawson was appointed Superintendent for Education in Nova Scotia, and in 1855, his remarkable powers as administrator assured his election as Principal of McGill University.

While continuing his teaching duties, he also found time to write several learned works on geology and zoology. His fundraising ability attracted much wealth to McGill, in particular the general financial support of Sir Donald Smith (cat. no. 128).

Like George Grant of Queen's University (cat. no. 70), Dawson was a strong advocate of higher education for women. It

69 *Sir William Dawson*   1889
29-1/2 x 23-1/4 po (74.9 x 59.1 cm) (s.v.)
INSCRIPTION: signature, b.d.: *Robert Harris*.
DOCUMENTS HARRIS: «J'attends présentement Sir William Dawson qui doit venir poser dans quelques minutes pour un portrait [terminé le 24 juin 1889] que je fais de lui pour le compte de la Société d'histoire naturelle.» (Lettre de Harris à sa mère, 10 juin 1889).

Sir William Dawson, un principal de McGill, est né en 1820, dans une famille d'immigrants écossais du comté de Pictou, en Nouvelle-Écosse. Après avoir passé son enfance à Pictou, il poursuit ses études à l'université d'Édimbourg où il obtient une maîtrise en géologie.

L'histoire naturelle et les expériences de chimie l'avaient fasciné à Édimbourg et, à son retour au Canada, il accompagna Sir Charles Lyell, l'éminent homme de science anglais, dans ses explorations géologiques de la Nouvelle-Écosse. En 1850, Dawson fut nommé surintendant de l'enseignement en Nouvelle-Écosse et, en 1855, ses remarquables talents d'administrateur lui valurent le poste de principal de l'université McGill.

Tout absorbé qu'il était par ses activités professorales, il publia néanmoins plusieurs ouvrages savants sur la géologie et la zoologie. Il eut le don de susciter la générosité de la grande bourgeoisie de la ville et obtint, notamment, pour McGill l'appui financier de Sir Donald A. Smith (qui deviendra plus tard Lord Strathcona, n° 128).

was because of his appeal to Sir Donald Smith (who built Royal Victoria College) that it became possible for women to enter McGill. Also like Grant, Dawson was convinced that a united Canada could never be achieved without a strong educational foundation. He thus took a broad view of the duties and privileges of the university as an intellectual centre. He paid close attention, as well, to the interests and the struggles of various schools and colleges in the Province of Quebec, especially at the elementary education level.

Sir William's greatest achievement as a pioneering educationalist was perhaps the maintenance of a balance between minority and majority opinions, in particular in preserving the intellectual freedom of the Protestant minority in Quebec. He was knighted in 1884.

MCGILL UNIVERSITY, MONTREAL

Tout comme George Grant (nº 70) de l'université Queen's, Dawson fut un fervent défenseur du droit de la femme à l'enseignement supérieur. C'est lui qui, ayant persuadé Sir Donald Smith (qui fit construire le Royal Victoria College), ouvrit aux femmes les portes de McGill. Comme Grant également, Dawson était convaincu que l'instruction est le pilier de l'unité nationale, ce qui explique ses idées libérales sur les obligations et les privilèges du centre intellectuel qu'est l'université. Il s'intéressait vivement aux écoles et aux collèges du Québec et, particulièrement, à tout ce qui concerne l'enseignement primaire.

Le plus grand exploit de cet éducateur d'avant-garde fut peut-être de maintenir le délicat équilibre entre les opinions de la majorité et celles de la minorité, et de préserver la liberté intellectuelle de la minorité protestante du Québec. En 1884, Dawson fut fait chevalier.

UNIVERSITÉ MCGILL, MONTRÉAL

---

70 *George Grant* 1889
29-3/4 x 24 in. (75.6 x 60.9 cm)
INSCRIPTION: signed and dated l.r., *Robert Harris 1889*.
HARRIS PAPERS: "I heard from the Kingston people [Sandford Fleming and the Rev. Dr. Campbell] about Principal Grant's portrait, which was unveiled in convocation hall on Wednesday last and it appears to give universal satisfaction." (Letter from Harris to his mother, dated 28 April 1889)

Like Dawson of McGill (cat. no. 69), George Grant came of Scottish parents. He was born at Stellarton in Pictou County, Nova Scotia, in 1835. His father was the village schoolmaster. The "Old Kirk" sent him to Scotland, along with other promising youths, to be educated for the ministry. He attended Glasgow University from 1853 to 1860 and came under the influence of that brilliant scholar and cleric, Norman McLeod (1812–72). While a student, Grant was for some time a social worker in the Glasgow slums.

His first ministry when he returned to Canada was in Georgetown, Prince Edward Island. His next call was to St. Matthew's Church, Halifax, where one of his friends and parishioners was the civil engineer, Sir Sandford Fleming (1827–1915), who took part in the first surveying expedition for the proposed C.P.R. Fleming invited Grant to accompany him, and Grant, in need of a holiday, went to the West Coast with the surveying party. Afterwards, Grant published his popular book *From Ocean to Ocean*, in which he described his impressions of the extent and

70 *George Grant* 1889
29-3/4 x 24 po (75.6 x 60.9 cm)
INSCRIPTION: signature et date, b.d.: *Robert Harris 1889*.
DOCUMENTS HARRIS: «De Kingston on m'apprend [Sanford Fleming et le révérend M. Campbell] que le portrait du principal Grant, dévoilé dans la salle de réunion mercredi dernier, semble satisfaire tout le monde.» (Lettre de Harris à sa mère, 28 avril 1889).

Tout comme Sir William Dawson (nº 69) de McGill, George Grant est d'origine écossaise. Il est né en 1835 à Stellarton dans le comté de Pictou (Nouvelle-Écosse). Son père était le maître d'école du village. Envoyé par l'«*Old Kirk*» en Écosse, avec d'autres jeunes gens pleins de promesses, pour se préparer au sacerdoce, il fréquenta l'université de Glasgow de 1853 à 1860 et y fit la connaissance du brillant humaniste et pasteur, Norman McLeod (1812–1872). Alors qu'il était encore étudiant, Grant fit du travail social dans les taudis de Glasgow.

De retour au Canada, il obtint son premier poste de pasteur à Georgetown (Î.-P.-É.). Appelé ensuite à desservir l'église St. Matthew's, à Halifax, il se lie d'amitié avec un de ses paroissiens, l'ingénieur Sir Sandford Fleming (1827–1915), qui doit prendre part à la première expédition dans l'Ouest pour étudier le tracé du Canadien Pacifique. Fleming invite Grant, qui a grand besoin de vacances, à l'accompagner; il suit le groupe jusqu'à la côte Ouest. Grant publie ensuite *From Ocean to Ocean*, qui connaît un grand succès, dans lequel il décrit la grandeur et la splendeur du

grandeur of Canada. This book was followed by articles in which he extolled the virtues of the country and recorded the progress of the railway. Behind his writings lay the firm message of the necessity for Confederation in a country of such desperate distances, and he warned of the dangers of what we now call separation, which an earlier writer named "dismemberment." "This Canada of ours," said Grant, enthusiastically, in an undated speech, "can become the youngest Anglo-Saxon nation working out for herself an individual character and destiny of her own on the last of the continents where such an experiment is practicable . . . Duty demands that we be true to our history. All of us must be Canada-first men."

In 1877 Grant left Halifax to take up his appointment as Principal of Queen's. It was said of him that he found Queen's a college and left it a university. He faced the challenge of an impoverished university with courage and energy; his first task, in 1878, was to launch a canvass which obtained about $140,000. The financial challenge was repeated again and again during his years at Queen's: if the University were to develop with facilities for specialization, for science, and for the intellectual centrality which was Grant's vision of the University, it must have money. He is still thought of as the "Great Principal," and his name is commemorated in Grant Hall, where, until recently, all Queen's University degrees were conferred.

In 1881 Harris made illustrations for Grant's *Picturesque Canada* (c. 1882) under the supervision of Sir Lucius O'Brien (1832–99).

PROVENANCE: Commissioned by the Board of Trustees, Queen's University.

EXHIBITIONS: *1889 Montreal Spring Exhibition*, no. 27; *1893 Montreal R.C.A.*, no. 69.

AGNES ETHERINGTON ART CENTRE
QUEEN'S UNIVERSITY AT KINGSTON

Canada. Le livre est suivi par des articles dans lesquels il exalte les vertus du pays et relate les progrès du chemin de fer. Dans tous ses écrits, il fait valoir la nécessité d'une confédération pour un pays aussi vaste et hétérogène que le Canada et met ses lecteurs en garde contre la séparation, qu'un auteur antérieur avait appelé «démembrement». «Notre patrie, le Canada, de proclamer Grant dans un discours dont on ignore la date, peut devenir le plus jeune pays anglo-saxon à se forger une identité et un destin qui lui soient propres, sur le dernier des continents où cela est encore possible... Notre devoir exige que nous soyons fidèles à notre histoire. Chacun d'entre nous doit être un partisan du Canada d'abord.»

En 1877, Grant quitte Halifax pour devenir le principal de Queen's. On a dit de lui qu'il avait transformé ce collège en université. Il a relevé avec courage, énergiquement, le défi que lui posait le collège apprauvri. Dès 1878, il lance une campagne qui lui rapporte quelque $140 000. Il aura souvent à répéter ce genre d'exploit, au cours de ses années à Queen's; chaque fois, en fait, qu'il voulait doter l'université d'installations qui la spécialiseraient, faciliter la recherche scientifique et faire de Queen's le grand centre intellectuel dont il rêvait. À la mémoire de celui qu'elle considère aujourd'hui encore comme son «grand principal», l'université a donné son nom à la salle où, jusqu'à très récemment, avait lieu la collation des grades.

En 1881, Harris exécuta, sous la surveillance de Sir Lucius O'Brien (1832–1899), des illustrations pour le *Picturesque Canada* de Grant, publié vers 1882.

HISTORIQUE: Exécuté sur commande du conseil d'administration de l'université Queen's.

EXPOSITIONS: *1889 Montréal, Printemps*, n° 27; *1893 Montréal, A.R.A.C.*, n° 69.

AGNES ETHERINGTON ART CENTRE
QUEEN'S UNIVERSITY AT KINGSTON

71 *Study for "Dr. R. Palmer Howard"*
1889
Oil on panel
14 x 11-3/8 in. (35.6 x 28.9 cm)
CONFEDERATION ART GALLERY AND
MUSEUM, CHARLOTTETOWN

71 *Étude pour Le docteur R. Palmer Howard*
1889
Huile sur bois
14 x 11-3/8 po (35.6 x 28.9 cm)
CONFEDERATION ART GALLERY AND
MUSEUM, CHARLOTTETOWN

72 *Dr. R. Palmer Howard* 1889
40-1/2 x 35-1/2 in. (102.9 x 90.2 cm)
INSCRIPTION: signed and dated l.l., *Robert Harris/1889.*

72 *Le docteur R. Palmer Howard* 1889
Huile sur bois
40-1/2 x 35-1/2 po (102.9 x 90.2 cm)
INSCRIPTION: signature et date, b.g.: *Robert Harris/1889.*

One of the most interesting discoveries (1972) in the search for Harris paintings was the fine portrait of Dr. Robert Palmer Howard, which hung for many years in the Nurses' Residence at the Montreal General Hospital. (The original sketch for this portrait, in Charlottetown, until 1972 remained unidentified.)

Of Irish descent, Howard was born in Montreal in 1823, where his father was a merchant. He was educated in Montreal and entered McGill University to study medicine. Further study, in Great Britain and France, followed. In 1849, Howard became a general practitioner in Montreal – and remained so till 1880 when he gave up surgery.

In 1856, Howard had been appointed Professor of Clinical Medicine at McGill, and in 1860 succeeded to the chair of Theory and Practice of Medicine. He was President of the Canadian Medical Association, of the College of Physicians and Surgeons, Quebec, and President of the Medico-Chirurgical Society of Quebec. He was elected a Fellow of the College of Physicians of Philadelphia and was also one of the Vice-Presidents of the Association of American Physicians. For twenty-two years he was one of the attending physicians and surgeons of the Montreal General Hospital and, for over thirty-three years, Secretary of that institution.

Howard's specialization was pneumonia and other pulmonary illnesses. One of the great chest-surgeons of the nineteenth century, Palmer Howard was for many years

Une des trouvailles les plus intéressantes (1972) que nous a livrée notre recherche des tableaux de Harris est le portrait du docteur Robert Palmer Howard qui, pendant de nombreuses années, a orné les murs de la résidence des infirmières de l'Hôpital général de Montréal. (L'esquisse originale de ce portrait, qui se trouvait à Charlottetown, n'a pu être identifiée qu'en 1972.)

D'origine irlandaise, Howard est né en 1823 à Montréal, où son père était négociant. Il passa son enfance à Montréal et étudia ensuite la médecine à l'université McGill, en Grande-Bretagne, puis en France. De retour au Canada, il s'installa en 1849 à Montréal où il pratiqua la médecine générale jusqu'en 1880, année où il abandonna la chirurgie.

En 1856, Howard fut nommé professeur de médecine clinique à McGill et, en 1860, devint titulaire de la chaire de la théorie et de la pratique médicales. Il fut président de l'Association canadienne des médecins, du Collège des médecins et chirurgiens du Québec et de la Medico Chirurgical Society du Québec. Il fut élu membre du College of Physicians de Philadelphie et fut l'un des vice-présidents de l'Association of American Physicians. Pendant vingt-deux ans, il fut médecin-chirurgien à l'Hôpital général de Montréal et, pendant plus de trente-trois ans, secrétaire de cet hôpital.

Palmer Howard était pneumologue. L'un des meilleurs chirurgiens du poumon du XIXe siècle, Howard fut longtemps le plus éminent médecin consultant au Canada. Ses travaux sur l'anémie pour le Congrès médical inter-

the leading consultant in Canada. His work on anaemia, prepared for the International Medical Congress in 1876, was considered at the time, and for many years after, one of the most important contributions to the subject. He was a teacher of Sir William Osler (cat. no. 134), and was for thirty years Chairman of the Medical Board of the Montreal General Hospital.

Harris, in this choice of pose, was obviously aware of the value Howard attached to bedside teaching. Howard stressed that, by assigning the duty of teaching to one person instead of leaving it indifferently to several members of the medical staff, one could secure efficient and regular bedside instructions.

EXHIBITION: *1919 Montreal*, no. 8.
THE MONTREAL GENERAL HOSPITAL

national de 1876 ont, pendant des années, fait autorité en la matière. Il eut Sir William Osler (n⁰ 134) pour élève et fut, pendant trente ans, président du conseil médical de l'Hôpital général de Montréal.

Harris, en peignant le portrait de Howard en train d'enseigner au chevet d'un malade, montre bien qu'il connaissait l'importance qu'attachait ce médecin à ce genre d'enseignement. Howard insistait également sur le fait qu'en donnant à un seul la tâche d'enseigner, au lieu de disperser indifféremment ce soin parmi plusieurs membres du personnel, on pouvait contrôler plus efficacement et de façon plus régulière les notions acquises au chevet du malade.

EXPOSITION: *1919 Montréal*, n⁰ 18.
HÔPITAL GÉNÉRAL DE MONTRÉAL

73 *Study for "Sir Alexander Galt"*   c. 1889
Graphite
9-3/4 x 7-1/4 in. (24.8 x 19 cm) (s)
INSCRIPTION: l.c., pencil, *Mr A T Galt.*

Study for a portrait not in the exhibition.

Galt, at one time a Minister of Finance, was Canadian High Commissioner to London from 1880 to 1883. He had been born in England and emigrated to Canada in 1835.

One of the promoters of the Grand Trunk Railway, Galt was delegate to the Charlottetown and Quebec conferences in 1864, and was one of the chief architects of the *British North America Act*. A firm believer in Canadian independence, he resigned from politics following a quarrel with Sir John A. Macdonald. In 1875, he was appointed a member of the Halifax Fisheries Commission. Died in Montreal in 1893.

EXHIBITION: *1967 Charlottetown*, no. 117.
CONFEDERATION ART GALLERY AND
MUSEUM, CHARLOTTETOWN

73 *Étude pour Sir Alexander Galt*   c. 1889
Mine de plomb
9-3/4 x 7-1/4 po (24.8 x 19 cm) (s.v.)
INSCRIPTION: b.c., au crayon: *Mr A T Galt.*

Le portrait exécuté à la suite de cette étude n'est pas présenté dans le cadre de cette exposition.

Né en Angleterre, Galt émigra au Canada en 1835. Ayant été ministre des finances, il fut haut-commissaire canadien à Londres de 1880 à 1883.

Il fut un des fondateurs du chemin de fer du Grand Tronc. Délégué aux conférences de Charlottetown et de Québec en 1864, il fut un des principaux artisans de l'Acte de l'Amérique du Nord britannique. Croyant fermement à l'indépendance canadienne, il abandonna la politique après une querelle avec Sir John A. Macdonald (n⁰ 42). Il fut nommé en 1875 membre de la Halifax Fisheries Commission. Il mourut à Montréal en 1893.

EXPOSITION: *1967 Charlottetown*, n⁰ 117.
CONFEDERATION ART GALLERY AND
MUSEUM, CHARLOTTETOWN

74 *John Crawford*   1890
54 x 47-1/2 in. (137.2 x 120.7 cm) (s)
INSCRIPTION: signed and dated l.r., *Robert Harris 1890.*
HARRIS PAPERS: "I'm pegging away hard [at] a portrait of Mr. Crawford the master of the Montreal Foxhounds, on horseback, and I intend painting him giving a Tallyho with the hounds and field coming up." (Letter from Harris to his mother, dated 20 December 1889) "I am all right again and am happy to say the portrait is going to be done in time after all. I may as well tell you what it looks like. Mr. Crawford, an old gentleman of 77, the Master of the hounds is on his horse, a dark brown one. He is in hunting costume looking back and waving his hat as

74 *John Crawford*   1890
54 x 47-1/2 po (137.2 x 120.7 cm) (s.v.)
INSCRIPTION: signature et date, b.d.: *Robert Harris 1890.*
DOCUMENTS HARRIS: «Je travaille ferme à un portrait de M. Crawford, le veneur de Montréal, que je compte peindre à cheval en train de crier taïaut, avec la meute et les cavaliers à l'arrière-plan.» (Lettre de Harris à sa mère, 20 décembre 1889).

«Je vais mieux et suis heureux de pouvoir affirmer que le portrait sera terminé à temps, après tout. Autant vous décrire de quoi il a l'air. M. Crawford, un vieux monsieur de 77 ans, maître d'équipage, est sur son cheval brun foncé. Vêtu de son costume de chasse, il est tourné en arrière et agite son chapeau

he gives the tally-ho to the riders coming up behind. The horse is looking off towards where the fox has gone and some of the hounds are rushing past the horse, one quite in the foreground. The background is a woodland glade and the landscape shows the hues of early autumn. The picture is about 4 feet by 5 feet canvas. It is to be presented at the annual hunt dinner, which takes place at the Windsor on the 23rd next." (Letter from Elizabeth Harris to her mother-in-law, dated 19 January 1890)

PROVENANCE: Presented to John Crawford Esq. M.F.H., by His Excellency Lord Stanley of Preston, Governor General of Canada; on behalf of the Montreal Hunt Club; Mrs. George Le Frois, New York.

MCCORD MUSEUM, MONTREAL

en criant taïaut aux cavaliers qui viennent, derrière lui. Le cheval regarde en avant, vers le renard, et la meute fonce à toute allure, dépassant le cheval. L'un des chiens est au premier plan. À l'arrière-plan, une éclaircie dans un paysage aux couleurs d'automne. Le tableau est une toile de 4 pieds sur 5 et sera présenté au dîner annuel de chasse, qui se tiendra au Windsor le 23 février.» (Lettre d'Elizabeth Harris à sa belle-mère, 19 janvier 1890).

HISTORIQUE: Présenté à John Crawford, Esq., M.F.H., par Son Excellence Lord Stanley of Preston, gouverneur général du Canada, au nom du Montreal Hunt Club; Mᵐᵉ George LeFrois, New York.

MUSÉE MCCORD, MONTRÉAL

---

75 *The Reverend Edward Harris and his Fiancée Florence Zwicker* 1890
23-3/4 x 29-3/4 in. (60.3 x 75.6 cm)
INSCRIPTION: signed and dated l.l., *Robert Harris 1890*; on reverse, *Rev Edward A. Harris, M.A.,/Rector of Mahone Bay/Miss Florrie Zwicker/Harry the horse/Cull the dog/ Mahone Bay, N.S./Painted at the Rectory/by Robert Harris, R.C.A., Aug. 4, 1890.*

Edward Harris was a brother of the artist. For another brother, see cat. no. 125.

CANON ROBERT CRITCHLOW TUCK, SUMMERSIDE, P.E.I.

75 *Le révérend Edward Harris et sa fiancée Florence Zwicker* 1890
23-3/4 x 29-3/4 po (60.3 x 75.6 cm)
INSCRIPTION: signature et date, b.g.: *Robert Harris 1890;* au verso (trad.): Le révérend *Edward A. Harris, M.A.,/Recteur de Mahone Bay/*Mˡˡᵉ *Florrie Zwicker/Harry,* le cheval/ *Cull,* le chien/*Mahone Bay,* N.-É./Peint au presbytère/par *Robert Harris,* A.R.A.C., *4 août 1890.*

Le modèle était un des frères de l'artiste. Voir également un autre frère de Harris (nᵒ 125).

LE CHANOINE ROBERT CRITCHLOW TUCK, SUMMERSIDE (Î.-P.-É.)

---

76 *Study for "Sir Joseph Hickson"* 1890
Charcoal
11 x 9-3/4 in. (27.9 x 24.8 cm)
INSCRIPTION: bottom edge, pencil, *Drawing for portrait of Sir Joseph Hickson painted in Montreal 12th April 1890. I changed the pose and did/not follow this/sketch at all.*

CONFEDERATION ART GALLERY AND MUSEUM, CHARLOTTETOWN

76 *Étude pour Sir Joseph Hickson* 1890
Fusain
11 x 9-3/4 po (27.9 x 24.8 cm)
INSCRIPTION: marge b., au crayon (trad.): Dessin pour le portrait de *Sir Joseph Hickson* peint à Montréal le *12* avril *1890.* J'ai changé la pose, délaissant complètement l'esquisse.

CONFEDERATION ART GALLERY AND MUSEUM, CHARLOTTETOWN

77 *Sir Joseph Hickson* 1890
48-3/4 x 42 in. (123.8 x 106.7 cm)
INSCRIPTION: signed l.l., *Robert Harris.*
HARRIS PAPERS: "Tough [Harris's dog] is rather under the weather today. I think he is depressed from having heard Sir Joseph Hickson offer me a fine bull dog the other day when he was sitting . . . ." (Letter from Harris to his mother, dated 2 March 1890) "Sir Joseph Hickson's portrait is now done to the satisfaction of everybody who has seen it. I shall keep it a fortnight as I want to send it to the [Montreal] Spring Exhibition which opens on the 25th of this month." (Letter from Harris to his mother, dated 6 April 1890)

Sir Joseph Hickson (1830–97) was born at Otterburn, Northumberland, and as a young man entered the service of the North Eastern Railway. In 1854, he was appointed Chief Accountant of the Grand Trunk Railway of Canada and by 1874 had risen to the position of General Manager, in which post he remained till his retirement in 1891.
EXHIBITION: *1890 Montreal Spring Exhibition*, no. 36.
THE NATIONAL GALLERY OF CANADA, OTTAWA (6701)
GIFT OF R.N. HICKSON, MONTREAL

77 *Sir Joseph Hickson* 1890
48-3/4 x 42 po (123.8 x 106.7 cm)
INSCRIPTION: signature, b.g.: *Robert Harris.*
DOCUMENTS HARRIS: «Tough [le chien de Harris] n'est pas dans son assiette aujourd'hui. Je crois qu'il est déprimé parce qu'il a entendu Sir Joseph me proposer un beau bouledogue, l'autre jour, en posant ...» (Lettre de Harris à sa mère, 2 mars 1890).
«Le portrait de Sir Joseph Hickson est terminé et il a plu à tous ceux qui l'ont vu. Je le garderai encore deux semaines, car je voudrais le présenter à l'exposition du printemps [à Montréal] qui commence le 25 de ce mois.» (Lettre de Harris à sa mère, 6 avril 1890.)

Sir Joseph Hickson est né en 1830 à Otterburn (Northumberland). Entré très jeune au service du chemin de fer du Nord-Est, il devint, en 1854, chef de la comptabilité au Grand Tronc. En 1874, il accéda au poste de directeur général, qu'il gardera jusqu'à sa retraite en 1891. Il mourut en 1897.
EXPOSITION: *1890 Montréal, Printemps*, n° 36.
GALERIE NATIONALE DU CANADA, OTTAWA (6701)
DON DE R.N. HICKSON, MONTRÉAL

78 *Hugh McLennan* c. 1890
28 x 22 in. (71.1 x 55.9 cm)
INSCRIPTION: signed l. l., *Robert Harris.*

The generous patronage extended to Robert Harris by the various members of the McLennan family is mentioned time and again in the Harris letters. It was through the McLennans that Harris first heard that Mrs. Putnam (cat. no. 46), his future mother-in-law, could offer him a home in Montreal.

Hugh McLennan, born in 1825, was self-educated and, like Harris as a young man, restless with ambition. After having worked as an agent for the stagecoach at Prescott, Ontario, he set up in business for himself, as wharfmonger and agent for lake boats at Kingston (one of which had Captain Putnam for Master).

In the winter of 1850–51, Hugh McLennan entered into a partnership in Montreal with his brother John, as an importer/exporter. It was at this time that Hugh McLennan renewed his acquaintance with Isabella Stewart, who had been twelve years old when first they met and who in September 1851 became his bride. The wedding ceremony took place in the home of James Ross (for Mrs. Ross, see cat. no. 153).

During the next few years John continued to operate the firm from Montreal, while Hugh lived in Chicago, concentrating on the

78 *Hugh McLennan* c. 1890
28 x 22 po (71.1 x 55.9 cm)
INSCRIPTION: signature, b.g.: *Robert Harris.*

Robert Harris mentionne sans cesse dans ses lettres l'appui généreux qu'il reçoit des divers membres de la famille McLennan. C'est des McLennan qu'il apprend, notamment, que Mme Putnam (n° 46) qui deviendra, par la suite, sa belle-mère, peut lui offrir une maison à Montréal.

Né en 1825, Hugh McLennan est autodidacte et, tout comme Harris dans sa jeunesse, brûle du désir de réussir. Après avoir travaillé en tant qu'agent pour une compagnie de diligences à Prescott (Ontario), il se met à son propre compte en tant que maître de quai et agent, à Kingston, des bateaux (dont un aura justement le capitaine Putnam pour maître) qui circulent sur les lacs.

Au cours de l'hiver 1850–1851, Hugh McLennan s'associe avec son frère John dans une entreprise d'import-export à Montréal. C'est au cours de cette période que Hugh McLennan renoue des liens avec Isabella Stewart, qu'il avait connue alors qu'elle était âgée de douze ans, et qui deviendra sa femme en septembre 1851. La cérémonie du mariage a lieu dans la maison de James Ross (Voir Mme Ross, n° 153).

Pendant les années qui suivent, John dirige, de Montréal, l'entreprise tandis que

grain trade. In 1867, Hugh returned to Montreal. His partnership with his brother eventually developed into the Montreal Transport Company. In 1872, Hugh was elected President of the Montreal Board of Trade, a position he held for twenty-five years. His large house and estate on Drummond Street became a centre of hospitality for visiting businessman from the Mid-West and New England States, as well as a gathering place for those connected with the C.P.R.

In a privately published history of the McLennan family, it is noted that McLennan's "personal appearance is well shown in the Harris portrait. Kindly expression, humour, intelligence." McLennan was about six feet tall, erect, and square-shouldered. He took no exercise as such and "lived in a generation when the mature, except golfers, for the most part played no games."

EXHIBITION: *1919 Montreal*, no. 10.

HUGH MCLENNAN, VANCOUVER

---

79 *Sir John Allen* 1892

43-1/4 x 32-3/4 in. (109.9 x 83.2 cm)

INSCRIPTION: signed and dated u.r., *Robert Harris.|–1892.–*

In 1892 Robert Harris travelled to Fredericton, New Brunswick, to paint a portrait, commissioned by the Law Society, of Sir John Campbell Allen (1817–98). Sir John, who had been appointed Chief Justice of the Supreme Court of New Brunswick in 1875, was born in Kingsclear, New Brunswick, in 1817. After his election to the House of Assembly in 1856, he became Solicitor-General and also Speaker of the Assembly. He was strongly opposed to Confederation and in 1865 was a delegate to Great Britain for the purpose of getting the British Government to accept New Brunswick's anti-Confederation objections. In due course, Sir John Allen became Chief Justice for that Province. He was knighted in 1889.

EXHIBITION: *1893 Montreal R.C.A.*, no. 69.

BARRISTERS' SOCIETY OF NEW BRUNSWICK, FREDERICTON

Hugh vit à Chicago où il se consacre au commerce des grains. En 1867, Hugh rentre à Montréal. De l'association des deux frères naît la Montreal Transport Company. En 1872, Hugh est élu président de la Chambre de commerce de Montréal, poste qu'il gardera pendant vingt-cinq ans. Sa grande maison et sa propriété, rue Drummond, deviennent un centre d'accueil pour les hommes d'affaires américains de passage à Montréal, ainsi qu'un lieu de rencontre pour tous ceux qui ont quelque lien avec le Canadien Pacifique.

Une étude privée de la famille McLennan indique que «le portrait de Harris fait très bien ressortir les caractéristiques de Hugh McLennan. Expression bienveillante, humour, intelligence». McLennan était un homme d'environ six pieds, aux épaules carrées et qui se tenait très droit. Il ne pratiquait aucun sport et «vécut en un temps où les adultes, hormis les golfeurs, ne jouaient tout simplement pas».

EXPOSITION: *1919 Montréal*, n° 10.

HUGH MCLENNAN, VANCOUVER

---

79 *Sir John Allen* 1892

43-1/4 x 32-3/4 po (109.9 x 83.2 cm)

INSCRIPTION: signature et date, h.d.: *Robert Harris.|–1892.–*

En 1892, Robert Harris se rendit à Fredericton (Nouveau-Brunswick) afin de faire le portrait de Sir John Campbell Allen pour le compte du Barreau de cette province. Né à Kingsclear (Nouveau-Brunswick) en 1817, Sir John fut nommé juge en chef de la Cour suprême du Nouveau-Brunswick en 1875. Élu député en 1856, il devint solliciteur-général et orateur de l'Assemblée. Fervent adversaire de la Confédération, en 1865, il fut envoyé en Angleterre pour exposer les objections du Nouveau-Brunswick et convaincre le gouvernement britannique de les accepter. Sir John devint, par la suite, juge en chef de cette province. Il fut fait chevalier en 1889. Il mourut en 1898.

EXPOSITION: *1893 Montréal, A.R.A.C.*, n° 69.

BARRISTERS' SOCIETY OF NEW BRUNSWICK, FREDERICTON

80 *Otto Jacobi* 1892
32 x 26-1/2 in. (81.3 x 67.3 cm)
INSCRIPTION: signed and dated u.r., *Robert Harris/1892.*

For a study toward this portrait, see cat. no. 61.

Jacobi was a close friend of Robert Harris, and for a while the two men had adjacent studios in Montreal. He was born in Königsberg (now Kaliningrad), East Prussia, and studied art in the Berlin Academy and at Düsseldorf. About 1837 he was appointed Court Painter at Wiesbaden. Jacobi came to Canada in 1860, lived for a while in Montreal, and in 1880 settled permanently in Toronto.

A charter member, in 1880, of the Royal Canadian Academy of Arts, and President (1890–93), Jacobi was also a member of the Ontario Society of Artists. For a short period he taught (though, it must be admitted, unsuccessfully) at the Ontario School of Art, and afterwards devoted himself to the pursuit of painting. He was a fine colourist, expert in the techniques of watercolour, and greatly respected and liked by all his fellow artists.

BIBLIOGRAPHY: MacTavish, *The Fine Arts in Canada*, repr. opp. p. 6.
EXHIBITIONS: *1893 Montreal R.C.A.*, no. 71; 1947, Toronto, Ontario Society of Artists, *75th Annual Spring Exhibition Including a Group of Paintings Selected from Works Exhibited During the First 50 Years of the Society's History*, no. 150.
THE NATIONAL GALLERY OF CANADA, OTTAWA (94)
GIFT OF THE ROYAL CANADIAN ACADEMY OF ARTS

80 *Otto Jacobi* 1892
32 x 26-1/2 po (81.3 x 67.3 cm)
INSCRIPTION: signature et date, h.d.: *Robert Harris/1892.*

Voir également une étude pour ce portrait (n° 61).

Jacobi était un grand ami de Robert Harris et, pendant quelque temps, les deux hommes eurent des ateliers contigus à Montréal. Né à Königsberg (maintenant Kaliningrad) en Prusse orientale, Jacobi étudia l'art à l'académie de Berlin et à Düsseldorf. Il devint, vers 1837, peintre de la cour à Wiesbaden. En 1860, il immigra au Canada. Il vécut d'abord à Montréal puis, à partir de 1880, à Toronto.

Membre originaire, en 1880, de la nouvelle Académie royale des arts du Canada, dont il fut le président de 1890 à 1893, Jacobi fit aussi partie de l'Ontario Society of Artists. Après avoir enseigné pendant quelque temps (sans grand succès, il faut le dire) à l'Ontario School of Art, il se consacra entièrement à la peinture. Excellent coloriste, versé dans les techniques de l'aquarelle, Jacobi fut respecté et aimé de ses collègues.

BIBLIOGRAPHIE: MacTavish: *The Fine Arts in Canada*, reprod. en regard de la p. 6.
EXPOSITIONS: *1893 Montréal, A.R.A.C.*, n° 71; 1947, Toronto, Ontario Society of Artists, *75th Annual Spring Exhibition Including a Group of Paintings Selected from Works Exhibited During the First 50 Years of the Society's History*, n° 150.
GALERIE NATIONALE DU CANADA, OTTAWA (94)
DON DE L'ACADÉMIE ROYALE DES ARTS DU CANADA

81 *Sir Oliver Mowat* 1892
92-3/8 x 64-3/8 in. (234.7 x 163.5 cm)
INSCRIPTION: signed and dated l.l., *Robert Harris, 1892.*
HARRIS PAPERS: "Portrait of Jacobi for R.C.A. National Gallery Ottawa, while there went to Toronto and painted full-length of Sir Oliver Mowatt [sic] done in his house from sittings there." (Sitter-book, undated entry)

The Honourable Sir Oliver Mowat, Premier of the Province of Ontario, was born in Kingston, in 1820. His father, a soldier who had served in the Peninsular War, was, like his mother, a native of Caithness, Scotland. They emigrated to Canada in 1816.

Mowat was apprenticed to John A. Macdonald's (cat. no. 42) law firm at the age of seventeen. Macdonald, only five years Mowat's senior, had only recently been called to the Bar. Mowat himself was called

81 *Sir Oliver Mowat* 1892
92-3/8 x 64-3/8 po (234.7 x 163.5 cm)
INSCRIPTION: signature et date, b.g.: *Robert Harris, 1892.*
DOCUMENTS HARRIS: «Portrait de Jacobi pour l'A.R.A.C., Galerie nationale, Ottawa, en ai profité pour aller à Toronto et faire un portrait en pied de Sir Oliver Mowatt [sic] qui a été exécuté à sa résidence d'après des séances de pose à cet endroit.» (Journal de travail de l'artiste, s.d.)

L'honorable Sir Oliver Mowat, un premier ministre de la province d'Ontario, est né à Kingston en 1820. Son père, ancien combattant de la guerre de la péninsule ibérique, et sa mère étaient originaires de Caithness (Écosse). Tous deux avaient immigré au Canada en 1816.

À l'âge de dix-sept ans, Oliver Mowat commence son apprentissage au service de John A. MacDonald (n° 42) dans un cabinet d'avocat. Macdonald, à cette époque, n'est que

in 1842 and quickly rose to eminence at the Chancery Bar.

Mowat's family background was strictly Conservative and naturally he also came under the directly Conservative influence of John A. Macdonald. Despite these influences, Oliver Mowat adopted the cause of the Liberals, from which party and policies he never waivered. For a period he served as Postmaster General in the Coalition Government of 1861. Later, as one of the delegates at the Quebec Conference, he assisted with the preliminary planning for Confederation.

In 1872, upon the retirement of his predecessor, Oliver Mowat was appointed Premier of Ontario, and his political experience as M.P. for North Oxford, combined with his legal acumen, enabled him to serve his province well. Liberal and progressive acts of legislation affecting higher education (particularly the University of Toronto), the introduction of the ballot in municipal and other elections, the revision of Provincial Statutes–these were but some of his achievements. Municipal loans, aid to public charities, and the liberalizing of the franchise are but a few of the well-considered and far-sighted bills introduced during his term of office. As leader of the Government, Mowat, was frequently embroiled in battle and disputes with his old colleague, Sir John A. Macdonald.

Mowat's assertion of provincial rights in the Boundary, Rivers and Streams Bill was finally recognized by the Dominion Government and, through that bill, served as one of the foundations of Ontario's economic development and wealth.

BIBLIOGRAPHY: Harper, *Painting in Canada: A History*, repr. p. 222.
PROVINCE OF ONTARIO, TORONTO

de cinq ans son aîné et vient juste d'être admis au barreau. Mowat sera lui-même inscrit au barreau en 1842 et parviendra à un rang élevé dans la carrière.

Élevé dans un milieu strictement conservateur, il subit naturellement l'influence conservatrice de John A. Macdonald. Cela ne l'empêchera cependant pas d'embrasser la cause des Libéraux, et de rester fidèle au parti et à ses politiques jusqu'à la fin de ses jours. Il fut ministre des postes pendant quelque temps dans le gouvernement de coalition de 1861. Il assista, à titre de délégué, à la conférence de Québec où il participa à l'élaboration du programme de la Confédération.

En 1872, Oliver Mowat devient premier ministre de l'Ontario, son prédécesseur ayant pris sa retraite; ce poste lui permettra de bien servir sa province grâce à son expérience politique acquise en tant que député de North Oxford et à sa profonde perspicacité en matière juridique. Au nombre de ses réalisations, citons les lois libérales et progressives qu'il promulgue en matière d'enseignement supérieur (surtout en ce qui concerne l'université de Toronto), l'introduction du scrutin dans les élections municipales et autres, et la révision des statuts provinciaux. Des projets de lois aussi judicieux et clairvoyants que les prêts municipaux, l'aide aux œuvres de charité et la libéralisation du droit de vote jalonnent son mandat. En tant que chef du gouvernement, toutefois, Mowat fut souvent à couteaux tirés avec son ancien collègue, Sir John A. Macdonald.

Les droits qu'il réclamait pour la province dans le Boundary, Rivers and Streams Bill furent finalement reconnus par le gouvernement fédéral et ils furent, par ce bill, à la base même du développement économique et de la prospérité de l'Ontario.

BIBLIOGRAPHIE: Harper: *La peinture au Canada, des origines à nos jours*, reprod. p. 222.
PROVINCE D'ONTARIO, TORONTO.

82 *Sir Leonard Tilley* 1892
49-3/4 x 40-1/4 in. (126.4 x 102.2 cm)
INSCRIPTION: signed and dated l.r., *Robert Harris. 1892.*

Samuel Leonard Tilley was born at Gagetown, New Brunswick, in 1818, and attended the local grammar school. At the age of thirteen, he became a clerk in an apothecary's office in Saint John. After having become a partner in his own business in the firm of Peters and Tilley, he ran for election to the Legislative Assembly in 1851. In 1854 he was appointed Provincial Secretary, and in the following year, introduced a bill to prevent the importation, manufacture, or sale of liquor in New Brunswick. It was opposed at third reading by a vote of 21 to 18. (In 1838, when the population of New Brunswick did not exceed 120,000, the consumption of rum, gin, and whisky was 312,298 gallons per annum, besides 64,579 gallons of brandy; and during the intervening seventeen years, the Temperance movement was not, perhaps, unjustified in its fears for the survival of the population.)
Tilley was a delegate to the conferences in Charlottetown and Quebec, and, in 1867, having resigned from the New Brunswick Government, he became Minister of Customs and, in 1873, Minister of Finance in the Dominion Government. When the Macdonald Government was once again re-elected, Tilley inaugurated the National Policy. In 1885 he was appointed for a second term as Lieutenant-Governor of New Brunswick. He died, in 1896, at Saint John.
PROVINCE OF NEW BRUNSWICK
DEPARTMENT OF SUPPLY AND SERVICES

82 *Sir Leonard Tilley* 1892
49-3/4 x 40-1/4 po (126.4 x 102.2 cm)
INSCRIPTION: signature et date, b.d.: *Robert Harris. 1892.*

Samuel Leonard Tilley est né à Gagetown (Nouveau-Brunswick) en 1818 et a fréquenté l'école primaire locale. À l'âge de treize ans, il devient commis chez un apothicaire de Saint-Jean. Devenu associé dans la firme de Peters et Tilley, il se présente, en 1851, aux élections de l'Assemblée législative. Nommé en 1854 secrétaire provincial, il dépose, l'année suivante, un projet de loi interdisant l'importation, la fabrication et la vente d'alcool au Nouveau-Brunswick, projet de loi qui sera défait à la troisième lecture par 21 voix contre 18. (En 1838, alors que la population du Nouveau-Brunswick ne dépassait pas 120 000 habitants, la province consommait, annuellement, 312 298 gallons de rhum, de gin et de whisky et 64 579 gallons de brandy. On comprend, à la lumière de ces statistiques, que le Mouvement pour la tempérance ait pu craindre, durant cette période, pour la survie de la population.)
Tilley participa aux conférences de Charlottetown et de Québec à titre de délégué et, s'étant démis de ses fonctions au sein du gouvernement du Nouveau-Brunswick, il devint ministre des douanes en 1867 et en 1873 ministre des finances du gouvernement fédéral. Après la réélection du gouvernement Macdonald, Tilley inaugura sa politique nationale. En 1885, il fut nommé pour la seconde fois lieutenant-gouverneur du Nouveau-Brunswick. Il mourut en 1896 à Saint-Jean.
PROVINCE DU NOUVEAU-BRUNSWICK
MINISTÈRE DES APPROVISIONNEMENTS
ET SERVICES, FREDERICTON

83 *Gilman Cheney* 1893
50-1/4 x 40 in. (127.7 x 101.6 cm)
INSCRIPTION: signed l.r., *Robert Harris.*
HARRIS PAPERS: "I am beginning a new portrait today, Mr. Cheyney [*sic*], head of the Dominion Express Co." (Letter from Harris to his mother, dated 6 February 1893) "I am waiting for my sitter, Mr. Cheyney, to arrive at nine o'clock, for he is an early bird." (Letter from Harris to his mother, dated 27 February 1893)
EXHIBITION: 1893, Chicago, World's Columbian Exposition, [exhibition by the Canadian Department of Fine Art], no. 57.
THE MONTREAL MUSEUM OF FINE ARTS
GIFT OF WILLIAM GILMAN CHENEY

83 *Gilman Cheney* 1893
50-1/4 x 40 po (127.7 x 101.6 cm)
INSCRIPTION: signature, b.d.: *Robert Harris.*
DOCUMENTS HARRIS: «Je commence un nouveau portrait aujourd'hui, celui de M. Cheyney [*sic*], directeur de la société Dominion Express.» (Lettre de Harris à sa mère, 6 février 1893).
«J'attends mon modèle, M. Cheyney [*sic*], à neuf heures, car il est un lève-tôt.» (Lettre de Harris à sa mère, 27 février 1893).
EXPOSITION: 1893, Chicago, [exposition du Canadian Department of Fine Art], *World's Columbian Exposition*, n° 57.
MUSÉE DES BEAUX-ARTS DE MONTRÉAL
DON DE WILLIAM GILMAN CHENEY

84 *James Ferrier* 1893
37 x 30 in. (94 x 76.2 cm) (s)
INSCRIPTION: signed l.r., *Robert Harris*.
HARRIS PAPERS: "My picture of Mr. A.F. Gault just completed and all who have seen it are most enthusiastic about it. You don't know perhaps about this loan exhibit [in the new gallery of the Art Association of Montreal, December 1893]. It is made up of pictures by the old masters and celebrated foreign artists with only four or five Canadian pictures. I have one of Senator Ferrier, A Chancellor of McGill!" (Letter from Harris to his mother, dated 2 December 1893)

Governor (1852–88), President of the Board of Governors (1885–88), and Chancellor (1885–88) of McGill, James Ferrier was born in Fifeshire, Scotland, in 1800. He emigrated to Canada in 1821 and became a leading Montreal merchant. A promoter of the Montreal and Lachine Railway, Ferrier became eventually a director of the Grand Trunk Railway. After holding office as Mayor of Montreal in 1847, he was elected to the Legislative Council of Canada. In 1867 he was called to the Senate of Canada, and in the same year, elected to the Legislative Council of Quebec. During his term of office, terrible fires swept the Quebec suburbs of Saint-Roch and Saint-Jean. Ferrier raised $40,000 for relief, among other things successfully memorializing Queen Victoria.
EXHIBITIONS: 1893, Montreal, Art Association of Montreal, *Seventeenth Loan Exhibition*, [no further information available]; *1919 Montreal*, no. 4.
MCGILL UNIVERSITY, MONTREAL

---

85 *Caricature of a Bishop* c. 1893
Pen and ink
6-3/4 x 4 in. (17.2 x 10.2 cm) (s)

Framed with cat. nos. 58, 86, 87, 93, 94.
EXHIBITION: *1967 Charlottetown*, no. 80 (one of six framed together).
CONFEDERATION ART GALLERY AND MUSEUM, CHARLOTTETOWN

---

86 *Caricature of a Bishop in Full Canonicals Playing the Organ* c. 1893
Red conté chalk and graphite
10 x 6-3/4 in. (25.4 x 17.2 cm) (s)

Framed with cat. nos. 58, 85, 87, 93, 94.
EXHIBITION: *1967 Charlottetown*, no. 80 (one of six framed together).
CONFEDERATION ART GALLERY AND MUSEUM, CHARLOTTETOWN

---

84 *James Ferrier* 1893
37 x 30 po (94 x 76.2 cm) (s.v.)
INSCRIPTION: signature, b.d.: *Robert Harris*.
DOCUMENTS HARRIS: «Viens de terminer le portrait de M. A.F. Gault qui suscite l'admiration de tous ceux qui l'ont vu. Vous n'êtes peut-être pas au courant de l'exposition de prêts [à la nouvelle galerie de l'Art Association of Montreal, décembre 1893]. Consacrée aux maîtres anciens et aux plus célèbres artistes étrangers, elle ne comprend que quatre ou cinq tableaux canadiens. Parmi ceux-là, mon sénateur Ferrier, chancelier de McGill!» (Lettre de Harris à sa mère, 2 décembre 1893.)

Successivement gouverneur (1852–1888), président (1885–1888) et chancelier (1885–1888) à McGill, James Ferrier est né dans le Fifeshire (Écosse) en 1800. Il s'établit au Canada en 1821 et devint un important négociant à Montréal. Promoteur du chemin de fer de Montréal et Lachine, Ferrier devint, par la suite, directeur du Grand Tronc. À la fin de son mandat en tant que maire de Montréal, il fut élu, en 1847, au Conseil législatif du Canada. En 1867, il devint sénateur à Ottawa et, la même année, fut élu au Conseil législatif du Québec. Au cours de son mandat, d'importants incendies dévastèrent les quartiers de Saint-Roch et de Saint-Jean à Québec. Ferrier réussit à réunir $40 000 en fonds pour venir en aide aux sinistrés, ayant obtenu, entre autres, un don de la reine Victoria.
EXPOSITIONS: 1893, Montréal, Art Association of Montreal, *Seventeenth Loan Exhibition*, [documentation incomplète]; *1919 Montréal*, n° 4.
UNIVERSITÉ MCGILL, MONTRÉAL

85 *Caricature d'un évêque* c. 1893
Plume, encre
6-3/4 x 4 po (17.2 x 10.2 cm) (s.v.)

Encadré avec les n°ˢ 58, 86, 87, 93 et 94.
EXPOSITION: *1967 Charlottetown*, n° 80 (qui comportait également les cinq autres).
CONFEDERATION ART GALLERY AND MUSEUM, CHARLOTTETOWN

86 *Caricature d'un évêque en grande tenue épiscopale jouant de l'orgue* c. 1893
Conté rouge et mine de plomb
10 x 6-3/4 po (25.4 x 17.2 cm)

Encadré avec les n°ˢ 58, 85, 87, 93 et 94.
EXPOSITION: *1967 Charlottetown*, n° 80 (qui comportait également les cinq autres).
CONFEDERATION ART GALLERY AND MUSEUM, CHARLOTTETOWN

87 *Caricature of the Reverend Canon Jacob Ellegood* c. 1893
Graphite
8 x 5 in. (20.3 x 12.7 cm) (s)
INSCRIPTION: u.r., red crayon, *Canon Ellegood*; bottom edge, pencil, *Canon Ellegood in Procession.*

Framed with cat. nos. 58, 85, 86, 93, 94. For a more reverential view of Ellegood, see cat. no. 102.
EXHIBITION: *1967 Charlottetown*, no. 80 (one of six framed together).
CONFEDERATION ART GALLERY AND MUSEUM, CHARLOTTETOWN

88 *Study for "Lord Aberdeen"* 1894
33 x 19 in. (83.8 x 48.3 cm) (s)
HARRIS PAPERS: "I may go up [to] Ottawa next week for a few days to work at Lord Aberdeen's portrait. He wrote the other day and asked me to stay at Rideau Hall When I liked to fix. However I will only start the picture now and go on with it in the autumn when they come to Montreal." (Letter from Harris to his mother, dated 11 June 1894) .

Study for a portrait not in the exhibition.
In the sitter-book is written (c. 1895): "Lord Aberdeen. Govr. Genl. to fit panel in Haddo Scotland." The original portrait does in fact now fit above the Wedgewood chimney-piece in the library at Haddo Hall, Aberdeenshire, Scotland. One wonders why, if their Excellencies had decided as early as 1894 to take the painting back with them to Scotland, they did not commission Harris to paint a replica for Government House during the next four years. As it is, in December 1898, when Harris returned to Canada from Europe, he wrote to his mother explaining why he and Bessie had gone to Montreal without first stopping off in Charlottetown: ". . . I feared I might get no commissions for portraits all winter if we did not turn up here. As it was I lost one, namely a replica of Lord Aberdeen's portrait (which I did two [*sic*] years ago for Government House, Ottawa.) They [the Aberdeens] wrote me as I was not there they had to get another artist to make a copy which they hoped would be satisfactory to me."
It is a splendid painting and one in which Harris borrowed a statesmanlike and kingly pose from one of Velasquez's portraits of Philip IV. Harris, like other Canadians, was immensely fond of Lord and Lady Aberdeen.
It was undoubtedly a matter of wise policy that has enabled the Dominion of Canada to have a succession of Scottish-born Governors

87 *Caricature du révérend chanoine Jacob Ellegood* c. 1893
Mine de plomb
8 x 5 po (20.3 x 12.7 cm) (s.v.)
INSCRIPTION: h.d., au crayon de pastel rouge (trad.): Le chanoine *Ellegood*; marge b., au crayon (trad.): Le chanoine *Ellegood* dans une procession.

Encadré avec les nᵒˢ 58, 85, 86, 93 et 94. Voir également un portrait moins caricatural d'Ellegood (nᵒ 102).
EXPOSITION: *1967 Charlottetown*, nᵒ 80 (qui comportait également les cinq autres).
CONFEDERATION ART GALLERY AND MUSEUM, CHARLOTTETOWN

88 *Étude pour Lord Aberdeen* 1894
33 x 19 po (83.8 x 48.3 cm) (s.v.)
DOCUMENTS HARRIS: «Il se peut que j'aille à Ottawa la semaine prochaine pour y travailler quelques jours au portrait de Lord Aberdeen. Il m'a écrit l'autre jour pour me demander de rester à Rideau Hall quand me plaira. Toutefois, je ne ferai que commencer le portrait maintenant et le continuerai à l'automne lorsqu'ils viendront à Montréal.» (Lettre de Harris à sa mère, 11 juin 1894).

Le portrait exécuté à la suite de cette étude n'est pas présenté dans le cadre de cette exposition.
Dans le journal de travail de l'artiste, on trouve la note suivante, qui date de 1895 environ: «Lord Aberdeen. Gouverneur général. À encastrer à Haddo en Écosse.» Le portrait original se trouve, en effet, au-dessus d'une cheminée Wedgewood dans la bibliothèque de Haddo Hall (Aberdeenshire, Écosse). On s'étonnera peut-être que Leurs Excellences n'en aient pas commandé, au cours des quatre années qui suivirent, une réplique pour la résidence du gouverneur général, puisqu'elles savaient, dès 1894, qu'elles ramèneraient le tableau en Écosse? Or, en décembre 1898, Harris revient d'Europe et rentre directement à Montréal avec Bessie, sans s'arrêter à Charlottetown. Il s'expliquera dans une lettre à sa mère: «J'avais peur de ne pas recevoir de commandes de portraits cet hiver si je n'apparaissais pas immédiatement ici. J'en ai déjà perdu une, celle de la réplique du portrait de Lord Aberdeen (que j'ai peint il y a deux ans [*sic*] pour la résidence du gouverneur général, Ottawa). Ils [les Aberdeen] m'ont écrit que, étant donné que j'étais absent, ils étaient obligés de demander à un autre peintre d'en faire une copie et qu'ils espéraient que j'en serais satisfait.»
Le tableau de Harris, qui a emprunté la noble et digne pose à l'un des portraits du

General, and when the future Marquess of Aberdeen returned to Scotland in 1898, the *Toronto Telegraph* commented that he "did more to popularize the office of Governor-General in Canada than any other representative that was ever sent to Ottawa."

Born in Edinburgh, Scotland, in 1847, and educated at St. Andrew's University and University College, Oxford, young Lord Aberdeen married Ishbell Maria, the daughter of the first Lord Tweedmouth, of Invernesshire. In addition to numerous honours from Canadian universities, he was Honorary Colonel of the Governor General's Foot Guards of Canada, and an Honourable Life Governor of the Victorian Order of Nurses. He was on the British Board of Directors of the Canadian Life Assurance Company, and a member of the Board of Control of the Pacific Cable Company. During the coronation of King George v and Queen Mary in 1911, the Marquess of Aberdeen carried the standard of the Dominion of Canada in the procession.

From 1881 to 1885 he was Lord High Commissioner to the General Assembly of the Church of Scotland, and twice served as Lord Lieutenant of Ireland.

While Lord Aberdeen was immensely popular in Canada, his Countess made almost as great an impression. At the time of her arrival in 1893, she was already a leader in the International Council of Women, and her first task was to call a rally in Toronto the following October. More than fifteen hundred women from across Canada attended. Lady Aberdeen consented to become the first President of the National Council of Women.

Lady Aberdeen was also chiefly responsible for the organization of the Victorian Order of Nurses, which was at first for the introduction of nurses into the rural areas of Canada, but was soon extended to larger cities such as Montreal and Toronto. This superb nursing service is still in existence today, thanks to Lady Aberdeen who overcame the objections of the Ontario Medical Association and others, and had both Sir Wilfrid Laurier and Lord Strathcona on her side. The v.o.n. finally achieved its Charter from Queen Victoria in May 1897.

Lady Aberdeen was the author of *Through Canada with a Kodak* (1893) and the *Canadian Journal* (edited for the Champlain Society in 1960).

BIBLIOGRAPHY: Smith, "The Royal Canadian Academy," repr. p. 310.
EXHIBITION: *1967 Charlottetown*, no. 48.
CONFEDERATION ART GALLERY AND
MUSEUM, CHARLOTTETOWN

roi Philippe IV peints par Velasquez, est splendide. Harris, comme d'autres Canadiens, avait beaucoup d'estime pour Lord Aberdeen et sa femme.

On ne peut que se féliciter des décisions qui ont valu au Dominion du Canada une série de gouverneurs généraux d'origine écossaise. Ainsi, lorsque le Lord d'Aberdeen et de Temair rentre en Écosse en 1898, le *Toronto Telegram* écrit, qu'il «a fait davantage pour rendre la charge de gouverneur général populaire au Canada que n'importe quel autre représentant jamais envoyé à Ottawa.»

Né à Édimbourg (Écosse) en 1847, Lord Aberdeen fit ses études à l'université St. Andrew's et au University College d'Oxford. Il épousa Ishbel Maria, fille du premier baron de Tweedmouth, d'Invernesshire. En plus des nombreux titres que lui conférèrent les universités canadiennes, Lord Aberdeen eut celui d'honorable colonel de la garde à pied du gouverneur général, et de gouverneur honorable à vie des infirmières de l'Ordre de Victoria. Il fut membre du conseil d'administration britannique de la Canadian Life Assurance Company et membre de l'office de contrôle de la Pacific Cable Company. Lors du couronnement du roi Georges V et de la reine Marie, en 1911, ce sera Lord Aberdeen qui portera l'étendard du Dominion du Canada dans le cortège.

De 1881 à 1885, il fut délégué de la Couronne à l'assemblée générale de l'Église d'Écosse. A deux reprises, il fut Lord-lieutenant d'Irlande.

Lord Aberdeen était très populaire au Canada, mais son épouse ne faisait pas moins grande impression. Au moment de son arrivée, en 1893, elle faisait déjà partie de la direction du Conseil international des femmes et sa première tâche fut d'organiser un grand rassemblement à Toronto le mois d'octobre suivant. Plus de quinze cents femmes venues de tous les coins du Canada y participèrent. Lady Aberdeen accepta alors de devenir la première présidente du Conseil national.

C'est à elle aussi que l'on doit l'organisation des infirmières de l'Ordre de Victoria dont le but, initialement, était de doter d'un service d'infirmières chaque district rural au Canada mais, plus tard, également les villes telles que Montréal et Toronto. Si cette excellente organisation existe encore aujourd'hui, c'est en grande partie parce que Lady Aberdeen a su réfuter les objections, entre autres, de l'Ontario Medical Association, et gagner l'appui de Sir Wilfrid Laurier et de Lord Strathcona. L'Ordre obtint finalement sa charte de la reine Victoria en mai 1897.

Lady Aberdeen fut également l'auteur de *Through Canada with a Kodak*, publié en

1893, et son *Canadian Journal* fut publié par la société Champlain en 1960.
BIBLIOGRAPHIE: Smith: *The Royal Canadian Academy*, reprod. p. 310.
EXPOSITION: *1967 Charlottetown*, n⁰ 48.
CONFEDERATION ART GALLERY AND MUSEUM, CHARLOTTETOWN

89   *Anonymous Copy of "Lord Aberdeen"*
1894
85-1/2 x 48-1/2 in. (217.2 x 123.2 cm)

See note on previous entry, cat. no. 88.
GOVERNMENT HOUSE, OTTAWA

89   *Copie anonyme de Lord Aberdeen*   1894
85-1/2 x 48-1/2 po (217.2 x 123.2 cm)

Voir le commentaire du n⁰ 88.
RÉSIDENCE DU GOUVERNEUR GÉNÉRAL, OTTAWA

90   *Study for "E.B. Eddy"*   1894
Brown conté chalk
18 x 14-3/8 in. (45.7 x 36.5 cm)
INSCRIPTION: dated u.l., pencil, *Study for portrait of/E.B. Eddy – Hull/abt 30 x 40 in/July/94.*
EXHIBITION: *1967 Charlottetown*, no. 115.
CONFEDERATION ART GALLERY AND MUSEUM, CHARLOTTETOWN

90   *Étude pour E.B. Eddy*   1894
Conté brun
18 x 14-3/8 po (45.7 x 36.5 cm)
INSCRIPTION: date, h.g., au crayon (trad.): *Étude pour le portrait de E.B. Eddy – Hull/approximativement 30 x 40 po/juillet/94.*
EXPOSITION: *1967 Charlottetown*, n⁰ 115.
CONFEDERATION ART GALLERY AND MUSEUM, CHARLOTTETOWN

91 *E.B. Eddy* 1894
51-1/8 x 41-3/8 in. (129.9 x 105.1 cm (s)
INSCRIPTION: signed l.r., *Robert Harris.*

The founder of one of the world's largest match companies was born near Bristol, Vermont, in 1827, son of Samuel Eddy and Clarissa Eastman. In 1851, when he was twenty-three years old, he first began to make matches by hand at Burlington, Vermont, later transferring his business to Wrightown (now Hull) in Canada East. (He also manufactured pails, washboards, and clothes pegs.) His first wife (née Zarda Diane Arnold) assisted him with the manufacturing of matches, and for the first five years their output was ten cases a day. At first, the Eddys sold the matches in a store near the wood-mill, or by horse and buggy, driving as far as Hamilton and selling cases en route, and replacing stocks with shipments sent on ahead. By 1870, though, the E.B. Eddy Company was shipping between fifty to seventy million boardfeet of lumber a year, in its sawmill making 125 cases of matches per day. In 1886 Eddy bought the rights to manufacture pressed fiberware and erected a groundwood pulp mill. In 1889 he built the first chemical pulp mill in Canada.

From 1871 to 1875, E.B. Eddy represented Ottawa County in the Quebec Legislative Assembly. He was elected Mayor of Hull in 1881.

In 1900, six years before Eddys' death, his plant was totally destroyed by fire at a loss of $3,000,000. At the time of the fire, the company was supplying newsprint to nearly all the newspapers in Canada. Within two years they had sufficiently recovered from the fire to have installed more paper-making machines than any other mill in the Province of Quebec.

EXHIBITION: *1895 Montreal Spring Exhibition*, no. 53.

THE E.B. EDDY COMPANY, OTTAWA-HULL

91 *E.B. Eddy* 1894
51-1/8 x 41-3/8 po (129.9 x 105.1 cm) (s.v.)
INSCRIPTION: signature, b.d.: *Robert Harris.*

Le fondateur d'une des plus grandes sociétés productrices d'allumettes au monde est né en 1827, près de Bristol (Vermont), de Samuel Eddy et de Clarissa Eastman. En 1851, âgé de vingt-trois ans, il commence à fabriquer des allumettes à la main, d'abord à Burlington (Vermont), puis à Wrightown (aujourd'hui Hull), dans l'Est du Canada. (Il fabriquait aussi des seaux, des planches de blanchisseuse et des pinces à linge.) Aidé de sa première femme (née Zarda Diane Arnold), il produisait, au cours des cinq premières années, jusqu'à dix caisses d'allumettes par jour qu'il vendait dans un magasin près de la scierie ou en parcourant le pays en voiture, allant même jusqu'à Hamilton en vendant des caisses en cours de route, se réapprovisionnant au moyen de chargements expédiés d'avance. Dès 1870, la société E.B. Eddy expédiait entre cinquante et soixante-dix millions de pieds de bois de construction par an de ses scieries et produisait 125 caisses d'allumettes par jour. En 1866, Eddy achetait les droits de fabrication du bois pressé et érigeait une usine de pâte mécanique. En 1889, il construisait la première usine chimique de pâte au Canada.

De 1871 à 1875, E.B. Eddy représentait le comté d'Ottawa à l'Assemblée législative du Québec. Il fut élu maire de Hull en 1881.

En 1900, six ans avant sa mort, un incendie ravageait complètement l'usine E.B. Eddy, ce qui représentait une perte de $3 000 000. La société fournissait à ce moment-là presque la totalité du papier journal utilisé au Canada. Il s'en remit toutefois rapidement puisque, en 1902, il possédait plus de machines à papier que toute autre usine dans la province de Québec.

EXPOSITION: *1895 Montréal, Printemps*, nᵒ 53.

COMPAGNIE E.B. EDDY, OTTAWA-HULL

92 *Study for "Mrs. E.B. Eddy"* 1894
Brown conté chalk
19-1/2 x 14 in. (49.5 x 35.6 cm)
INSCRIPTION: l.r., pencil, *Study for portrait of Mrs. Eddy.*

Study for a portrait not in the exhibition.
This drawing is of E.B. Eddy's (cat. no. 91) second wife, née Jennie Grahl Hunter, whom he married in 1894.
CONFEDERATION ART GALLERY AND MUSEUM, CHARLOTTETOWN

92 *Étude pour Mme E.B. Eddy* 1894
Conté brun
19-1/2 x 14 po (49.5 x 35.6 cm)
INSCRIPTION: b.d., au crayon (trad.): Étude pour le *portrait* de Mme *Eddy.*

Le portrait exécuté à la suite de cette étude n'est pas présenté dans le cadre de cette exposition.
Le modèle était la seconde femme, née Jennie Grahl Hunter, de E.B. Eddy (n° 91). Ils se marièrent en 1894.
CONFEDERATION ART GALLERY AND MUSEUM, CHARLOTTETOWN

93 *Caricature of Bishop A.C.A. Hall* 1894
Pen and sepia ink
6 x 4 in. (15.3 x 10.2 cm) (s)
INSCRIPTION: dated l.r., *Dr. Hall/Bishop of Vermont/6th Oct 94/St. John's.*

Framed with cat. nos. 58, 85, 86, 87, 94.
Arthur Crawshay Alliston Hall (1847–1930), born and educated in England, was influenced by the Oxford Movement (see note on cat. no. 7). He returned to England after disappointment of preferment in Massachusetts, but was recalled to become Bishop of Vermont in 1893.
EXHIBITION: *1967 Charlottetown*, no. 80 (one of six framed together).
CONFEDERATION ART GALLERY AND MUSEUM, CHARLOTTETOWN

93 *Caricature de l'évêque A.C.A. Hall* 1894
Plume, sépia
6 x 4 po (15.3 x 10.2 cm) (s.v.)
INSCRIPTION: date, b.d. (trad.): *Dr. Hall/évêque du Vermont/6* octobre *94/St. John's.*

Encadré avec les n°s 58, 85, 86, 87 et 94.
Arthur Crawshay Alliston Hall naquit en 1847 en Angleterre et y fit ses études. Il subit l'influence de l'«*Oxford Movement*» (voir le commentaire du n° 7). N'ayant pu accéder au siège épiscopal du Massachusetts, il retourna en Angleterre; rappelé, il devint néanmoins évêque du Vermont en 1893. Il mourut en 1930.
EXPOSITION: *1967 Charlottetown*, n° 80 (qui comportait également les cinq autres).
CONFEDERATION ART GALLERY AND MUSEUM, CHARLOTTETOWN

94 *Caricature of ?The Reverend E. Wood*
1894
8-3/4 x 6-3/4 in. (22.2 x 17.2 cm) (s)
INSCRIPTION: signed and dated l.r., *R. H. 23 Dec/94;* l.c., *Revnd. E. Wood*

Framed with cat. nos. 58, 85, 86, 87, 93.
EXHIBITION: *1967 Charlottetown*, no. 80 (one of six framed together).
CONFEDERATION ART GALLERY AND MUSEUM, CHARLOTTETOWN

94 *Caricature du révérend E. Wood* (?)
1894
8-3/4 x 6-3/4 po (22.2 x 17.2 cm) (s.v.)
INSCRIPTION: signature et date (trad.), b.d.: *R.H. 23* décembre*/94;* inscription, *b.c.: Revnd. E. Wood.*

Encadré avec les n°s 58, 85, 86, 87 et 93.
EXPOSITION: *1967 Charlottetown*, n° 80 (qui comportait également les cinq autres).
CONFEDERATION ART GALLERY AND MUSEUM, CHARLOTTETOWN

95 *?James Morgan* 1895
10-3/4 x 8-3/4 in. (27.3 x 22.2 cm) (s)
INSCRIPTION: l.c., pencil, *sketch for portrait of James Morgan.*

Framed with cat. no. 113. There are no notes or letters to confirm the identification of the man in the inscription.
CONFEDERATION ART GALLERY AND MUSEUM, CHARLOTTETOWN

95 *James Morgan* (?) 1895
10-3/4 x 8-3/4 po (27.3 x 22.2 cm) (s.v.)
INSCRIPTION: b.c., au crayon (trad.): esquisse pour le *portrait* de *James Morgan.*

Encadré avec le n° 113. L'identité du modèle n'est spécifiée dans aucune note ou lettre.
CONFEDERATION ART GALLERY AND MUSEUM, CHARLOTTETOWN

96 *Ruth Harris* 1896
31 x 20 in. (78.7 x 50.8 cm)
INSCRIPTION: signed l.l., *Robert Harris*; top edge, *RUTH HARRIS ÆTATIS III*; on reverse, dated u.r., *Portrait of/RUTH M.L. HARRIS/(daughter of/Rev. E. Harris M.A.)/ painted from life/in St. James Rectory/Mahone, N.S./by Robert Harris/P.R.C.A./August 1896.*

Daughter of one of Harris's brothers (cat. no. 75), the sitter became Mrs. E.L. Tuck.
THE REVEREND AND MRS. E.L. TUCK, CHARLOTTETOWN

96 *Ruth Harris* 1896
31 x 20 po (78.7 x 50.8 cm)
INSCRIPTION: signature, b.g.: *Robert Harris*; marge h.: *RUTH HARRIS ÆTATIS III*; au verso, date, h.d. (trad.): *Portrait de/ RUTH M.L. HARRIS/(fille du/révérend E. Harris M.A.)/peint d'après nature/au presbytère St. James/Mahone* (N.-É.)/par *Robert Harris/P.R.C.A./*août *1896.*

Le modèle était la fille du frère de Harris (n° 75). Elle devint, par la suite, Mme E.L. Tuck.
LE RÉVÉREND ET MME E.L. TUCK, CHARLOTTETOWN

97 *Dr. Francis Shepherd* 1896
30 x 24 in. (76.2 x 60.9 cm) (s), painted oval
INSCRIPTION: signed l.r., *Robert Harris.*

Dr. Shepherd was Chief Surgeon at the Montreal General Hospital. Dr. H.E. MacDermott, in his *History of the Montreal General Hospital*, declares that from a historical point of view, "few men occupied such a large place in the story of the hospital as Shepherd, who seems to spread all over its life. He could speak at first hand of almost the earliest men in its staff."
Shepherd saw the hospital expand. Not only was he Professor of Anatomy at McGill, he was Dermatologist at the General Hospital, and illustrated his lectures with his own skilled drawings. He donated a large collection of surgical and pathological specimens to the University, and it was one of the great sorrows of his life when the collection was totally destroyed in the fire of 1906 which

97 *Le docteur Francis Shepherd* 1896
30 x 24 po (76.2 x 60.9 cm) (s.v.), peint en ovale
INSCRIPTION: signature, b.d.: *Robert Harris.*

Le docteur Shepherd était chirurgien en chef à l'Hôpital général de Montréal. Le docteur H.E. MacDermott note dans son histoire de l'hôpital que, du point de vue historique, «peu d'hommes ont occupé une aussi grande place dans l'histoire de l'hôpital que Shepherd, qui semble avoir pénétré toutes les facettes de son activité. Il pouvait vous parler, pour les avoir connus personnellement, même des plus anciens membres de son personnel.»
Shepherd fut témoin de l'expansion de l'hôpital. Il y travailla de longues années en tant que dermatologiste, tout en donnant à McGill, des cours d'anatomie qu'il relevait par d'excellents dessins techniques, de sa main. Il dota l'université d'une vaste collection de spécimens chirurgicaux et

gutted the Museum and Medical Building.

Shepherd had a reputation as an autocrat. Being a policy-maker, and a powerful one at that, he persuaded the Board of Governors, in 1910, that the Hospital should remain on its present site and not move to another uptown. It was Dr. Shepherd, also, who, in 1890, had opposed the suggestion that the Montreal General Hospital should amalgamate with the Royal Victoria Hospital, because he felt the terms proposed by the new hospital were too sweeping, and that the General Hospital would lose its identity.

Shepherd also found time for the arts, as Chairman of the Board of the Art Association of Montreal (1906–11, 1918–29). He was also Chairman of the Board of the National Gallery of Canada (1924–29).

EXHIBITIONS: *1896 Montreal R.C.A.*, no. 73; *1919 Montreal*, no. 50.

THE MONTREAL GENERAL HOSPITAL

pathologiques dont la perte, dans un incendie qui ravagea le musée et le bâtiment de la Faculté de médecine en 1906, l'affligea profondément.

Shepherd passait pour un autocrate. Volontaire et homme puissant, c'est lui qui persuada le conseil des gouverneurs, en 1910, de ne pas déplacer l'hôpital à un nouveau site plus loin du centre de la ville. C'est encore lui qui, en 1890, s'opposa véhémentement à la fusion de l'Hôpital général de Montréal avec l'hôpital Royal Victoria parce que, selon lui, les conditions proposées étaient trop radicales et que l'Hôpital général perdrait son identité.

Le docteur Shepherd consacra également une partie de son temps aux arts puisqu'il fut de 1906 à 1911, puis de 1918 à 1929, président du conseil de l'Art Association of Montreal. Il fut également président du conseil de la Galerie nationale du Canada de 1924 à 1929.

EXPOSITIONS: *1896 Montréal, A.R.A.C.*, no 73; *1919 Montréal*, no 50.

HÔPITAL GÉNÉRAL DE MONTRÉAL

98 *Study for "Sir Henry Strong"* 1896
Pastel crayon
16 x 12-1/4 in. (40.6 x 31.1 cm)
INSCRIPTION: l.r., pencil, *Sir Henry Strong, Justic* [sic] *sketch for portrait in Court House, Ottawa.*
CONFEDERATION ART GALLERY AND MUSEUM, CHARLOTTETOWN

98 *Étude pour Sir Henry Strong* 1896
Crayon de pastel
16 x 12-1/4 po (40.6 x 31.1 cm)
INSCRIPTION: b.d., au crayon (trad.): *Sir Henry Strong*, juge en chef, esquisse pour un *portrait* destiné au palais de justice, *Ottawa.*
CONFEDERATION ART GALLERY AND MUSEUM, CHARLOTTETOWN

99   *Study for "Sir Henry Strong"*   1896
Graphite and chalk
18-1/4 x 15 in. (46.4 x 38.1 cm)
INSCRIPTION: signed l.r., *Robt Harris*; bottom
edge, pencil, *Study for portrait of Chief Justice Sir Henry Strong for Courtroom Ottawa.*
EXHIBITION: *1967 Charlottetown*, no. 116, repr.
CONFEDERATION ART GALLERY AND
MUSEUM, CHARLOTTETOWN

99   *Étude pour Sir Henry Strong*   1896
Mine de plomb et craie
18-1/4 x 15 po (46.4 x 38.1 cm)
INSCRIPTION: signature, b.d.: *Robt Harris;*
marge b., au crayon (trad.): Étude pour le
portrait du juge en chef *Sir Henry Strong*
destiné à la salle d'audience du palais de
justice à *Ottawa.*
EXPOSITION: *1967 Charlottetown*, nº 116,
reprod.
CONFEDERATION ART GALLERY AND
MUSEUM, CHARLOTTETOWN

100   *Sir Henry Strong*   1896
53-1/8 x 43-3/4 in. (134.9 x 111.1 cm)
INSCRIPTION: signed u.l., *Robert Harris.*

The future first Chief Justice of the Supreme Court of Canada came to Canada with his parents in 1836 from Poole, Dorset, where he had been born in 1825. Educated in Quebec, he studied law at Bytown (Ottawa) and Toronto and was called to the Bar of Upper Canada in 1849. When the Supreme Court was organized in 1875 he was appointed a puisne judge. He was a judge of the Court of Chancery of Ontario from 1874–75.

In 1897 he became a member of the Imperial Privy Council and a member of the Judicial Committee of the Privy Council.

Harris began painting this portrait late in 1895, with sittings in Ottawa, and completed it in March 1896.
CANADA DEPARTMENT OF PUBLIC WORKS,
OTTAWA

100   *Sir Henry Strong*   1896
53-1/8 x 43-3/4 po (134.9 x 111.1 cm)
INSCRIPTION: signature, h.g.: *Robert Harris.*

Celui qui devait être le premier juge en chef de la Cour suprême du Canada, Samuel Henry Strong, est né à Poole (Dorset), en 1825. Il immigra avec ses parents au Canada en 1836. Ayant poursuivi ses études à Québec, il fit son droit à Bytown (Ottawa) et à Toronto. Il fut admis au barreau du Haut-Canada en 1849. Il fut nommé juge-conseiller à la Cour suprême lorsque celle-ci fut créée en 1875, après avoir été, de 1874 à 1875, juge à la Cour de chancellerie de l'Ontario.

En 1897, il devint membre du Conseil privé impérial et membre du comité juridique du Conseil privé.

Robert Harris commença ce portrait à Ottawa, vers la fin de 1895, pour le terminer en mars 1896.
MINISTÈRE FÉDÉRAL DES TRAVAUX
PUBLICS, OTTAWA

101 *Lady Allan* 1897
38 x 24-1/4 in. (96.5 x 61.6 cm) (s)
INSCRIPTION: signed l.l., on pedestal, *Robert Harris.*

Wife of the Montreal financier Sir Montague Allan, second son of Sir Hugh Allan (cat. no. 44), Lady Allan (née Margaret Ethel Mackenzie) was one of the leaders of Montreal Society in the 1890s. Among many other philanthropies, she endowed the Allan Pavilion of the Royal Victoria Hospital.

Montague Allan commissioned this portrait of his wife from Harris in April 1897.

EXHIBITION: *1897 Montreal Spring Exhibition*, no. 55 (as *Portrait, Mrs. H. Montagu Allen*).

ROYAL VICTORIA HOSPITAL,
MONTREAL, QUEBEC

101 *Lady Allan* 1897
38 x 24-1/4 po (96.5 x 61.6 cm) (s.v.)
INSCRIPTION: signature, b.g. (sur le piédestal): *Robert Harris.*

Épouse du financier montréalais Sir Montague Allan, deuxième fils de Sir Hugh Allan (n° 44), Lady Allan, née Margaret Ethel Mackenzie, fit partie de l'élite de la société montréalaise dans les années 1890. On lui doit, parmi d'autres œuvres philanthropiques, la dotation du pavillon Allan de l'hôpital Royal Victoria.

En avril 1897, Sir Montague Allan commanda à Harris ce portrait de sa femme.

EXPOSITION: *1897 Montréal, Printemps*, n° 55 (*Portrait, Mrs. H. Montagu Allen*).

HÔPITAL ROYAL VICTORIA, MONTRÉAL

102 *The Reverend Canon Jacob Ellegood*
1897
85-3/4 x 48-1/2 in. (217.8 x 123.2 cm)
INSCRIPTION: signed l.r., *Robert Harris.*

This delightful portrait was presented to Canon Ellegood by his congregation at the Church of St. James the Apostle, Montreal, on the occasion of his jubilee in 1898.

Canon Ellegood, who was a descendant of United Empire Loyalists, was born in Dumfries, New Brunswick, in 1824. He was educated at local schools, at Kings College, and then at Bishop's College. After his ordination in 1849, he served as assistant in Christ Church Cathedral in Montreal. For some years he was in charge of St. Anne's Chapel, Montreal – a church which was eventually destroyed in a terrible fire. It was through Ellegood's efforts that the magnificent Church of St. James the Apostle – with its rectory and other buildings – was erected, and in 1864 he was appointed its Rector.

He was Chaplain to the Third Regiment of the Victoria Rifles with the honorary rank of Captain. In 1908 he was appointed Honourable Major of the Regiment. The newspaper *The Montreal Witness* referred to him as the "grand old patriarch of Canadian Anglicanism."

For a gentle caricature by Harris, see cat. no. 87.

EXHIBITION: *1898 Montreal Spring Exhibition*, no. 46.

THE CHURCH OF ST. JAMES THE APOSTLE,
MONTREAL

102 *Le révérend chanoine Jacob Ellegood*
1897
85-3/4 x 48-1/2 po (217.8 x 123.2 cm)
INSCRIPTION: signature, b.d.: *Robert Harris.*

Ce ravissant portrait a été offert au chanoine Ellegood par ses paroissiens de l'église St. James the Apostle, à Montréal, à l'occasion de ses cinquante ans de sacerdoce, en 1898.

Le chanoine Ellegood, un descendant des Loyalistes, est né à Dumfries (Nouveau-Brunswick), en 1824. Il fit ses études dans les écoles locales d'abord, puis à Kings et à Bishop's College. Ordonné ministre en 1849, il devint vicaire à la cathédrale Christ Church de Montréal. Au cours des années suivantes, il desservit la chapelle St. Anne's de Montréal, qui fut malheureusement détruite au cours d'un terrible incendie. C'est grâce à Ellegood que fut construite la somptueuse église St. James the Apostle, avec son presbytère et les bâtiments connexes. En 1864, Ellegood en devint le recteur.

Il fut aumônier du troisième régiment des Victoria Rifles, avec le rang de capitaine et, à partir de 1908, celui d'honorable major du régiment. Le journal *The Montreal Witness*, le qualifia de «grand patriarche de l'anglicanisme canadien».

Voir également le commentaire sur sa caricature (n° 87).

EXPOSITION: *1898 Montréal, Printemps*, n° 46.

THE CHURCH OF ST. JAMES THE APOSTLE,
MONTRÉAL

103 *Study for "Bruce Price"* 1897
10-3/4 x 5-3/4 in. (27.3 x 14.6 cm) (s)
INSCRIPTION: u.l., pencil. *Sketch for portrait of/Bruce Price.*

Study for a portrait not in the exhibition. Framed with cat. no. 104.

Bruce Price was born in Cumberland, Maryland, in 1845 and studied architecture in Baltimore and abroad. He designed many well-known buildings in the southern United States before taking his family to New York where his first major architectural complex, Tuxedo Park, was built. He built many individual homes for the wealthy at Newport, Rhode Island, and Bar Harbor, Maine.

Price was hired by Sir Donald Smith (later to become Lord Strathcona; see cat. no. 128) to design Royal Victoria College and McGill University. While in Canada, or working out of his Boston office, Bruce Price designed the Château Frontenac, Quebec City, the Banff Springs Hotel, Alberta, the Windsor Street Station, Montreal, and Place Viger Railway Station for the C.P.R. It has been suggested by Professor Alan Gowans that Bruce Price gave to Canada a national style in architecture.

Price won the gold medal for architecture at the Paris Exposition, 1900, and he was the choice of a committee of Japanese architects who made an extended world tour for the purpose of selecting the architect for a palace in Tokyo for the Crown Prince of Japan.

Price was immensely popular in Montreal, and the St. James Club created the post of permanent visitor for him, a post which he was the only man ever to hold.

Mr. and Mrs. Bruce Price had the further distinction of being the parents of Emily Post.

The Prices travelled regularly from New York to Montreal for sittings in Harris's studio. Alas, two years of search have failed to find the missing portraits – which were apparently sold in 1960 from the Emily Post Estate. The sketches here exhibited would appear to be the final studies. Bruce Price died in 1903.

CONFEDERATION ART GALLERY AND
MUSEUM, CHARLOTTETOWN

103 *Étude pour Bruce Price* 1897
10-3/4 x 5-3/4 po (27.3 x 14.6 cm) (s.v.)
INSCRIPTION: h.g. au crayon (trad.): Étude pour le *portrait* de/*Bruce Price.*

Le portrait exécuté à la suite de cette étude n'est pas présenté dans le cadre de cette exposition. Encadré avec le n° 104.

Né à Cumberland (Maryland) en 1845, Bruce Price étudia l'architecture à Baltimore et à l'étranger. Il avait déjà conçu plusieurs édifices célèbres dans le Sud des États-Unis lorsqu'il s'installa avec sa famille à New York où son premier grand ensemble architectural, le Tuxedo Park, sera construit. Il fut aussi l'architecte de nombreuses résidences pour de riches particuliers à Newport (Rhode Island) et à Bar Harbor (Maine).

Price fut engagé par Sir Donald Smith (qui deviendra, plus tard, Lord Strathcona; n° 128) pour le Royal Victoria College et l'université McGill. Price se vit confier, pendant son séjour au Canada, puis à son cabinet de Boston, la tâche de dessiner le Château Frontenac à Québec, le Banff Springs Hotel en Alberta, la gare Windsor à Montréal, ainsi que la gare du Canadien Pacifique, place Viger. Selon le professeur Alan Gowans, on pourrait affirmer que Bruce Price a réellement doté le Canada d'un style national d'architecture.

En 1900, Price remporta la médaille d'or d'architecture à l'exposition de Paris et se vit confier, par une commission d'architectes japonais qui faisait le tour du monde à la recherche d'un architecte, la tâche de construire à Tokyo le palais du prince héritier du Japon. Price jouit d'une grande popularité à Montréal et le St. James Club créa, à son intention, le titre de visiteur permanent, auquel il fut le seul à avoir droit. (À M. et Mme Bruce Price revient aussi l'honneur d'être les parents d'Emily Post).

Pour permettre à Harris de faire leur portrait, les Price voyagèrent régulièrement entre New York et Montréal pour poser à l'atelier du peintre. Malheureusement, deux ans de recherche n'ont pas permis de retrouver leurs portraits, qui ont apparemment été vendus en 1960 par les responsables de la succession d'Emily Post. Les esquisses de cette exposition en seraient les études définitives. Bruce Price mourut en 1903.

CONFEDERATION ART GALLERY AND
MUSEUM, CHARLOTTETOWN

104 *Study for "Mrs. Bruce Price"* 1897
10-3/4 x 5-3/4 in. (27.3 x 14.6 cm) (s)
INSCRIPTION: upper edge, pencil, *Sketch for portrait of Mrs. Bruce Price.*

Study for a portrait not in the exhibition. Framed with cat. no. 103.
CONFEDERATION ART GALLERY AND
MUSEUM, CHARLOTTETOWN

104 *Étude pour Mme Bruce Price* 1897
10-3/4 x 5-3/4 po (27.3 x 14.6 cm) (s.v.)
INSCRIPTION: marge h., au crayon (trad.):
Étude pour le *portrait* de Mme *Bruce Price.*

Le portrait exécuté à la suite de cette étude n'est pas présenté dans le cadre de cette exposition. Encadré avec le n° 103.
CONFEDERATION ART GALLERY AND
MUSEUM, CHARLOTTETOWN

105 *Peter Redpath* 1897
43-7/8 x 35-3/4 in. (111.5 x 90.8 cm)
INSCRIPTION: signed l.r., *Robert Harris –;* on reverse, *Presented to the Montreal General Hospital by Mrs. Redpath, 1897.*

On 11 March 1897, Robert Harris received a letter from Mrs. Peter Redpath, then living in England, commissioning a portrait of her late husband (died 1894) for the Montreal General Hospital, at $750. "She to send frame which she has out, if it will do." On the fifteenth of the same month Harris received another letter commissioning him to paint a portrait of herself "for McGill College to correspond with that of her late husband painted by me." On 11 April, Mrs. Redpath wrote again, this time to add a further commission, a portrait of herself for the "library, McGill College." By the middle of June, after further correspondence, Harris appears to have completed all four portraits, and on 24 June he delivered the portrait of Peter Redpath to the General Hospital. In December 1897, the sitter-book entry reads, "Mr. G.W. Redpath, Painted sketch of later Peter Redpath over an old head cut out of a picture of them they had to destroy in London. Paid." – but he doesn't say how much.

Peter Redpath, sugar manufacturer, was born in Montreal in 1821. He studied business methods in England, then returned to Canada and entered his father's sugar refinery. He endowed a chair of Natural Philosophy at McGill University, and also built and endowed a library building and museum, to both of which institutions he gave many gifts of historical value. He was for many years President of the Montreal General Hospital. He retired from business in 1879 to Chislehurst, England, where he died.

105 *Peter Redpath* 1897
43-7/8 x 35-3/4 po (111.5 x 90.8 cm)
INSCRIPTION: signature, b.d.: *Robert Harris;* au verso (trad.): Offert à l'Hôpital général de Montréal par Mme *Redpath, 1897.*

Le 11 mars 1897, Robert Harris reçut une lettre de Mme Peter Redpath (qui résidait à ce moment-là en Angleterre), lui demandant de peindre le portrait de son défunt mari (mort en 1894), portrait qu'elle voulait léguer à l'Hôpital général de Montréal. Elle était prête à payer $750 et à «envoyer le cadre qu'elle avait, s'il convenait». Le 15 du même mois, il recevait une autre lettre de Mme Redpath, qui commandait, cette fois, son propre portrait «pour McGill College, pendant de celui de son défunt mari peint par moi.» Le 11 avril, Mme Redpath écrivait de nouveau, pour commander un autre portrait d'elle-même pour la «bibliothèque de McGill College.» Vers la mi-juin, après un autre échange de lettres, il semble que Harris avait terminé les quatre portraits et, le 24 de ce mois, il faisait livrer celui de Peter Redpath à l'Hôpital général. Dans son journal de travail on peut lire, en date de décembre 1897: «M. G.W. Redpath, ai fait une esquisse de feu Peter Redpath à partir d'une vieille image les représentant et qu'ils ont dû détruire à Londres. Payé.» – mais il ne mentionne pas le montant reçu.

Peter Redpath, le fabricant de sucre, est né à Montréal en 1821. Il étudia la gestion en Angleterre, puis revint au Canada où il travailla à la raffinerie de son père. Il dotera une chaire de philosophie naturelle à l'université McGill et construira et équipera une bibliothèque et un musée, auxquels il fournira plusieurs objets d'une grande valeur historique. Pendant de nombreuses années,

il fut président de l'Hôpital général de Montréal. Il se retira des affaires en 1879 et s'installa à Chislehurst, en Angleterre, où il mourut.
MUSÉE MCCORD, MONTRÉAL

106 *The Girl with the Pink Bow* 1898
18-1/4 x 14 in. (46.4 x 35.6 cm)
INSCRIPTION: signed l.r., *Robert Harris.*
BIBLIOGRAPHY: [J.G.], "Studio Talk," repr.
p. 67.
CONFEDERATION ART GALLERY AND
MUSEUM, CHARLOTTETOWN

106 *La fille à la boucle rose* 1898
18-1/4 x 14 po (46.4 x 35.6 cm)
INSCRIPTION: signature, b.d.: *Robert Harris.*
BIBLIOGRAPHIE: [J.G.]: *Studio Talk*, reprod.
p. 67.
CONFEDERATION ART GALLERY AND
MUSEUM, CHARLOTTETOWN

107 *John Hammond* 1898
24 x 20 in. (60.9 x 50.8 cm)
INSCRIPTION: signed l.r., *Robert Harris.*

107 *John Hammond* 1898
24 x 20 po (60.9 x 50.8 cm)
INSCRIPTION: signature, b.d.: *Robert Harris.*

One of Harris' fellow-Academicians and friends was the painter, John Hammond, who was born in Montreal and had a very adventurous life, starting work in a marble mill at the age of nine (at the age of eleven deciding to become an artist). At the age of twenty-three Hammond joined the militia during the Fenian Uprisings. After leaving the army, Hammond travelled to England with his brother and then, again with his brother, sailed to New Zealand in search of gold. In 1870 back in Canada, he was part of the Transcontinental survey team for the building of a railway. Back in Montreal he worked for a while for William Notman, the photographer, along with Otto Jacobi (cat. nos. 61, 80). It was around this period (the 1870s) that Hammond decided to become a full-time painter, and, thus, fulfill his boyhood ambitions.

He was elected to the Ontario Society of Artists in 1873 and by 1880 had moved to Saint John, New Brunswick, where he established himself as a portrait-painter. Then he returned to Europe in 1885 and for a while, in Holland, painted with James Mc-Neil Whistler, and then, going to France, worked for a time with the French Barbizon painter, Millet. Later travels took him to Italy. He became a full member of the Royal Canadian Academy in 1893.

Harris eut pour ami et collègue à l'Académie le peintre John Hammond, né à Montréal, qui connut une vie des plus aventureuses. À neuf ans, il travaillait déjà dans une marbrerie (à onze ans, il décida de devenir artiste). À vingt-trois ans, il s'engagea dans l'armée, au moment où éclata le soulèvement des Fenians. Ayant terminé son service, Hammond se rendit en Angleterre avec son frère, puis tous deux partirent pour la Nouvelle-Zélande y chercher de l'or. De retour au Canada en 1870, il fit partie du groupe d'experts qui prirent part aux études en vue de la construction du chemin de fer transcontinental. Plus tard, à Montréal, il travailla pendant un certain temps, en compagnie d'Otto Jacobi (nos 61 et 80), chez le photographe William Notman. C'est au cours de ces années (1870) que Hammond décida de se consacrer entièrement à la peinture, réalisant ainsi son rêve d'enfance.

Élu membre de l'Ontario Society of Artists en 1873, il repartit bientôt, cette fois, pour le Nouveau-Brunswick, et s'installa en 1880 à Saint-Jean en tant que portraitiste. À peine quelques années plus tard, en 1885, il retournait en Europe; il se rendit d'abord en Hollande, où il peignit brièvement en compagnie de James McNeil Whistler, puis en France, où il travailla quelque temps avec François Millet, le peintre de Barbizon. Plus

It was John Hammond who was appointed first Curator of the Owens Art Gallery, in Saint John, and later supervised its move to Sackville, New Brunswick. From 1907 to 1919, Hammond was Head of the School of Art at Mount Allison University. He was one of the artists commissioned by Sir William Van Horne (1843–1915) to paint a number of murals and other works showing the scenery of Western Canada, and the development of the C.P.R.

EXHIBITIONS: *1898 Montreal Spring Exhibition*, no. 48; *1898 Toronto R.C.A.*, no. 49; 1967, Sackville, Nova Scotia, Owens Art Gallery, Mount Allison University, *John Hammond, R.C.A., 1843–1939: Retrospective Exhibition*, no. 19.

KATHARINE HAMMOND KRUG, WATERLOO, ONTARIO

tard, il visitera aussi l'Italie. Il devint membre de l'Académie royale des arts du Canada en 1893.

Premier conservateur de l'Owens Art Gallery à Saint-Jean, c'est lui qui présida au transfert de celle-ci à Sackville (Nouveau-Brunswick). De 1907 à 1919, Hammond fut directeur de l'école des beaux-arts de l'université Mount Allison. Il fut l'un des peintres que Sir William Van Horne (1843–1915) chargea d'exécuter une série de peintures murales sur l'Ouest canadien et la construction du chemin de fer du Canadien Pacifique.

EXPOSITIONS: *1898 Montréal, Printemps*, nº 48; *1898 Toronto, A.R.A.C.*, nº 49; 1967, Sackville (Nouveau-Brunswick), Owens Art Gallery, Mount Allison University, *John Hammond, R.C.A., 1843–1939: Retrospective Exhibition*, nº 19.

KATHARINE HAMMOND KRUG, WATERLOO (ONTARIO)

108 *Steady and Unafraid* 1898
30-1/8 x 24-1/4 in. (76.5 x 61.6 cm)
INSCRIPTION: signed l.l., *Robert Harris.*
PROVENANCE: Donated by Harris to the Royal Canadian Academy Patriotic Fund Exhibition, 1914: purchased by the father of the present owner.
EXHIBITIONS: *1897 Montreal Spring Exhibition*, no. 61 (as *Come if you dare*); *1898 Toronto R.C.A.*, no. 50 (as "*Come, if you Dare*"); 1914, Toronto/Winnipeg/Halifax/St. John/Quebec/Montreal/Ottawa/London/Hamilton/, Royal Canadian Academy of Arts, *An Exhibition of Pictures Given by Canadian Artists in Aid of the Patriotic Fund*, no. 4, repr.

JUNE M. SMITH, THETFORD MINES, QUEBEC

108 *Sans peur et sans reproche* 1898
30-1/8 x 24-1/4 po (76.5 x 61.6 cm)
INSCRIPTION: signature, b.g.: *Robert Harris*
HISTORIQUE: Don de l'artiste à l'A.R.A.C. pour la *Patriotic Fund Exhibition*, 1914. Acquise par le père du propriétaire actuel.
EXPOSITIONS: *1897 Montréal, Printemps*, nº 61 (*Come if you dare*); *1898 Toronto, A.R.A.C.*, nº 50 (*Come if you dare*); 1914, Toronto / Winnipeg / Halifax / Saint-Jean / Québec / Montréal / Ottawa / London / Hamilton, A.R.A.C., *An Exhibition of Pictures Given by Canadian Artists in Aid to the Patriotic Fund* nº 4, reprod.

Mˡˡᴱ JUNE M. SMITH, THETFORD MINES (QUÉBEC)

109 *John Try-Davies* 1898
26 x 16 in. (66.1 x 40.7 cm) (s)
INSCRIPTION: signed l.l., *Robert Harris.*

Among the names of charter subscribers to the establishment of the Montreal General Hospital, on 1 May 1819, there appears John Try, father of Harris's friend and fellow-member of the Pen and Pencil Club in Montreal. Harris illustrated a book of Try-Davies' short stories. *A Semi-Detached House and Other Stories*, published in 1900. Try-Davies was closely associated with the Montreal General Hospital and was on the Board of Directors of the Mount Royal Club.
EXHIBITIONS: *1898 Montreal Spring Exhibition*, no. 51 (as *The Miniature*); *1898 Toronto R.C.A.*, no. 51 (as *Looking at the Miniature*).
THE MONTREAL GENERAL HOSPITAL

109 *John Try-Davies* 1898
26 x 16 po (66.1 x 40.7 cm) (s.v.)
INSCRIPTION: signature, b.g.: *Robert Harris.*

Parmi les signataires de la charte de l'Hôpital général de Montréal, fondé le 1er mai 1819, figure John Try, père de l'ami et collègue de Harris au Pen and Pencil Club à Montréal. Harris a illustré *A Semi-Detached House and other Stories*, un recueil de nouvelles écrites par Try-Davies, publié en 1900. Try-Davies a lui aussi été étroitement lié à l'Hôpital général de Montréal et a fait partie du conseil d'administration du Mount Royal Club.
EXPOSITIONS: *1898 Montréal, Printemps*, nº 51 (*The Miniature*); *1898 Toronto, A.R.A.C.*, nº 51 (*Looking at the Miniature*).
HÔPITAL GÉNÉRAL DE MONTRÉAL

110 *Young Canada* 1898
23-1/2 x 19-1/2 in. (59.7 x 49.5 cm)
INSCRIPTION: signed l.r., *Robert Harris.*
BIBLIOGRAPHY: [J.G.], "Studio Talk," repr. p. 66.
EXHIBITIONS: *1898 Montreal Spring Exhibition*, no. 52; *1900 Ottawa R.C.A.*, no. 51.
THE NATIONAL GALLERY OF CANADA, OTTAWA (142)
GIFT OF MISS. C. HILL

110 *Jeune Canada* 1898
23-1/2 x 19-1/2 po (59.7 x 49.5 cm)
INSCRIPTION: signature, b.d.: *Robert Harris.*
BIBLIOGRAPHIE: [J.G.]: *Studio Talk*, reprod. p. 66.
EXPOSITIONS: *1898 Montréal, Printemps*, nº 52; *1900 Ottawa, A.R.A.C.*, nº 51.
GALERIE NATIONALE DU CANADA, OTTAWA (142)
DON DE MLLE C. HILL

111 *Charles Alexander* 1899
30 x 24 in. (76.2 x 60.9 cm) (s)
INSCRIPTION: signed l.r., *Robert Harris.*

While emigrating at the age of twenty-two, in 1840, Charles Alexander was shipwrecked off the coast of Newfoundland. Three years later, he had managed to establish a successful confectionary business in Montreal. In time he was to become one of the city's leading philanthropists, and was for many years a member of the Board of Management of the Montreal General Hospital. Among his other gifts, he contributed over $200,000 for the establishment of the Outdoor Department of that hospital.
THE MONTREAL GENERAL HOSPITAL

111 *Charles Alexander* 1899
30 x 24 po (76.2 x 60.9 cm) (s.v.)
INSCRIPTION: signature, b.d.: *Robert Harris.*

En 1840, le bateau qui amène Charles Alexander, alors âgé de vingt-deux ans, au Canada, fait naufrage dans les eaux terre-neuviennes. Il s'établit à Montréal où, trois ans plus tard, il possède une prospère maison de confection. Il deviendra par la suite l'un des plus importants philantropes de la ville et siègera, pendant de longues années, au conseil de direction de l'Hôpital général de Montréal, auquel il fera don, entre autres, de $200 000 pour l'établissement d'un service des consultations externes.
HÔPITAL GÉNÉRAL DE MONTRÉAL

112 *Portrait of a French Canadian* 1899
16 x 14 in. (40.6 x 35.6 cm)
INSCRIPTION: signed l.r., *Robert Harris.*
BIBLIOGRAPHY: [J.G.], "Studio Talk," p. 69,
repr. (as *Portrait Study*).
EXHIBITION: *1899 Montreal R.C.A.*, no. 65.
O'NEILL COLLEGIATE AND VOCATIONAL
INSTITUTE,
ONTARIO COUNTY BOARD OF EDUCATION,
OSHAWA, ONTARIO

112 *Portrait d'un Canadien français* 1899
16 x 14 po (40.6 x 35.6 cm)
INSCRIPTION: signature, b.d.: *Robert Harris.*
BIBLIOGRAPHIE: [J.G.]: *Studio Talk*, reprod.
p. 69 (*Portrait Study*).
EXPOSITION: *1899 Montréal, A.R.A.C.*, n° 65.
O'NEILL COLLEGIATE AND VOCATIONAL
INSTITUTE
ONTARIO COUNTY BOARD OF EDUCATION,
OSHAWA (ONTARIO)

113 *Study for "Chancellor R.W.
Heneker"* 1900
10-3/4 x 8-3/4 in. (27.3 x 22.2 cm)
INSCRIPTION: signed l.l., pencil, *1st study/for
Portrait/Dr. Heneker/R. Harris.*

Framed with cat. no. 95.
CONFEDERATION ART GALLERY AND
MUSEUM, CHARLOTTETOWN

113 *Étude pour Le chancelier R. W. Heneker*
1900
10-3/4 x 8-3/4 po (27.3 x 22.2 cm)
INSCRIPTION: signature, b.g., au crayon
(trad.): 1ère étude/pour un *Portrait/Dr. Hene-
ker/R. Harris.*

Encadré avec le n° 95.
CONFEDERATION ART GALLERY AND
MUSEUM, CHARLOTTETOWN

114 *Chancellor R.W. Heneker* 1900
33 x 28 in. (83.8 x 71.1 cm)
INSCRIPTION: signed l.l., *Robert Harris.*

Chancellor of Bishop's University and
President of the Eastern Townships Bank
from 1874–1902, Richard William Heneker
was born in Dublin in 1823. Educated privately and partly at the University College
School, London, he studied architecture, and
at the age of nineteen entered the office of Sir
Charles Barry, the architect of the new
palace of Westminster.

Later, Heneker travelled in France, Germany, and Italy to study continental architecture. (While posing for Robert Harris,
Heneker told the artist he remembered the
building of the National Gallery in London.)
After several years practising his profession
as an architect, in 1855 he accepted an offer
to succeed Alexander Galt (cat. no. 73) as
Commissioner in Canada for the British
American Land Company. In 1859 he assisted in establishing the Eastern Townships
Bank, and in 1866, in conjunction with Lord
Mount Stephen (see cat. no. 11, inscription),

114 *Le chancelier R.W. Heneker* 1900
33 x 88 po (83.8 x 71.1 cm)
INSCRIPTION: signature, b.g.: *Robert Harris.*

Chancelier de Bishop's University et président de l'Eastern Townships Bank de 1874
à 1902, Richard William Heneker est né à
Dublin en 1823. Élève de l'University College
School, à Londres, il se spécialise en architecture. À l'âge de dix-neuf ans, il est employé chez Sir Charles Barry, l'architecte du
nouveau palais de Westminster.

Plus tard, il fit des voyages en France, en
Allemagne et en Italie pour étudier l'architecture européenne. (En posant pour Harris,
il lui parlera de la construction de la National
Gallery à Londres.) Après quelques années
d'expérience professionnelle, il accepta, en
1855, de succéder à Alexander Galt (n° 73)
au poste de commissaire au Canada de la
British American Land Company. En 1859,
il participa à la fondation de l'Eastern Townships Bank, et en 1866, il fonda, avec Lord
Mount Stephen (voir l'inscription du n° 11),
les usines Paton Tweed à Sherbrooke. Il
devint, en 1858, chancelier de Bishop's

established the Paton Tweed Mills at Sherbrooke. He became Chancellor of Bishop's University, Lennoxville, in 1858, and Chairman of the Board of Trustees at a later period.

In addition to receiving an honorary M.A. from Bishop's, Heneker also received an honorary LL.D. from McGill. Active in the affairs of the Anglican Church, he served as a delegate to the Diocesan, Provincial, and General Synods. He also sat in the first General Synod of the Consolidated Church of England in Canada.

His eldest son, Richard Tuson Heneker, K.C., was solicitor to the C.P.R. His second son, General Sir William Charles Gifford Heneker, K.C.M.G., K.C.B., D.S.O., died in England in 1939, while his youngest son, Lt. Col. Frederick Christian Heneker, was killed in action in 1916. His daughter, Frances, predeceased him by six years in 1905.

BISHOP'S UNIVERSITY,
LENNOXVILLE, QUEBEC

University, à Lennoxville (Québec) et, plus tard, président du conseil d'administration de l'université.

En plus de se voir décerner un diplôme honoraire de maîtrise ès arts à Bishop's, Heneker reçut un doctorat en droit à McGill. Très actif au sein de l'Église anglicane, Heneker assista, en tant que délégué, aux synodes diocésains, provinciaux et généraux de celle-ci. Il participa également au premier synode général de la Consolidated Church of England au Canada.

Son fils aîné, Richard Tuson Heneker, K.C., sera l'avocat du Canadien Pacifique. Son deuxième fils, Sir William Charles Gifford Heneker, K.C.M.G., K.C.B., D.S.O., général de l'armée, mourut en Angleterre en 1939, tandis que le cadet, le lieutenant-colonel Fredrick Christian Heneker fut tué au combat en 1916. Sa fille, Frances, mourut en 1905, six ans avant son père.

BISHOP'S UNIVERSITY, LENNOXVILLE
(QUÉBEC)

---

115 *The Man Behind the Gun* 1900
27-5/8 x 31-1/8 in. (70.2 x 79 cm)
INSCRIPTION: signed and dated l.r., *Robert Harris. 1900*; dated on reverse, *George Rutherford Caverhill/Born 8th November 1896/Painted in Montreal 1900.*
HARRIS PAPERS: "This was painted year of Boer War." (Sitter-book, undated entry)

The sitter was George Rutherford Caverhill.
EXHIBITION: *1901 Montreal Spring Exhibition*, no. 57 (as *George Rutherford, Son of George Caverhill, Esq*).
MRS. A. LOUISE KIRKLAND, ISLINGTON, ONTARIO

115 *L'homme derrière le fusil* 1900
27-5/8 x 31-1/8 po (70.2 x 79 cm)
INSCRIPTION: signature et date, b.d.: *Robert Harris 1900*; inscription et date, au verso (trad.): *George Rutherford Caverhill/Né 8 novembre 1896/*Peint à Montréal *1900.*
DOCUMENTS HARRIS: «Ce portrait fut peint la première année de la guerre des Boers.» (Journal de travail de l'artiste, s.d.).

Le modèle était George Rutherford Caverhill.
EXPOSITION: *1901 Montréal, Printemps*, nº 57 (*George Rutherford, Son of George Caverhill, Esq.*).
MME A. LOUISE KIRKLAND, ISLINGTON (ONTARIO)

---

116 *Miss Innocence* 1900
31-3/4 x 25 in. (80.7 x 63.5 cm)
INSCRIPTION: signed l.r., *Robert Harris—*.
PROVENANCE: Gift of Mr. John A. Soule, 1953.

The sitter is the daughter of Mr. and Mrs. Gordon Smithers of Montreal.
THE ART GALLERY OF HAMILTON

116 *Mademoiselle Innocence* 1900
31-3/4 x 25 po (80.7 x 63.5 cm)
INSCRIPTION: signature, b.d.: *Robert Harris—*.
HISTORIQUE: Don de M. John A. Soule, 1953.

Le modèle est la fille de M. et Mme Gordon Smithers de Montréal.
THE ART GALLERY OF HAMILTON

117 *Gordon Reed* 1900
48 x 24-7/8 in. (121.9 x 63.2 cm)
INSCRIPTION: signed and dated l.r., *Robert Harris. 1900*; u.l., *GORDON*.
EXHIBITIONS: *1967 Charlottetown*, no. 58.
MCCORD MUSEUM, MONTREAL

117 *Gordon Reed* 1900
48 x 24-7/8 po (121.9 x 63.2 cm)
INSCRIPTION: signature et date, b.d.: *Robert Harris. 1900;* inscription, h.g.: *GORDON*.
EXPOSITION: *1967 Charlottetown*, nº 58.
MUSÉE MCCORD, MONTRÉAL

118 *William Tuck* 1900
43-1/4 x 33 in. (109.9 x 83.8 cm)
INSCRIPTION: signed l.l., *Robert Harris*; dated and signed on reverse, *Hon. Tuck/Chief Justice of New Brunswick/painted from sittings in Montreal, Jan 1900/by Robert Harris P.R.C.A.*
HARRIS PAPERS: "C.F. Coster, 120 Prince William St. John N.B. Letter from him 29th Nov fixing for portrait of Chief Justice of N.B. as per my letter. Sitting to begin in January next. $400. Frame $60." (Sitter-book, undated entry) "The Chief Justice Tuck of N.B. came here last week and I have just finished portrait of him, to his great satisfaction, for the Court in Fredericton. He is a jolly old boy and knows several Island people." (Letter from Harris to his mother, dated 25 January 1900)

William Henry Tuck (1831–1913) was born at Saint John, New Brunswick and educated at Mount Allison University (D.C.L., 1874). He practiced law in Saint John and was Chief Justice for the Province of New Brunswick from 1896 to 1908. He died at Saint John.

118 *William Tuck* 1900
43-1/4 x 33 po (109.9 x 83.8 cm)
INSCRIPTION: signature, b.g.: *Robert Harris*; inscription, date et signature, au verso (trad.): *Hon. Tuck*/Juge en chef du Nouveau-Brunswick/peint à la suite de séances à Montréal, janvier *1900*/par *Robert Harris P.R.C.A.*
DOCUMENTS HARRIS: «C.F. Coster, 120, rue Prince William, Saint-Jean (Nouveau-Brunswick). Accepte dans sa lettre du 29 novembre les arrangements que je lui proposais au sujet du portrait du juge en chef du Nouveau-Brunswick. Les séances de pose commenceront en janvier prochain. $400. Cadre $60.» (Journal de travail de l'artiste, s.d.).
«Le juge en chef Tuck du Nouveau-Brunswick est venu ici la semaine dernière et je viens de terminer son portrait pour la Cour de Fredericton, à sa grande satisfaction. C'est un homme qui a le sens de l'humour et il connaît plusieurs personnes de l'Île-du-Prince-Édouard.» (Lettre de Harris à sa mère, 25 janvier 1900).

William Henry Tuck, né à Saint-Jean (Nouveau-Brunswick) en 1831, a fait ses études à l'université Mount Allison (D.C.L., 1874). Ayant pratiqué le droit à Saint-Jean, il fut juge en chef du Nouveau-Brunswick de 1896 à 1908. Il mourut à Saint-Jean en 1913.

EXHIBITIONS: *1900 Montreal Spring Exhibition*, no. 47; *1900 Ottawa R.C.A.*, no. 50.
BARRISTERS' SOCIETY OF NEW BRUNSWICK, FREDERICTON

EXPOSITIONS: *1900 Montréal, Printemps*, nᵒ 47; *1900 Ottawa, A.R.A.C.*, nᵒ 50.
BARRISTERS' SOCIETY OF NEW BRUNSWICK, FREDERICTON

---

119 *Dr. Robert Craik* 1901
42-1/2 x 32-1/4 in. (108 x 81.9 cm) (s)
INSCRIPTION: signed u.r., *Robert Harris.*

One of the most distinguished of nineteenth-century academics, Dr. Robert Craik was connected with the McGill University Faculty of Medicine from 1856 to 1907. He began his professional career as demonstrator of Anatomy and Curator of the Medical Museum from 1857 to 1861, when he was appointed Professor of Chemistry, a post he held for ten years. A Fellow, 1876–77 and 1889–1902, he was appointed Emeritus Professor in the Faculty of Medicine from 1879–89, and Dean of that Faculty from 1889–1901, Professor of Hygiene, 1889–95, and Public Health, 1895–1901.

He was appointed to the Chair of Strathcona Professor of Hygiene and Public Health, 1901–02, and from 1902 to 1907 was a member of the University's Board of Governors.
EXHIBITIONS: *1909 Montreal Spring Exhibition*, no. 168; *1919 Montreal*, no. 2.
MCGILL UNIVERSITY, MONTREAL

119 *Le docteur Robert Craik* 1901
42-1/2 x 32-1/4 po (108 x 81.9 cm) (s.v.)
INSCRIPTION: signature, h.d.: *Robert Harris.*

Le docteur Robert Craik, un des professeurs les plus éminents du XIXᵉ siècle, enseigna à la Faculté de médecine de l'université McGill de 1857 à 1907. Il commença sa carrière professionnelle en tant que professeur d'anatomie et conservateur du musée de médecine (1857–1861). En 1861, il devint professeur de chimie, poste qu'il gardera pendant dix ans. Agrégé de 1876 à 1877 et de 1889 à 1902, il fut professeur honoraire de la Faculté de médecine de 1879 à 1889, doyen de cette faculté de 1889 à 1901, professeur d'hygiène de 1889 à 1895 et de santé publique de 1895 à 1901.

De 1901 à 1902, il fut titulaire de la chaire Strathcona d'hygiène et de santé publique et, de 1902 à 1907, membre du conseil d'administration de l'université.
EXPOSITIONS: *1909 Montréal, Printemps*, nᵒ 168; *1919 Montréal*, nᵒ 2.
UNIVERSITÉ MCGILL, MONTRÉAL

---

120 *Frederic Nicholls* 1901
50 x 40 in. (127 x 101.6 cm)
INSCRIPTION: signed l.r., *Robert Harris.*

The Honourable Frederic Nicholls was born in England in 1856. Little is known of his schooling except that, before emigrating to Canada in 1874 at the age of eighteen, he spent a year or two in Stuttgart seeking technical knowledge about electricity.

He couldn't have chosen a worse period to emigrate to Canada, for 1874 was the year of extreme depression and unemployment. However, young Nicholls spent five years in Ottawa listening and watching, and as a young Conservative became deeply interested in matters such as the inequalities of the Reciprocity Treaty, free trade, tariffs and the Conservative National Policy.

By 1879 Nicholls had moved to Toronto, where he was appointed Assistant Secretary and, later, Secretary to the Canadian Manufacturers Association. In 1882 he purchased an Ottawa paper called *Industrial World*, which he transferred to Toronto and renamed the *Canadian Manufacturer*. He was the first editor in Canada to advocate protective tariff, and was eventually elected President of the Canadian Press Club.

Nicholls, in addition to his political activities, concerned himself with the development of electricity in the Province of

120 *Frederic Nicholls* 1901
50 x 40 po (127 x 101.6 cm)
INSCRIPTION: signature, b.d.: *Robert Harris.*

L'honorable Frederic Nicholls est né en Angleterre en 1856. De ses études on sait seulement qu'avant d'émigrer au Canada en 1874, à l'âge de dix-huit ans, il passa un an ou deux à Stuttgart pour étudier l'électricité.

Il arriva au Canada alors que le pays était en pleine dépression et que le chômage était à son paroxysme. Au cours de ses cinq premières années à Ottawa cependant, le jeune Nicholls en profita pour se renseigner et observer la situation. Jeune Conservateur, il s'intéressa vivement aux injustices du traité de réciprocité, au libre échange, aux tarifs et à la politique nationale des Conservateurs.

En 1879, Nicholls s'établissait à Toronto où il devint secrétaire adjoint puis secrétaire de l'Association canadienne des manufacturiers. En 1882, il acheta un journal d'Ottawa, l'*Industrial World* (qu'il renommera *Canadian Manufacturer*) et dont il établit le siège à Toronto. Nicholls fut le premier journaliste au Canada à préconiser le tarif protecteur et il fut, par la suite, élu président du Club de la presse canadienne.

En plus de s'intéresser à la politique, Nicholls désirait participer au développement des installations électriques en Ontario. Il fut le fondateur de la Toronto Incandes-

Ontario, and organized the Toronto Incandescent Electric Light Company, the first company to adopt the system of underground cables. Nicholls was President of the National Electric Light Association of America, being the first Canadian to hold that position. He eventually became President of Canadian General Electric, having defeated Edison General Electric Company, his major American competitor, in their attempt to take over the power at Sudbury. Considering his interest in the engineering, development, and distribution of electric power (particularly as it was used for electric streetcars), it is not surprising that Nicholls foresaw, in 1878, that Canada was on the eve of a great railway era. As president or vice-president of at least sixteen industrial enterprises, from steel companies to shipping firms, from electric power companies to railroads, Nicholls saw to it that Canada had her share of the power resources of the falls at Niagara.

A keen yachtsman, big-game hunter, and golfer, Senator Nicholls owned one of the finest art collections in Toronto. He also had a good collection of books and a large conservatory in which he cultivated rare orchids, cinerarias, and palms. As Harris confirms for us in this fine portrait, Nicholls customarily wore a small bouquet from his conservatory.

Harris made two further replicas of this portrait with slight variations, both for presentation to companies in which Nicholls was interested.

MRS. R.J. CURRIE GARDNER, TORONTO

cent Electric Light Company, la première à adopter le système des câbles souterrains. Nicholls fut, de plus, le premier président canadien de la National Electric Light Association of America. Il devint, par la suite, président de la société Canadian General Electric, après avoir triomphé de l'Edison General Electric, son principal concurrent américain, dans la lutte pour le contrôle des installations électriques à Sudbury. Il n'est pas étonnant, lorsqu'on connaît le vif intérêt qu'il portait aux questions relatives au génie électrique, au développement et à la distribution du courant électrique (notamment l'utilisation qu'on en faisait pour les tramways électriques), que Nicholls ait pressenti, dès 1878, que le Canada allait pénétrer dans l'ère des grands chemins de fer. À titre de président ou de vice-président d'au moins seize entreprises industrielles (œuvrant dans des domaines très diversifiés, de l'acier au transport, de l'électricité aux chemins de fer), Nicholls a veillé à ce que le Canada obtint sa part de l'énergie hydraulique des chutes du Niagara.

Excellent yachtman, chasseur de gros gibier et golfeur, le sénateur Nicholls possèdait aussi une des plus riches collections d'art de Toronto, en plus d'une bonne bibliothèque et d'une serre dans laquelle il cultivait de rares orchidées, des cinéraires et des palmiers. Comme nous le confirme Harris dans cet élégant portrait, Nicholls avait l'habitude de porter quelques fleurs provenant de sa serre.

Harris a aussi exécuté deux copies (à quelques détails près) de ce portrait, à l'intention de compagnies auxquelles Nicholls s'intéressait.

MME R.J. CURRIE GARDNER, TORONTO

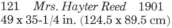

121   *Mrs. Hayter Reed*   1901
49 x 35-1/4 in. (124.5 x 89.5 cm)
INSCRIPTION: signed and dated l.l., *Robert Harris-1901.*
HARRIS PAPERS: "Agreed to do portrait of her [Mrs. Hayter Reed] for $600, size indefinite. (I really am doing it much larger than I intended at starting.)" (Letter from Harris to his mother, undated)

Born Kate Armour in 1856, the oldest child of the large family of Judge John Douglas Armour of Cobourg, Ontario, she was first married to Grosvenor Lowry of Tarrytown, New York. After Lowry's death, she married Hayter Reed in 1894. Reed was Indian Commissioner in Manitoba and the Northwest Territories and later, in 1900, Manager of the Château Frontenac Hotel.

From all accounts Mrs. Hayter Reed was supposed to have been an extremely intelligent, charming, and vital woman – respon-

121   *Mme Hayter Reed*   1901
49 x 35-1/4 po (124.5 x 89.5 cm)
INSCRIPTION: signature et date, b.g.: *Robert Harris-1901.*
DOCUMENTS HARRIS «Ai accepté de faire un portrait d'elle [Mme Hayter Reed] pour $600, dimensions à établir. Je le fais en réalité beaucoup plus grand que je ne le prévoyais au départ.» (Lettre de Harris à sa mère, s.d.).

Née Kate Armour en 1856, le modèle était la fille aînée d'une famille nombreuse, celle du juge John Douglas Armour de Cobourg (Ontario). Veuve de Grosvenor Lowry de Tarrytown (New York), elle épousa Hayter Reed en 1894. Reed fut commissaire des Indiens au Manitoba et dans les Territoires du Nord-Ouest avant de se voir confier, en 1900, la direction de l'hôtel Château Frontenac.

De l'avis de tous Mme Hayter Reed était une femme charmante, intelligente et d'une

sible for the redecorating of most of the C.P.R. hotels. (She also bought and sold antiques.) The proud possessor of a pass for the C.P.R. for herself and her family, given to her by Lord Shaughnessy, she travelled frequently between Quebec City, Montreal, Ottawa, and the Maritimes.
EXHIBITIONS: *1900 Montreal Spring Exhibition*, no. 58; *1967 Charlottetown*, no. 59.
MCCORD MUSEUM, MONTREAL

grande vitalité. C'est à elle que l'on doit notamment la redécoration de la plupart des hôtels du Canadien Pacifique. (Elle achetait et vendait également des antiquités.) Fière détentrice d'un laissez-passer que lui avait donné Lord Shaughnessy et qui lui permettait, à elle et à sa famille, de voyager gratuitement à bord des trains du Canadien Pacifique, elle fit souvent la navette entre Québec, Montréal, Ottawa et les Maritimes.
EXPOSITIONS: *1900 Montréal, Printemps*, nº 58; *1967 Charlottetown*, nº 59.
MUSÉE MCCORD, MONTRÉAL

---

122   *Study for "Sir Louis Davies"*   1902
Graphite
11-1/2 x 8-1/2 in. (29.2 x 21.6 cm)
INSCRIPTION: l.l., *Sir Louis Davies.*

    Framed with cat. no. 123.
CONFEDERATION ART GALLERY AND
MUSEUM, CHARLOTTETOWN

122   *Étude pour Sir Louis Davies*   1902
Mine de plomb
11-1/2 x 8-1/2 po (29.2 x 21.6 cm)
INSCRIPTION: b.g.: *Sir Louis Davies.*

    Encadré avec le nº 123.
CONFEDERATION ART GALLERY AND
MUSEUM, CHARLOTTETOWN

---

123   *Study for "Sir Louis Davies"*   1902
Graphite
11-1/2 x 8-1/2 in. (29.2 x 21.6 cm)
INSCRIPTION: l.l., *Sir Louis Davies.*

    Framed with cat. no. 122.
CONFEDERATION ART GALLERY AND
MUSEUM, CHARLOTTETOWN

123   *Étude pour Sir Louis Davies*   1902
Mine de plomb
11-1/2 x 8-1/2 po (29.2 x 21.6 cm)
INSCRIPTION: b.g.: *Sir Louis Davies.*

    Encadré avec le nº 122.
CONFEDERATION ART GALLERY AND
MUSEUM, CHARLOTTETOWN

124 *Sir Louis Davies* 1902
34-1/2 x 30-1/2 in. (87.6 x 77.5 cm)
INSCRIPTION: signed l.l., *Robert Harris.*

Davies was born in 1845 in Charlottetown, Prince Edward Island, and was the son of the Honourable Benjamin Davies, a shipbuilder of Orwell, Prince Edward Island, and who became, after his election to the local Legislative Assembly, Post Master General and Colonial Secretary. Later he was appointed Chairman of the Board for the construction of the Prince Edward Island Railway.

Davies was educated at the Central Academy, Charlottetown, which was the old name for Prince of Wales College; after, he studied law at the Inner Temple, in the Chambers of the Attorney General, Sir Thomas Chitty. He then returned to Charlottetown to practice law, taking up the case of tenants opposed to absentee landlords.

Following his father's example, Davies was elected a member of the Prince Edward Island Parliament in 1872. A prominent Liberal, he was for four years leader of the opposition, but in 1876 became Attorney General and Premier. In 1882 he was elected federal Liberal M.P. for Queen's County. Aside from his spirited defense of Sir Wilfrid Laurier when the latter came under Opposition attack for his discussions of Reciprocity with the United States, it was Davies' insistence that brought about legislation that lowered Canadian tariffs on imports from Britain – a result which earned him the title of "Father of British Preference." After his appointment as Minister of Marine and Fisheries, Davies took part in various conferences between Colonial and other governments regarding fishing rights and boundaries, in particular pressing Canada's side in disputes with the United States.

Davies was appointed to the Supreme Court of Canada in 1901 and elevated to Chief Justice in 1918. Davies was President of the Merchants Bank, Prince Edward Island, President of the Canadian Branch of the St. John's Ambulance Association, and Governor and Chairman of the Board of Management of St. Luke's Hospital. He was a member of the Ottawa Archeological Society and also a member of the Dickens Fellowship.

At the time of Davies' appointment to the Supreme Court, Harris was commissioned to paint the portrait presented to him by the grateful constituents in Queen's County.
EXHIBITION: *1903 Ottawa R.C.A.*, no. 57.
CANADA DEPARTMENT OF PUBLIC WORKS, OTTAWA

124 *Sir Louis Davies* 1902
34-1/2 x 30-1/2 po (87.6 x 77.5 cm)
INSCRIPTION: signature, b.g.: *Robert Harris.*

Davies est né à Charlottetown (Île-du-Prince-Édouard), en 1845. Il était le fils de l'honorable Benjamin Davies, constructeur de navires d'Orwell (Île-du-Prince-Édouard) qui devint, après son élection à l'Assemblée législative provinciale, ministre des postes et ministre des colonies. Il fut plus tard nommé président de la commission chargée de la construction des chemins de fer de l'Île-du-Prince-Édouard.

Davies fit ses études à la Central Academy de Charlottetown qui allait plus tard devenir le Prince of Wales College; puis, il étudia le droit à l'Inner Temple, dans l'étude du procureur général, Sir Thomas Chitty. Revenu à Charlottetown pour y exercer le droit, il défendit la cause des fermiers contre les absentéistes.

Comme son père, Davies fut élu député au parlement de l'Île-du-Prince-Édouard en 1872. Membre éminent du parti libéral, il fut pendant quatre ans chef de l'opposition avant de devenir, en 1876, procureur général et premier ministre. En 1882, il fut élu député du comté de Queen's aux Communes, où il défendit ardemment Sir Wilfrid Laurier (1841–1919) en butte aux attaques de l'opposition par suite de ses objections à propos de la réciprocité avec les États-Unis. Son dévouement à cette cause amena le gouvernement à voter une législation qui eut pour effet de réduire les tarifs douaniers canadiens sur les importations britanniques, ce qui lui valut le titre de «Père de la préférence britannique». Nommé ministre de la marine et des pêcheries, Davies participa à diverses conférences entre le gouvernement colonial et les autres gouvernements au sujet des droits et des limites de pêche, soutenant en particulier la position du Canada dans ses conflits avec les États-Unis.

Davies fut nommé juge de la Cour suprême du Canada en 1901 et il en devint le juge en chef en 1918. Davies fut président de la Merchants Bank à l'Île-du-Prince-Édouard, président de la division canadienne des Ambulanciers Saint-Jean, et directeur et président du conseil d'administration de l'hôpital Saint-Luc. Il fut membre de l'Ottawa Archeological Society et, grand admirateur de Charles Dickens, membre de la Dickens Fellowship.

C'est au moment où Davies fut nommé juge à la Cour suprême que ses anciens électeurs du comté de Queen's commandèrent à Harris ce portrait qu'ils lui présentèrent.
EXPOSITION: *1903 Ottawa, A.R.A.C.*, nº 57.
MINISTÈRE FÉDÉRAL DES TRAVAUX PUBLICS, OTTAWA

125 *Thomas Harris* c. 1902
Oil on panel
16 x 12 in. (40.7 x 30.5 cm)
INSCRIPTION: signed and dated l.r., *R. Harris.*
1902.

One of Harris's brothers. For another, see
cat. no. 75.
EXHIBITION: *1967 Charlottetown*, no. 61.
CONFEDERATION ART GALLERY AND
MUSEUM, CHARLOTTETOWN

125 *Thomas Harris* c. 1902
Huile sur bois
16 x 12 po (40.7 x 30.5 cm)
INSCRIPTION: signature et date, b.d.: *R.*
Harris. 1902.

Le modèle était le frère de l'artiste. Voir
également un autre frère de Harris (n° 75).
EXPOSITION: *1967 Charlottetown*, n° 61.
CONFEDERATION ART GALLERY AND
MUSEUM, CHARLOTTETOWN

126 *Charles Hosmer* 1902
40 x 30 in. (101.6 x 76.2 cm)
INSCRIPTION: signed l.l., *Robert Harris.*

One of the greatest pioneers of modern
telegraphic communication, Charles Hosmer
was born at Coteau Landing, Quebec. He left
school at fourteen to work for the Grand
Trunk Railway as a telegraphist, and within
a year was in charge of the office. At the age
of twenty he was appointed Manager of the
Kingston Office of the Dominion Telegraph
Company. In 1886, after serving as President
and Manager of the Canadian Mutual Telegraph Company, he was offered management
of the whole C.P.R. telegraph system. At the
same time, he was appointed Director of the
Postal Telegraph Company and Vice-President of the Commercial Cable Company.

By 1899 Hosmer resigned from telegraph
work; he became President of Ogilvie's Flour
Mills and Director of both the C.P.R. and the
Bank of Montreal. He continued his interest
in all matters telegraphic, however, and was
a Director of some of the largest telegraph
and cable companies in the world.

It is interesting to note that Charles
Hosmer was a Councillor of the Montreal
Art Association from 1902 to 1921, and a
patron of many contemporary painters in-
cluding Horne Russell and Harris.
EXHIBITION: *1905 Montreal Spring Exhibi-*
tion, no. 67; 1972, Halifax, Centennial Gal-
lery, Nova Scotia Museum of Fine Arts,
Halifax Portraits, no. 13.
MRS. DONALD J. OLAND, HALIFAX

126 *Charles Hosmer* 1902
40 x 30 po (101.6 x 76.2 cm)
INSCRIPTION: signature, b.g.: *Robert Harris.*

Un des grands pionniers de la communication télégraphique moderne, Charles Hosmer est né à Coteau-Landing (Québec). Il
quitta l'école à quatorze ans pour devenir
télégraphiste au Grand Tronc et, à peine
un an plus tard, devint responsable du
bureau. À vingt ans, il fut nommé directeur
du bureau de la société Dominion Telegraph
à Kingston. Vers 1886, après avoir été président et directeur de la Canadian Mutual
Telegraph Company, le Canadien Pacifique
lui offrait la direction de tout son réseau
télégraphique. Il fut, en même temps,
nommé directeur de la société Postal Telegraph et vice-président de la Commercial
Cable.

Vers 1899, Hosmer abandonna la télé-
graphie pour devenir président de l'Ogilvie's
Flour Mills et directeur du Canadien Pacifique et de la Banque de Montréal. Il n'en
continua pas moins, cependant, de s'intéresser aux communications télégraphiques
et il fit partie du conseil d'administration de
quelques-unes des plus grandes compagnies
de télégraphe et de câble du monde.

Il est intéressant de constater que Charles
Hosmer fut conseiller de l'Art Association
of Montreal de 1902 à 1921 et le mécène de
nombreux artistes contemporains dont George Horne Russell (1861–1933) et Harris.
EXPOSITION: *1905 Montréal, Printemps*, n° 67;
1972, Halifax, Centennial Gallery, Nova
Scotia Museum of Fine Arts, *Halifax Por-*
traits, n° 13.
Mᵐᵉ DONALD J. OLAND, HALIFAX

127　*Mrs. Charles Hosmer*　1902
30 x 24 in. (76.2 x 60.9 cm), painted oval
INSCRIPTION: signed l.l., *Robert Harris.*
EXHIBITION: 1972, Halifax, Centennial Gallery, Nova Scotia Museum of Fine Arts, *Halifax Portraits*, no. 14.
MRS. DONALD J. OLAND, HALIFAX

127　*Mme Charles Hosmer*　1902
30 x 24 po (76.2 x 60.9 cm), peint en ovale
INSCRIPTION: signature, b.g.: *Robert Harris.*
EXPOSITIONS: 1972, Halifax, Centennial Gallery, Nova Scotia Museum of Fine Arts, *Halifax Portraits*, n° 14.
MME DONALD J. OLAND, HALIFAX

128　*Lord Strathcona*　1902
87 x 60-1/2 in. (221 x 153.7 cm)
INSCRIPTION: signed l.r., *Robert Harris.*

The Honourable Colonel, the Right Honourable Donald Alexander Smith, First Baron Strathcona and Mount Royal, was born in Forres, Scotland, in 1820. He entered the service of the Hudson's Bay Company at the age of eighteen, and for the next thirty years was stationed on the Labrador coast. In 1869 he was given the responsibility of the company's Office in Montreal, and in the following years he rose to become President and Chief Commissioner, and, eventually Governor of the Hudson's Bay Company.

At the time of the Riel Rebellion, Smith was appointed by the Dominion Government to head the board of inquiry, and subsequently held political appointments representing Winnipeg in the Manitoba Assembly, and for ten years, from 1870 to 1880, as representative for Selkirk in the House of Commons. He opposed the government of Sir John A. Macdonald (cat. no. 42) at the time of what became known as the "Pacific Scandals." From 1887 till 1896, he represented Montreal West.

His fortune, which was enormous, was based on his holdings as an owner of the St. Paul, Minneapolis and Manitoba Railway.

From 1880 Smith was an enthusiastic supporter of the C.P.R., and five years later he was given the honour of driving the "last spike" at Craigellachie, British Columbia – the subject of the well-known photograph.

He was principal benefactor of McGill University, and he and Lord Mount Stephen (see cat. no. 11, inscription) both donated one million dollars for the building of the Royal Victorial Hospital. In time he became not only President of the Bank of Montreal, but Chancellor of McGill and Lord Rector

128　*Lord Strathcona*　1902
87 x 60-1/2 po (221 x 153.7 cm)
INSCRIPTION: signature, b.d.: *Robert Harris.*

L'honorable colonel, le très honorable Sir Donald Alexander Smith, premier baron de Strathcona and Mount Royal, est né à Forres (Écosse) en 1820. Il entra au service de la Compagnie de la baie d'Hudson à l'âge de dix-huit ans et passa les trente années suivantes sur la côte du Labrador. En 1869, on lui confia la direction du bureau de la compagnie à Montréal et, au cours des années suivantes, il fut promu président et directeur général de la Compagnie de la baie d'Hudson au Canada avant d'en devenir le gouverneur.

Au moment de la rébellion de Riel, le gouvernement du Dominion nomma Smith à la tête de la commission d'enquête. Par la suite, il sera député de Winnipeg à l'Assemblée législative du Manitoba et, de 1870 à 1880, député de Selkirk à la Chambre des communes. Il prit position contre le gouvernement de Sir John A. Macdonald (n° 42) au moment des scandales du Canadien Pacifique. De 1887 à 1896, il fut député de Montréal-Ouest.

Sa fortune colossale provenait principalement des actions qu'il possèdait en tant que propriétaire du St. Paul, Minneapolis and Manitoba Railway.

À partir de 1880, Smith se révéla un partisan enthousiaste du Canadien Pacifique et, cinq ans plus tard, il eut l'honneur d'enfoncer le «*last spike*» à Craigellachie (Colombie britannique), moment que perpétue une photographie célèbre.

Il fut le principal bienfaiteur de l'université McGill et, tout comme Lord Mount Stephen (voir l'inscription au n° 11), il donna un million de dollars pour la construction de l'hôpital Royal Victoria. Il sera

and Chancellor of Aberdeen University. He personally paid for the equipment of the cavalry force which would eventually win its battle honours during the Boer War as the "Strathcona Horse."

Lord Strathcona was Canadian High Commissioner to Great Britain from 1896 till his death in 1914.

EXHIBITIONS: *1909 Montreal Spring Exhibition*, no. 167; *1919 Montreal*, no. 17.

MCGILL UNIVERSITY, MONTREAL

président de la Banque de Montréal, chancelier de McGill et recteur et chancelier de l'université d'Aberdeen. Il équipa à lui seul tout un corps de cavalerie qui gagnera ses galons durant la guerre des Boers sous le nom de «*Strathcona Horse*».

Lord Strathcona fut haut-commissaire du Canada à Londres de 1896 à sa mort en 1914.

EXPOSITIONS: *1909 Montréal, Printemps*, n° 167; *1919 Montréal*, n° 17.

UNIVERSITÉ MCGILL, MONTRÉAL

129   *Alice Sutherland*   1902
44-1/4 x 30-1/2 in. (112.4 x 77.4 cm)
INSCRIPTION: signed l.l., *Robert Harris*; dated and signed on reverse, *Painted in Montreal 1902 by Robert Harris P.R.C.A. Portrait of Miss Alice Sutherland.*

"I have always hoped that viewers would look upon it as a beautiful work of art rather than as a portrait of myself," wrote Mrs. H. Y. Russel (née Alice Sutherland) in reply to a request for biographical data. She is the daughter of Dr. William Dunbar Sutherland who emigrated from Scotland and studied for his M.D. at McGill in the 1870s. He and Francis Shepherd (cat. no. 97) were fellow-surgeons at the Montreal General Hospital in the days of William Osler (cat. no. 134).

Mrs. Russel was born in Montreal in 1882 and educated at the Trafalgar School. Later she went to McGill, studying chiefly archaeology and economics, the latter course with Stephen Leacock. She made frequent visits to Great Britain and Europe – in Switzerland at the outbreak of the Second World War. She married Hugh Yelverton Russel, a mining engineer who, at the time of his death in 1924 was Manager of the Western Division of Chemical Industries Limited (C.I.L.) and Subsidiaries. They had three sons; two served in the Royal Canadian Navy, the eldest being lost in a British submarine.

MRS. H.Y. RUSSEL, PIERREFONDS MANOR, PIERREFONDS, QUEBEC

129   *Alice Sutherland*   1902
44-1/4 x 30-1/2 po (112.4 x 77.4 cm)
INSCRIPTION: signature, b.g.: *Robert Harris*; date et signature, au verso (trad.): Peint à Montréal *1902* par *Robert Harris P.R.C.A. Portrait* de Mlle *Alice Sutherland.*

En réponse à notre demande de données biographiques, Mme H.Y. Russel, née Alice Sutherland, nous écrivit: «J'ai toujours espéré que l'on verrait dans ce tableau une très belle œuvre d'art plutôt que mon portrait.» Mme Russel est la fille du docteur William Dunbar Sutherland qui émigra d'Écosse et obtint son doctorat en médecine à McGill dans les années 1870. Il fut chirurgien et collègue du docteur Francis Shepherd (n° 97) à l'Hôpital général de Montréal du temps de William Osler (n° 134).

Mme Russel est née à Montréal en 1882. Elle fit ses études à la Trafalgar School. Ensuite, à McGill, elle étudia principalement l'archéologie et, avec Stephen Leacock, l'économie. Elle fit de nombreux voyages en Grande-Bretagne et en Europe et elle était en Suisse lorsque s'est déclarée la Seconde guerre mondiale. Elle avait épousé Hugh Yelverton Russel, ingénieur des mines qui, au moment de sa mort en 1924, était directeur pour l'Ouest du Canada de la société C.I.L. et ses filiales. Ils eurent trois fils; deux serviront dans la Marine royale canadienne et l'aîné sera porté disparu lors du naufrage d'un sous-marin britannique.

MME H.Y. RUSSEL, MANOIR DE PIERREFONDS, PIERREFONDS (QUÉBEC)

130 *The Reverend Dr. Harvey MacVicar*
1903
37 x 31 in. (94 x 78.8 cm)
INSCRIPTION: signed u.r., *Robert Harris.*

The Reverend Donald Harvey MacVicar was a distinguished theologian of Scottish ancestry whose special contribution to Canadian life was establishing the Presbyterian College, Montreal, of which he became Principal and first professor of Divinity.

Born at South End, close to Campbelltown, Argyleshire, Scotland, in 1831, he was the seventh son of twelve children. When brought with the rest of the family to Canada in 1835, he (as his son later remarked in his biography) "could only prattle in Gaelic and had to act in pantomime when sent to borrow an axe from a neighbour."

Presbyterian College, Montreal, was first discussed at a meeting in Bank Street in 1864, but it would be three years before MacVicar and his fellow-ministers obtained approval from the Assembly. By then they had settled to their own, and everyone else's, satisfaction such Calvinistic obstacles as to whether or not to allow instrumental music in kirk – in view of the relevant text from the Book of Job that "the wicked rejoice at the sound of the organ."

On the afternoon of 15 December 1902 his class gathered to hear his lecture on Pedagogics. MacVicar, always noted for punctuality, was so late in making an appearance that some students went to his study. They found him dead at his desk, victim of a heart attack. "I am good for ten more years of work," he had just written to friends.

Shortly before this calamity, students and alumni, as evidence of the esteem in which he was regarded, persuaded Principal MacVicar to sit for his portrait. The portrait, "in the execution of which he manifested much interest and satisfaction," was completed a few days before his death. It was unveiled, at Convocation in David Morrice Hall, in the spring of 1903.

EXHIBITION: *1903 Montreal Spring Exhibition*, no. 71.

THE PRESBYTERIAN COLLEGE, MONTREAL

130 *Le révérend Donald MacVicar, principal*
1903
37 x 31 po (94 x 78.8 cm)
INSCRIPTION: signature, h.d.: *Robert Harris.*

Le révérend Donald Harvey MacVicar fut un théologien distingué d'origine écossaise dont l'apport particulier à la vie canadienne fut la fondation du Presbyterian College de Montréal; il en devint le principal et le premier professeur de théologie.

Né en 1831 à South End, près de Campbelltown (Argyleshire) en Écosse, il était le septième d'une famille de douze enfants. Lorsqu'il émigra au Canada avec ses parents en 1835, comme le faisait plus tard remarquer son fils dans sa biographie, il «ne pouvait que babiller le gaélique et devait recourir à la pantomime lorsqu'on l'envoyait emprunter une hache chez un voisin».

Il fut d'abord question de la fondation du Presbyterian College de Montréal lors d'une réunion de la rue Bank en 1864, mais ce n'est que trois ans plus tard que MacVicar et ses collègues obtinrent l'approbation de l'assemblée. Ils avaient alors, à la satisfaction générale, aplani des obstacles calvinistes tel celui de savoir si on pouvait ou non tolérer la musique instrumentale à l'église puisqu'il était dit dans le Livre de Job que «les méchants jubilent au son de l'orgue».

L'après-midi du 15 décembre 1902, sa classe se réunit pour son cours de pédagogie. MacVicar, renommé pour sa ponctualité, tarda tellement à se présenter que quelques étudiants se rendirent à son bureau. Ils le trouvèrent mort à son pupitre, victime d'une crise cardiaque. Il venait d'écrire à des amis: «Je peux travailler encore durant dix ans.»

Peu avant ce malheur, les élèves et les anciens du collège avaient persuadé le principal MacVicar de poser pour son portrait, ce qui est un éloquent témoignage de l'estime qu'ils lui portaient. Le portrait, «pour lequel il manifesta beaucoup d'intérêt et dont il semblait fort satisfait», fut terminé quelques jours avant sa mort. Il fut dévoilé à la cérémonie de collation de grades, dans le David Morrice Hall, au printemps de 1903.

EXPOSITION: *1903 Montréal, Printemps*, n° 71.

THE PRESBYTERIAN COLLEGE, MONTRÉAL

131 *The Countess of Minto* 1903
52 x 38 in. (132.1 x 96.5 cm)
INSCRIPTION: signed l.r., *Robert Harris.*
HARRIS PAPERS: "I went to Ottawa last Monday morning to get sittings from Lady Minto. There is a fairly good light in the Ball Room and they had got what I wanted there. I stayed in Ottawa till Thursday afternoon and as she gave me long sittings the picture went well. I got luncheon there every day and as there were a good many visitors there it was quite interesting. The Countess of Antrim used to read part of the time during the sittings." (Letter from Harris to his mother, dated 18 January 1903)

Mary Caroline, Countess of Minto, was the daughter of General The Hon. Charles Grey. The Art Association of Montreal commissioned this portrait of their patroness in 1902.
For a portrait of the Earl of Minto, see cat. no. 140.
EXHIBITIONS: *1903 Montreal Spring Exhibition*, no. 69; *1903 Ottawa R.C.A.*, no. 56; *1904 Montreal R.C.A.*, (not in cat.); 1904, St. Louis, Louisiana Purchase Exposition, (not in cat.); *1919 Montreal*, no. 35; 1941, Montreal, Art Association of Montreal, [Portrait paintings loaned from private collections in Montreal], no. 24; 1960, Montreal, Montreal Museum of Fine Arts, *Eleven Artists in Montreal 1860–1960*, no. 28; 1967, Montreal, 1941, Montreal Museum of Fine Arts, *Underground Art*, [no further information available]; *1967 Charlottetown*, no. 63.
THE MONTREAL MUSEUM OF FINE ARTS
PURCHASED 1903, TEMPEST FUND

131 *La comtesse de Minto* 1903
52 x 38 po (132.1 x 96.5 cm)
INSCRIPTION: signature, b.d.: *Robert Harris.*
DOCUMENTS HARRIS: « Je suis allé à Ottawa lundi dernier pour préparer les séances de pose de Lady Minto. La salle de bal est assez bien éclairée et ils y avaient mis ce que je voulais. Je suis resté à Ottawa jusqu'au jeudi après-midi et comme la comtesse m'a accordé de longues séances, le portrait avançait bien. J'ai déjeuné chez elle tous les jours et comme elle avait bon nombre de visiteurs, c'était intéressant. La comtesse d'Antrim avait l'habitude de lire durant une partie des séances.» (Lettre de Harris à sa mère, 18 janvier 1903).

Mary Caroline, comtesse de Minto, était la fille de l'honorable général Charles Grey. Les membres de l'Art Association of Montreal commandèrent ce portrait de leur mécène en 1902.
Voir également le portrait du comte de Minto (n⁰ 140).
EXPOSITIONS: *1903 Montréal, Printemps*, n⁰ 69; *1903 Ottawa, A.R.A.C.*, n⁰ 56; *1904 Montréal, A.R.A.C.* (ne fait pas partie du catalogue); 1904, St. Louis, *Louisiana Purchase Exhibition* (ne fait pas partie du catalogue); *1919 Montréal*, n⁰ 35; 1941, Montréal, Art Association of Montreal, [*Portrait paintings loaned from private collections in Montreal*], n⁰ 24; 1960, Montréal, Musée des beaux-arts de Montréal, *Onze Artistes de Montréal, 1860–1960*, n⁰ 28; 1967, Montréal, Musée des beaux-arts de Montréal, *Underground Art* [documentation incomplète]; *1967 Charlottetown*, n⁰ 63.
MUSÉE DES BEAUX-ARTS DE MONTRÉAL
ACQUIS EN 1903, FONDS TEMPEST

132 *David Morrice* 1903
29-1/4 x 24 in. (74.3 x 60.9 cm) (s), oval
INSCRIPTION: signed l.r., *Robert Harris.*
HARRIS PAPERS: "I dare say Tom will know of one of my subjects at present, Mr. David Morrice. His son has been on the other side for a good many years now and has many a success in Paris as a landscape painter. He does very fine things indeed." (Letter from Harris to his mother, dated 9 June 1903) "The two portraits I am at [Mr. and Mrs. Morrice] go on all right though Mr. Morrice is a most aggravating sitter, as his business often interfers with his keeping appointments just at the last moment." (Letter from Harris to his mother, dated 17 June 1903)

David Morrice, referred to in the *Montreal Star* as a "True Merchant Prince," was born at St. Martin's, Perthshire, Scotland, in 1849, and established himself in Canada in

132 *David Morrice* 1903
29-1/4 x 24 po (74.3 x 60.9 cm) (s.v.), ovale
INSCRIPTION: signature, b.d.: *Robert Harris.*
DOCUMENTS HARRIS: « Tom aura sans doute entendu parler de l'un de mes sujets actuels, M. David Morrice. Son fils est en Europe depuis bon nombre d'années et remporte beaucoup de succès à Paris comme paysagiste. Il fait de très belles choses.» (Lettre de Harris à sa mère, 9 juin 1903).
«Les deux portraits que je suis en train de peindre [ceux de M. et Mᵐᵉ David Morrice] avancent bien, quoique M. Morrice soit un modèle absolument insupportable, ses affaires l'empêchant souvent à la dernière minute de venir aux séances de pose!» (Lettre de Harris à sa mère, 17 juin 1903).

David Morrice, que le *Montreal Star* appela un «vrai prince du commerce», est né en 1849 à St. Martin's (Perthshire) en Écosse. Il s'établit au Canada en 1863. L'un

1863. One of the best authorities on cotton in the Dominion, he was, according to the *Montreal Gazette*, President of Penman's Limited, Canadian Coloured Cotton Company, Canadian Cottons Limited, and the Montreal Investment and Freehold Company.

He was a Senator and also Chairman of the Board of Management of the Presbyterian College, where, at the cost of $80,000 he erected David Morrice Hall. By 1911 the *Montreal Star* rated Morrice as a millionaire. Certainly he was one of the most generous philanthropists of his time. He contributed various handsome sums to the Montreal General Hospital, the Tuberculosis Association, the Presbyterian College, and donated (among other gifts) $10,000 to the Art Association of Montreal.

David Morrice was, of course, father of the artist James Wilson Morrice.

EXHIBITIONS: *1912 Montreal Spring Exhibition*, no. 182; *1918 Montreal Spring Exhibition*, no. 152; *1919 Montreal*, no. 12.
DAVID R. MORRICE, MONTREAL

des meilleurs spécialistes du coton dans le Dominion, il fut selon la *Montreal Gazette*, président de Penman's Limited, de Canadian Coloured Cotton Company, de Canadian Cottons Limited et de la Montreal Investment and Freehold Company.

Il fut sénateur et président du conseil d'administration du Presbyterian College où il fit construire, au coût de $80 000, le David Morrice Hall. Vers 1911, le *Montreal Star* considérait Morrice comme un millionnaire. Il fut certainement l'un des plus généreux philanthropes de son temps. Il offrit généreusement diverses sommes à l'Hôpital général de Montréal, à la Ligue antituberculeuse et au Presbyterian College, et il fit don, entre autres, de $10 000 à l'Art Association of Montreal.

L'artiste James Wilson Morrice était le fils de David Morrice.

EXPOSITIONS: *1912 Montréal, Printemps*, nº 182; *1918 Montréal, Printemps*, nº 152; *1919 Montréal*, nº 12.
DAVID R. MORRICE, MONTRÉAL

133 *Mrs. David Morrice* 1903
29 x 23-1/2 in. (73.2 x 59.7 cm) (s), oval
INSCRIPTION: signed l.l., *Robert Harris.*
DAVID R. MORRICE, MONTREAL

133 *Mme David Morrice* 1903
29 x 23-1/2 po (73.2 x 59.7 cm) (s.v.), ovale
INSCRIPTION: signature, b.g.: *Robert Harris.*
DAVID R. MORRICE, MONTRÉAL

134 *Sir William Osler* 1903
47-1/2 x 33-1/2 in. (120.7 x 85.1 cm) (s)
INSCRIPTION: signed l.l., *Robert Harris–*.
HARRIS PAPERS: "Just about Christmas, I
think, Dr. Osler of Baltimore is going to give
me some sittings for a proposed portrait."
(Letter from Harris to his mother, dated 6
December 1903)

One of the great surgeons of the nineteenth
century, William Osler was born at Bond
Head, Upper Canada, in 1849. He was
educated at Trinity College School, Port
Hope, and McGill University – where he
was awarded his M.D. in 1872. He then went
on to further studies in Vienna and London.

For ten years Osler was on the staff of
McGill Medical School (1875–85), and was
lecturer in Clinical Medicine at the University
of Philadelphia between 1884 and 1889,
when he was appointed to Johns Hopkins
University, Baltimore. From 1905 till his
death, Osler was Regius Professor of Medicine
at Oxford University.

He married the widow of Dr. G.W. Gross,
the subject of a famous painting by Thomas
Eakins. In addition to numerous academic
honours, Osler was elected a Fellow of the
Royal Society in 1891.
EXHIBITIONS: *1904 Montreal R.C.A.*, no. 87;
1919 Montreal, no. 39.
MCGILL UNIVERSITY, MONTREAL

134 *Sir William Osler* 1903
47-1/2 x 33-1/2 po (120.7 x 85.1 cm) (s.v.)
INSCRIPTION: signature, b.g.: *Robert Harris–*.
DOCUMENTS HARRIS: «Aux environs de Noël,
je crois, le docteur Osler de Baltimore m'accordera
quelques séances de pose pour un
portrait.» (Lettre de Harris à sa mère, décembre 1903.)

L'un des plus éminents chirurgiens du
XIXᵉ siècle, Sir William Osler est né en 1849
à Bond Head dans le Haut-Canada. Il fit ses
études à la Trinity College School de Port
Hope et à l'université McGill, où il obtint
son doctorat en médecine en 1872. Il poursuivit
ensuite ses études à Vienne et à Londres.

De 1875 à 1885, il fit partie du personnel
enseignant de l'École de médecine de
McGill. Il fut professeur de médecine clinique
à l'université de Philadelphie de 1884 à
1889, année où il fut nommé à l'université
John Hopkins de Baltimore. De 1905 à sa
mort en 1919, il fut professeur royal de
médecine à l'université d'Oxford.

Il épousa la veuve du docteur G.W. Gross,
modèle d'une toile célèbre de Thomas
Eakins. Outre ses nombreux titres universitaires,
Osler reçut celui de membre de la
Royal Society en 1891.
EXPOSITIONS: *1904 Montréal, A.R.A.C.*, nᵒ 87;
1919 Montréal, nᵒ 39.
UNIVERSITÉ MCGILL, MONTRÉAL

135 *Bartlett McLennan* 1904
23-1/2 x 15-3/8 in. (59.7 x 39.1 cm) (s)
INSCRIPTION: signed l.l., *Robert Harris*.

Bartlett McLennan, son of Hugh McLennan
(cat. no. 78), was born in Chicago in the
1860s. He was named Bartlett after the
Reverend Dr. Bartlett of New England
Church, Chicago (later President of Dartmouth College).

McLennan graduated from the Royal
Military College, Kingston, in 1889, and for
a time was field engineer with the C.P.R. He
then entered the Montreal office of Kingman
Brown and Company and from 1899 till the
outbreak of the war in 1914 succeeded his
father as head of the Montreal Transportation Company.

Bartlett McLennan was especially fond of
those very aristocratic forms of sport, hunting
and polo. He rode regularly with the
Montreal Hunt Club, for which the portrait
in this exhibition was painted in 1904, had
two seasons with the South of Ireland Hunt,
and in 1913–14 with the Duke of Beaufort.
Bartlett had great skill in forming a hunter,
and the Earl of Minto (cat. no. 140) said of
one of the hunters Bartlett had trained that
"he had as perfect manners as any horse he

135 *Bartlett McLennan* 1904
23-1/2 x 15-3/8 po (59.7 x 39.1 cm) (s.v.)
INSCRIPTION: signature, b.g.: *Robert Harris*.

Bartlett McLennan, le fils de Hugh McLennan
(nᵒ 78), est né dans les années 1860 à
Chicago. Il reçut son prénom en l'honneur du
révérend Bartlett, de l'Église de la Nouvelle-Angleterre
à Chicago (qui deviendra, plus
tard, président de Dartmouth College).

Diplômé du Royal Military College de
Kingston en 1889, McLennan travailla
quelque temps comme ingénieur de campagne
à la compagnie de chemin de fer du
Canadien Pacifique. Il entra ensuite au
service de la Kingman Brown and Company
de Montréal, puis, de 1899 à la déclaration
de la guerre en 1914, remplaça son père à la
tête de la Montreal Transportation Company.

Bartlett McLennan affectionnait particulièrement
les sports très aristocratiques
de la chasse à courre et du polo. Il chassait
régulièrement avec le Montreal Hunt Club
(qui commanda ce portrait à Harris en
1904); il passa deux saisons avec le South of
Ireland Hunt et, en 1913–1914, il chassa
avec le duc de Beaufort. McLennan avait
beaucoup d'aptitude pour dresser les che-

had ever ridden.'' Bartlett McLennan, on the other hand, remarked that he had learned more about how to deal with his fellows from sport than from any other of his occupations.

In 1915 Bartlett McLennan was a Major of the famous 42nd Royal Highland Regiment, "The Black Watch," and by the time he was killed in action in 1918, he had obtained the rank of Lieutenant Colonel. He was posthumously awarded the D.S.O. for bravery.

LT. COL. H.C.T. MACDOUGALL, MONTREAL

vaux de chasse. Parlant d'un cheval dressé par McLennan, le comte de Minto (n° 140) affirma qu'il s'agissait d'un des meilleurs chevaux qu'il ait jamais montés. De son côté, Bartlett McLennan faisait souvent remarquer que les sports lui avaient appris davantage en matière de relations avec ses semblables que toute autre activité.

En 1915, Bartlett McLennan était major du célèbre 42e Royal Highland Regiment, le «Black Watch», et, lorsqu'il fut tué au front en 1918, il venait à peine d'être promu au grade de lieutenant-colonel. On lui décerna, à titre posthume, un D.S.O. pour sa bravoure.

LIEUTENANT-COLONEL H.C.T. MACDOUGALL, MONTRÉAL

---

136 *Sketchbook Page Related to "The Earl of Minto": Colouring, Dimensions, and Sittings* 1904
Graphite
6-7/8 x 4 in. (17.4 x 10.2 cm)

Framed with cat. nos. 137, 138, 139.
CONFEDERATION ART GALLERY AND MUSEUM, CHARLOTTETOWN

136 *Page du cahier de croquis consacrée au Comte de Minto: indications sur les couleurs, les dimensions et les séances de pose* 1904
Mine de plomb
6-7/8 x 4 po (17.4 x 10.2 cm)

Encadrée avec les nos 137, 138 et 139.
CONFEDERATION ART GALLERY AND MUSEUM, CHARLOTTETOWN

137 *Sketchbook Page Related to "The Earl Minto": A Rejected Pose* 1904
Graphite
6-7/8 x 4 in. (17.4 x 10.2 cm)

Framed with cat. nos. 136,138, 139.
CONFEDERATION ART GALLERY AND MUSEUM, CHARLOTTETOWN

137 *Page du cahier de croquis consacrée au Comte de Minto: une des poses rejetées* 1904
Mine de plomb
6-7/8 x 4 po (17.4 x 10.2 cm)

Encadrée avec les nos 136, 138 et 139.
CONFEDERATION ART GALLERY AND MUSEUM, CHARLOTTETOWN

---

138 *Sketchbook Page Related to "The Earl of Minto": Near-Final Notes on Hand and Riding Crop* 1904
Graphite
6-7/8 x 4 in. (17.4 x 10.2 cm)

Framed with cat. nos. 136, 137, 139.
CONFEDERATION ART GALLERY AND MUSEUM, CHARLOTTETOWN

138 *Page du cahier de croquis consacrée au Comte de Minto: dessin de la main et de la cravache presque identique à celui du portrait terminé* 1904
Mine de plomb
6-7/8 x 4 po (17.4 x 10.2 cm)

Encadrée avec les nos 136, 137 et 139.
CONFEDERATION ART GALLERY AND MUSEUM, CHARLOTTETOWN

---

139 *Sketchbook Page Related to "The Earl of Minto": Notes on Riding Crop* 1904
Graphite
6-7/8 x 4 in. (17.4 x 10.2 cm)

139 *Page du cahier de croquis consacrée au Comte de Minto: notes sur la cravache* 1904
Mine de plomb
6-7/8 x 4 po (17.4 x 10.2 cm)

Framed with cat. nos. 136, 137, 138.
CONFEDERATION ART GALLERY AND
MUSEUM, CHARLOTTETOWN

Encadrée avec les nᵒˢ 136, 137 et 138.
CONFEDERATION ART GALLERY AND
MUSEUM, CHARLOTTETOWN

140 *Gilbert John, 4th Earl of Minto, K.G.,
P.C., G.C.S.I., G.C.M.G., G.C.I.E., D.L.,
1845–1914* 1904
56 x 36 in. (142.3 x 91.5 cm) (s)
INSCRIPTION: signed l.l., *Robert Harris.*

The Earl and Countess of Minto were as
popular in Canada as had been Lord and
Lady Aberdeen (see cat. nos. 88, 89). Robert
and Elizabeth Harris appear to have been
particularly well-favoured by their Excellencies, and long after they had returned to
Scotland, there was still an exchange of
Christmas cards and the occasional note.

The Earl of Minto, Gilbert John Murray
Kynynmoud Elliot, born in London, had
been educated at Eton and Trinity College,
Cambridge, and in 1867 was Commissioned
in the Scots Guards. However, in 1879 he
resigned his Commission and went to
Lincolnshire, where he indulged in the pur-
suits and sportsmanlike activities of gentleman rider. He rode four times in the Grand
National, England's famous steeple-chase,
and in the 1876 race, succeeded in breaking
his neck. Having survived this near-disaster,
he became a foreign correspondent and did a
tour of duty in Spain with the Carlist army
and, later on, in Turkey during the Russo-
Turkish war. He was also present during the
second Afgan war in 1879. During the Egyp-
tian war of 1882, he fought with the mounted
infantry at Ismailia.

After his marriage in 1883, Minto was
appointed military secretary to Lord Lansdowne in Canada and saw action during the
Riel Rebellion. He was offered an appointment as commandant of the North West
Mounted Police, but instead returned to Scotland to his own voluntary corps of the
Border Mounted Rifles.

As Governor General ("the most constitu-
tional Governor we have had," according to
Sir Wilfrid Laurier), he rode with the Montreal Hunt Club, enjoying the company of fine
horsemen such as Colonel Bartlett McLennan (cat. no. 135).

Minto ended his varied and distinguished
career as Viceroy of India. He died in Scotland at Minto in 1914.

For a portrait of the Countess of Minto,
see cat. no. 131.
EXHIBITION: *1919 Montreal*, no. 11.
THE COUNTESS OF MINTO, O.B.E.

140 *Gilbert John, 4ᵉ comte de Minto, K.G.,
C.P., G.C.S.I., G.C.M.G., G.C.I.E., D.L.,
1845–1914* 1904
56 x 36 po (142.3 x 91.5 cm) (s.v.)
INSCRIPTION: signature, b.g.: *Robert Harris.*

Le comte et la comtesse de Minto jouis-
saient au Canada d'une popularité comparable à celle de Lord et de Lady Aberdeen
(voir nᵒˢ 88 et 89). Leurs Excellences semblaient favoriser particulièrement Robert et
Elizabeth Harris et, longtemps après leur
retour en Écosse, ils continuèrent à échanger
des cartes de Noël et à leur écrire un mot à
l'occasion d'événements particuliers.

Né à Londres en 1845, Gilbert John
Murrary Kynynmoud Elliott, comte de
Minto, fit ses études à Eton et au Trinity College de Cambridge. En 1867, il fut nommé à
un commandement dans la garde écossaise.
Il démissiona toutefois en 1879 et se rendit
dans le Lincolnshire où il s'adonna aux occupations et activités d'un gentleman-rider. Il
participa quatre fois au Grand National, le
célèbre steeple-chase anglais mais, en 1876,
il sortit gravement blessé de l'épreuve. Après
cet accident qui aurait pu lui être fatal, il
devint correspondant à l'étranger et partit
en service en Espagne avec l'armée carliste
et, plus tard, en Turquie durant la guerre
russo-turque. Il prit également part, en 1879,
à la seconde guerre afghane. Au cours de la
campagne d'Égypte, en 1882, il combattit
dans l'infanterie à cheval, à Ismaïlia.

Après son mariage, en 1883, il fut nommé
secrétaire militaire de Lord Lansdowne au
Canada et joua un rôle actif au moment de
la rébellion de Riel. On lui offrit le poste de
commandant de la North West Mounted
Police, mais il préféra rentrer en Écosse pour
servir dans son propre corps franc, le Border
Mounted Rifles.

Devenu gouverneur général du Canada
(«le gouverneur le plus constitutionnel que
nous ayons eu» selon Sir Wilfrid Laurier), il
participa aux activités du Montreal Hunt
Club, appréciant la compagnie de bons cavaliers tels que le colonel Bartlett McLennan
(nᵒ 135). Le comte de Minto termina sa
remarquable carrière comme vice-roi des
Indes. Il mourut à Minto (Écosse), en 1914.

Voir également le portrait de la comtesse
de Minto (nᵒ 131).
EXPOSITION: *1919 Montréal*, nᵒ 11.
LA COMTESSE DE MINTO, O.B.E., LONDRES

141　*R.B. Angus*　1905
43-1/4 x 39-3/8 in. (109.9 x 100 cm)
INSCRIPTION: signed l.r., *Robert Harris –*.
HARRIS PAPERS: "Last night I went to a meeting (dinner) of the chairmen of committee of the Mount Royal Club (12 there). Afterward they had an unveiling of portraits of Lord Strathcona and Mr. R.B. Angus which I have just finished for the Club. The pictures I'm glad to say gave great satisfaction." (Letter from Harris to his mother, dated 16 April 1907)

R.B. Angus, President of the Bank of Montreal from 1910 to 1913, was born in Bathgate, Scotland, in 1831. He trained with the Manchester and Liverpool Bank before sailing for Canada in 1857, when he joined the Bank of Montreal. He became General Manager in 1869 for a period of ten years.

Best known to Canadians for his part in the "syndicate" (cat. no. 11) formed in 1880 to construct the C.P.R., he had amassed a fortune from his holdings in the St. Paul, Minneapolis and Manitoba Railway. (He became General Manager of it in 1879.) Angus was one of the directors of the C.P.R. until his death in 1922.

EXHIBITION: *1919 Montreal*, no. 18.
THE MOUNT ROYAL CLUB, MONTREAL

141　*Richard B. Angus*　1905
43-1/4 x 39-3/8 po (109.9 x 100 cm)
INSCRIPTION: signature, b.d.: *Robert Harris –*.
DOCUMENTS HARRIS: «Hier soir, je suis allé à une réunion (dîner) des présidents de comité du Mount Royal Club (12 membres présents). Après le dîner, on a dévoilé les portraits de Lord Strathcona et de M. R.B. Angus que je viens de terminer pour le Club. Je suis heureux de dire que ces toiles ont beaucoup plu.» (Lettre de Harris à sa mère, 16 avril 1907).

Richard Bladworth Angus, président de la Banque de Montréal de 1910 à 1913, est né à Bathgate (Écosse) en 1831. Il fit son apprentissage à la Manchester and Liverpool Bank avant de s'embarquer pour le Canada en 1857, et d'entrer au service de la Banque de Montréal. En 1869, il en devint le directeur général pour une période de dix ans.

Surtout connu des Canadiens pour sa participation au Syndicat (nº 11) formé en 1880 en vue de la construction de la ligne du chemin de fer du Canadien Pacifique, il retira une fortune des actions qu'il possédait dans celle du St. Paul, Minneapolis and Manitoba Railway (dont il devint directeur général en 1879). Angus fut l'un des directeurs des chemins de fer du Canadien Pacifique jusqu'à sa mort en 1922.

EXPOSITION: *1919 Montréal*, nº 18.
THE MOUNT ROYAL CLUB, MONTRÉAL

142　*Margery Davidson ("Mary Morison")* 1905
Oil on board
24 x 18-1/4 in (60.9 x 46.3 cm), oval
INSCRIPTION: signed u.l., *Robert Harris*

The sitter was Margery Davidson of Montreal. Harris quotes the Burns line, with his usual erratic spelling: "A thocht ungentle canna be, the thocht of Mary Morrison."

On 19 August 1901, Robert Harris visited the Kirkyard at Mauchline, Scotland, and made a drawing of the tombstone of Adjutant John Morison of the 104th Regiment who died at Mauchline in 1804, aged eighty. On the same stone is written *"Also his daughter Mary, the poet's bonnie Mary Morison who died 20 June 1971 aged 20."*

Harris was an admirer of Robert Burns and as a young man did a series of illustrations to *Tam O'Shanter*, and he was fond of quoting the Bard.

We have not been able to trace any explanation of the title of this portrait. It was presented by the artist's widow to the Art Association of Montreal in 1919, in memory of her husband.

EXHIBITIONS: *1906 Ottawa R.C.A.*, no. 101;

142　*Margery Davidson («Mary Morison»)* 1905
Huile sur panneau
24 x 18-1/4 po (60.9 x 46.3 cm), ovale
INSCRIPTION: signature, h.g.: *Robert Harris*.

Le modèle était Margery Davidson de Montréal.

«Un rude sentiment ne peut être le sentiment de Mary Morrison [*sic*].»

Le 19 août 1901, Robert Harris se rendit au cimetière de Mauchline (Écosse), et exécuta un dessin de la pierre tombale du major John Morison du 104e régiment, décédé à Mauchline en 1804 à l'âge de quatre-vingts ans. Est également inscrit sur la même pierre (trad.): Ainsi que sa fille *Mary*, la gentille *Mary Morison* du poète, décédée le *20 juin 1871*, à l'âge de *20* ans.

Harris était un admirateur de Robert Burns; il exécuta, dans sa jeunesse, une série d'illustrations pour *Tam O'Shanter*. Il aimait d'ailleurs beaucoup citer le barde.

Nous n'avons pas trouvé d'explication du titre de ce tableau qui fut offert, en 1919, à l'Art Association of Montreal par la veuve de l'artiste, en mémoire de son mari.
EXPOSITIONS: *1906 Ottawa, A.R.A.C.*, nº 101; *1908 Montréal, Printemps*, nº 70; *1908 To-*

1908 Montreal Spring Exhibition, no. 70; *1908 Toronto R.C.A.*, no. 69; *1912 Montreal Spring Exhibition*, no. 68; *1919 Montreal*, no. 70; *1967 Charlottetown*, no. 73; 1972, Fredericton, Beaverbrook Art Gallery, *Canadian Painting: Yesterday and Today 1800–1960*, no. 8.

BEAVERBROOK ART GALLERY, FREDERICTON

ronto, *A.R.A.C.*, nᵒ 69; *1912 Montréal, Printemps*, nᵒ 68; *1919 Montréal*, nᵒ 70; *1967 Charlottetown*, nᵒ 73; 1972, Fredericton, Beaverbrook Art Gallery, *Canadian Painting Yesterday and Today, 1800–1960*, nᵒ 8.

BEAVERBROOK ART GALLERY, FREDERICTON

143 *Anna Leonowens* 1905
29 x 24 in. (73.7 x 60.9 cm), oval
INSCRIPTION: signed l.l., *Robert Harris –*.

The mother-in-law of Thomas Fyshe (cat. no. 155), Anna (Mrs. Thomas Leigh Leonowens) published her famous book *The English Governess at the Court of Siam* (1870). Mrs. Leonowens not only taught English to the Heir Apparent but was influential enough to impart such a strong sense of justice in her young charge that when eventually he became king, one of the first changes he brought about was the abolition of slavery throughout Siam.

The brooch which she is wearing represents one of the dragon-shaped gondolas of the Royal Household. The portrait was commissioned by Thomas Fyshe in June 1905.

EXHIBITIONS: *1906 Montreal Spring Exhibition*, no. 90; *1967 Charlottetown*, no. 74.

DR. T.G. FYSHE, HAMILTON, ONTARIO

143 *Anna Leonowens* 1905
29 x 24 po (73.7 x 60.9 cm), ovale
INSCRIPTION: signature, b.g.: *Robert Harris –*.

Belle-mère de Thomas Fyshe (nᵒ 155), Anna Leonowens (Mᵐᵉ Thomas Leigh) publia en 1870 son fameux livre *The English Governess at the Court of Siam*. Non seulement enseigna-t-elle l'anglais à l'héritier présomptif du royaume de Siam, mais elle eut suffisamment d'influence pour inculquer un tel sens de la justice à son jeune élève que celui-ci inaugurera son règne par l'abolition de l'esclavage dans le pays.

La broche qu'elle porte représente une des gondoles en forme de dragon de la Maison royale. Le portrait fut commandé en 1905 par Thomas Fyshe.

EXPOSITIONS: *1906 Montréal, Printemps*, nᵒ 90; *1967 Charlottetown*, nᵒ 74.

Dᴿ T.G. FYSHE, HAMILTON (ONTARIO)

144 *William Weir* 1905
55-1/4 x 40-1/4 in. (140.3 x 102.2 cm)
INSCRIPTION: signed l.r., *Robert Harris*.

The distinguished jurist Mr. William Weir was the author of two legal treatises, *The Municipal Code of the Province of Quebec* (1889) and *The Civil Code of the Province of Quebec* (1890). Born in Montreal in 1858, he graduated from McGill University and, in 1881, was called to the Bar of Quebec.

Weir represented Argenteuil in the Legislative Assembly of Quebec from 1897 to 1910, and was Speaker of the Assembly (1905–06) when Harris painted this portrait. He became successively Minister of Public Works and Provincial Treasurer. In 1910 he was appointed puisne judge of the Supreme Court of Quebec. He died in England in 1929.

ASSEMBLÉE NATIONALE DU QUÉBEC, QUEBEC

144 *William Weir* 1905
55-1/4 x 40-1/4 po (140.3 x 102.2 cm)
INSCRIPTION: signature, b.d.: *Robert Harris*.

Le distingué juriste William Weir fut l'auteur de deux ouvrages de droit, *Le code municipal de la province de Québec* (1889) et *Le code civil de la province de Québec* (1890). Né à Montréal en 1858, il était diplômé de l'université McGill et fut inscrit au barreau du Québec en 1881.

Député d'Argenteuil à l'Assemblée législative du Québec de 1897 à 1910, Weir était l'orateur de l'Assemblée (1905–1906) au moment où Harris peignit son portrait. Par la suite, il devint successivement ministre des travaux publics et trésorier provincial. En 1910, il fut nommé juge-conseiller à la Cour suprême du Québec. Il mourut en Angleterre en 1929.

ASSEMBLÉE NATIONALE DU QUÉBEC, QUÉBEC

145 *Mrs. Robert Lindsay* c. 1905
30-1/8 x 24 in. (76.5 x 60.9 cm)
INSCRIPTION: signed l.r., *Robert Harris.*

Mrs. Lindsay (née Mary Heloise Bagg), who died in 1938, was the daughter of Stanley Bagg and wife of Robert Lindsay, also of Montreal.

Harris painted many portraits of the Lindsay and Bagg families – both of them, being extensive landowners, involved in the development and expansion of Montreal.

EXHIBITIONS: *1906 Montreal Spring Exhibition*, no. 93; *1919 Montreal*, no. 33.
THE MONTREAL MUSEUM OF FINE ARTS
GIFT OF THE REVEREND SYDENHAM AND MRS.
LINDSAY, 1970

145 *Mme Robert Lindsay* c. 1905
30-1/8 x 24 po (76.5 x 60.9 cm)
INSCRIPTION: signature, b.d.: *Robert Harris –.*

Mme Lindsay (née Mary Heloise Bagg) était la fille de Stanley Bagg et fut la femme de Robert Lindsay, tous deux de Montréal. Elle mourut en 1938.

Harris peignit plusieurs portraits des familles Lindsay et Bagg, des grands propriétaires fonciers dont les noms sont associés au développement et à l'expansion de Montréal.

EXPOSITIONS: *1906 Montréal, Printemps*, n° 93; *1919 Montréal*, n° 33.
MUSÉE DES BEAUX-ARTS DE MONTRÉAL
DON DU RÉVÉREND SYDENHAM ET
DE MME LINDSAY

146 *Robertson Macaulay* 1906
42 x 35 in. (106.7 x 88.9 cm) (s)
INSCRIPTION: signature l.r. (now obscured by frame), *Robert Harris.*

Robertson Macaulay, who became President of the Sun Life Assurance Company of Canada in 1889, was born in Fraserburgh, Aberdeenshire, in 1833 – the son of Kenneth Macaulay, a mariner sailing out of Fraserburgh. (It has been said that "Robertson Macaulay, though born in Aberdeenshire, always maintained that he was a Hebridean, his people on his father's side having resided in Lewis for several generations.")

Robertson Macaulay crossed from Leith to Quebec on a timber-boat early in 1854, and appears to have settled in Hamilton, Ontario. The following year, 1855, his mother, Margaret, came with her family to join him. Meanwhile, Robertson, while in Aberdeen, had become friendly with a Barbara Maria Reid of Edinburgh, born in 1830, the daughter of Thomas Bassett Reid. He persuaded her to come to Canada which she did in 1859, and the two were married that year. At the time of Robertson Macaulay's marriage he was working as accountant with the Canada Life Assurance Company in Hamilton, and remained there for some sixteen years, resigning in 1872 after some difference of opinion to join a small Ontario life company.

In 1874 the young Sun Mutual Life Insurance Company of Montreal invited Robertson Macaulay to join its small staff as Secretary. He accepted and his long association with Sun Life began on 2 August 1874. By 27 November 1883 he had been named Managing Director of the Company (now known as Sun Life Assurance Company of Canada), a title he still retained when elected

146 *Robertson Macaulay* 1906
42 x 35 po (106.7 x 88.9 cm) (s.v.)
INSCRIPTION: signature, b.d. (maintenant sous le cadre): *Robert Harris.*

Robertson Macaulay, qui devint président de la compagnie d'assurance-vie Sun Life du Canada en 1889, est né en 1833 à Fraserburgh (Aberdeenshire); il était le fils de Kenneth Macaulay, marin de Fraserburgh. On a dit que Robertson Macaulay, quoique né dans l'Aberdeenshire, a toujours maintenu qu'il était un Hébridais, la famille de son père ayant vécu à Lewis durant plusieurs générations.

Robertson Macaulay vint de Leith à Québec sur un bateau à bois au début de 1854 et semble s'être établi à Hamilton (Ontario). L'année suivante, sa mère, Margaret, vint le rejoindre avec sa famille. Entre-temps, à Aberdeen, Robertson devint l'ami d'une certaine Barbara Maria Reid, fille de Thomas Basset Reid, née à Édimbourg en 1830. Il la persuada de venir au Canada, ce qu'elle fit en 1859, et l'épousa la même année. À cette époque, il était comptable à la Canada Life Assurance Company d'Hamilton; il y resta quelque 16 ans et démissionna à la suite d'un différend, en 1872, pour entrer au service d'une petite compagnie d'assurances de l'Ontario.

En 1874, la jeune Sun Mutual Life Insurance Company of Montreal offrit à Robertson Macaulay le poste de secrétaire. Il accepta et commença le 2 août 1874 une longue et fructueuse carrière au sein de la compagnie. Vers le 27 novembre 1883, il fut nommé directeur général de celle-ci (devenue, entretemps, la Sun Life Assurance Company of Canada), titre qu'il garda lorsqu'il fut élu président le 15 octobre 1889. Il abandonna le poste de directeur général, en

President on 15 October 1889. He relinquished the post of Managing Director with advancing age in May 1908 but remained President until his death which occurred in Montreal on 27 September 1915. His son, Thomas Bassett Macaulay, succeeded him in the Presidency.

A letter to Robert Harris dated 12 June 1896 from T.B. Macaulay, Secretary of the Sun Life Assurance Company compliments him on his portrait of Robertson Macaulay, and contained a cheque for one thousand and sixty dollars. The existence of this letter led to an erroneous dating of the portrait which was, in fact not commissioned till February 1906, through Abner Kingman on behalf of his fellow directors. Kingman himself did not become a director of Sun Life till 1902, remaining in office till 1930. Harris' sitter-book records payment in full having been made in June 1906.

The Macaulays were related to Lord Babington Macaulay who hailed from Stornoway. In 1929, Robertson Macaulay's son, T.B. Macaulay visited Lewis and had a book *A Summary of a Visit to Lewis* privately printed in Stornoway, mentioning the fact that he was the first of the Canadian Macaulays to visit their native Hebrides.

EXHIBITIONS: *1907 Montreal R.C.A.*, no. 96; *1919 Montreal*, no. 9.

SUN LIFE ASSURANCE COMPANY OF CANADA

raison de son grand âge, en mai 1908, mais il demeura président jusqu'à sa mort, survenue à Montréal le 27 septembre 1915. Son fils, Thomas Bassett Macaulay, lui succéda à la présidence.

T.B. Macaulay, secrétaire de la Sun Life Assurance Company, dans une lettre en date du 12 juin 1896 adressée à Robert Harris, félicitait l'artiste pour son portrait de Robertson Macaulay; il faisait de plus état d'un chèque de mille soixante dollars. Cette lettre engendra une erreur dans la datation de ce portrait, qui ne fut commandé qu'en février 1906 par Abner Kingman au nom des autres membres du conseil de direction. Kingman ne fut d'ailleurs pas nommé au poste de directeur de la Sun Life avant 1902; il conserva ce poste jusqu'en 1930. Le journal de travail de l'artiste mentionne que tout était acquitté en juin 1906.

Les Macaulay étaient apparentés à Lord Babington Macaulay qui vint de Stornoway. En 1929, T.B. Macaulay, le fils de Robert Macaulay, se rendit à l'île Lewis et, à Stornoway, publia à compte d'auteur *A Summary of a Visit to Lewis* dans lequel il affirme qu'il fut le premier Macaulay d'origine canadienne à visiter l'archipel des Hébrides de ses ancêtres.

EXPOSITIONS: *1907 Montréal, A.R.A.C.*, n° 96; *1919 Montréal*, n° 9.

SUN LIFE DU CANADA, COMPAGNIE D'ASSURANCE-VIE

---

147 *?Lady Barron* c. 1906
40 x 30 in. (101.6 x 76.2 cm)
INSCRIPTION: signed l.l., *Robert Harris.*

Née Louise Stevenson Brown. The only indication we have of the identity of the sitter was her name beneath a photograph showing her against a different background.

EXHIBITION: *1967 Charlottetown*, no. 66.

CONFEDERATION ART GALLERY AND MUSEUM, CHARLOTTETOWN

147 *Lady Barron* (?) c. 1906
40 x 30 po (101.6 x 76.2 cm)
INSCRIPTION: signature, b.g.: *Robert Harris.*

Le modèle était née Louise Stevenson Brown. Le seul renseignement que nous ayons concernant l'identité du modèle de ce portrait est le nom inscrit sous une photographie qui le représente sur un arrière-plan différent.

EXPOSITION: *1967 Charlottetown*, n° 66.

CONFEDERATION ART GALLERY AND MUSEUM, CHARLOTTETOWN

148 *John Bell Carruthers* c. 1906
30 x 24 in. (76.2 x 60.9 cm), painted oval
INSCRIPTION: signed l.r., *Robert Harris*.

John Bell Carruthers, the eldest son of John Carruthers (cat. no. 68), was born in Kingston in 1854 and was educated there and in Paris. In 1881 he married Lillie Burpee, eldest daughter of The Honourable Isaac Burpee, P.C., Saint John, New Brunswick.

A vice-president of the Kingston and Montreal Forwarding Company, he was a benefactor of Queen's University and was one of the twelve Governors appointed for the School of Mining, later signing the declaration for the Incorporation of the School of Mining and Agriculture.

In 1890 he laid the cornerstone of Carruthers Hall, a science building at Queen's University named for his father, John Carruthers, who had died in 1889.

AGNES ETHERINGTON ART CENTRE
QUEEN'S UNIVERSITY AT KINGSTON

149 *Portrait of a Lady* c. 1906
30-1/8 x 24-1/8 in. (76.5 x 61.3 cm)
INSCRIPTION: signed l.r., *Robert Harris*.

The day after Robert Harris had been commissioned by Mr. Baumgarten to paint a portrait of R.B. Angus (cat. no. 141) for the Mount Royal Club, he and his wife sailed for Europe and spent the remainder of the month in Munich. We would place this portrait among those associated with his stay in Germany, when he worked in the studio loaned to him by the Baroness von Schene-Kosboth.

EXHIBITION: *1967 Charlottetown*, no. 52.

CONFEDERATION ART GALLERY AND
MUSEUM, CHARLOTTETOWN

148 *John Bell Carruthers* c. 1906
30 x 24 po (76.2 x 60.9 cm), ovale
INSCRIPTION: signature, b.d.: *Robert Harris*.

John Bell Carruthers, fils aîné de John Carruthers (n° 68), est né à Kingston en 1854. Il poursuivit ses études dans sa ville natale et à Paris. En 1881, il épousa Lillie Burpee, fille aînée de l'honorable Isaac Burpee, C.P., de Saint-Jean (Nouveau-Brunswick).

Vice-président de la Forwarding Company de Kingston et de Montréal et bienfaiteur de l'université Queen's, il fut l'un des douze gouverneurs de la School of Mining, et signa, plus tard, la déclaration de l'incorporation de la School of Mining and Agriculture.

En 1890, il posa la pierre angulaire du Carruthers Hall, l'immeuble des sciences de l'université Queen's, nommé ainsi en l'honneur de son père, John Carruthers, décédé en 1889.

AGNES ETHERINGTON ART CENTRE
QUEEN'S UNIVERSITY AT KINGSTON

149 *Portrait d'une dame* c. 1906
30-1/8 x 24-1/8 po (76.5 x 61.3 cm)
INSCRIPTION: signature, b.d.: *Robert Harris*.

Le lendemain du jour où M. Baumgarten demandait à Robert Harris de peindre le portrait de R.B. Angus (n° 141) pour le Mount Royal Club, Harris et sa femme s'embarqèrent pour l'Europe et passèrent le reste du mois à Munich. C'est au cours de ce séjour en Allemagne, où il travailla dans un atelier que lui avait prêté la baronne von Schene-Kosboth, que Harris aurait exécuté de portrait.

EXPOSITION: *1967 Charlottetown*, n° 52.

CONFEDERATION ART GALLERY AND
MUSEUM, CHARLOTTETOWN

150 *John Molson* 1907
29-3/8 x 23-3/8 in. (74.6 x 59.4 cm) (s)
INSCRIPTION: signed l.l., *Robert Harris.*
HARRIS PAPERS: M. Molson. To paint him according to agreement made several years ago. $400. 24 x 30 1907 30th Nov on acct $300. (Sitter-book, entry dated ?30 November 1907)

Since John Henry Robinson Molson died at his home "Piedmont," in Montreal, in 1897, this portrait must have been arranged by McGill authorities posthumously, and painted from a photograph.

John Henry Robinson Molson, was born in 1826, and was educated in Montreal at a private and well-known school run by Dr. Black. At the age of fifteen, in 1841, he was taken on a visit to England and Scotland, where, along with his father, he inspected a number of breweries and distilleries. The following year, he was sent on a trip through various towns in Upper Canada, including Toronto, and in 1842 entered Upper Canada College, where he remained for one year.

In 1843, at the age of seventeen, he went to work in the family brewery, and in 1844 was formally apprenticed to Thomas and William Molson and Company for a period of three years "to faithfully serve and obey his masters, keep their secrets and do no damage to them or see it done by others without giving them instant information thereof."

In time, following a further period with English breweries by 1850, according to the Molson family biographer, Mr. Merrill Denison, John Henry Robinson was the best technically trained brewer there had yet been in the family.

Among his other interests, John H.R. Molson, became a Vice-President of Molson's Bank, succeeding Thomas Workman (cat. no. 43) as President in 1889. He was also actively associated with the Montreal Street Railway, the Scottish Life Assurance Company, and the City and District Savings Bank. He gave generously of time and money to McGill University, the Fraser Institute, and as far as McGill was concerned "so generous were he and Mrs. Molson with gifts to it, that he was offered the Chancellorship, but he declined in favour of Sir Donald Smith, later Lord Strathcona [cat. no. 128]."

Of particular interest was his endowment of the Verdun Protestant Hospital for the Insane. In 1892, in addition to earlier gifts, he presented the Verdun Hospital with funds for the erection of a Molson pavilion and gymnasium. A Dr. Maurice Buck of London, Ontario, had been a world pioneer in the introduction of games and exercises as an aid in mental therapy, and Molson's gift,

150 *John Molson* 1907
29-3/8 x 23-3/8 po (74.6 x 59.4 cm) (s.v.)
INSCRIPTION: signature, b.g.: *Robert Harris.*
DOCUMENTS HARRIS: «M. Molson. Peindre selon l'entente intervenue il y a plusieurs années. $400. 24 x 30. 1907 30 novembre, $300 en acompte.» (Journal de travail de l'artiste, 30 novembre 1907?).

John Henry Robinson Molson mourut en 1897 à sa résidence «Piedmont» de Montréal. Ce portrait serait, par conséquent, une œuvre posthume commandée par les autorités de McGill. Il aurait été exécuté par Harris d'après une photographie.

John Molson est né en 1826. Il étudia à Montréal dans une école privée renommée que dirigeait M. Black. En 1841, à l'âge de quinze ans, il se rendit, en compagnie de son père, en Angleterre et en Écosse pour y visiter des brasseries et des distilleries. L'année suivante, il parcourut les principales villes du Haut-Canada, dont Toronto, et s'inscrivit à l'Upper Canada College où il étudia un an.

En 1843, à l'âge de dix-sept ans, il commença à travailler pour la brasserie familiale et devint, en 1844, apprenti à la Thomas and William Molson and Company. Il y demeurera trois ans pour apprendre à «servir loyalement ses maîtres, leur obéir et garder leurs secrets de fabrication; ne leur causer aucun dommage ni tolérer que d'autres le fassent sans les informer sans tarder».

Selon Merrill Denison, le biographe de la famille Molson, John Henry Robinson fut, après un autre séjour dans des brasseries anglaises en 1850, le brasseur le mieux entraîné de la famille pour l'époque.

John H.R. Robinson devint, par ailleurs, vice-président de la Molson's Bank et, en 1889, succéda à Thomas Workman (nº 43) au poste de président. Il s'occupa également activement du Montreal Street Railway, de la Scottish Life Assurance Company et de la City and District Savings Bank. Il consacra généreusement une partie de son temps et de ses deniers à l'université McGill et au Fraser Institute. En ce qui a trait à McGill, «M. et Mᵐᵉ Molson dotèrent si généreusement l'université qu'on lui offrit la chancellerie, offre qu'il déclina, préférant laisser cet honneur à Sir Donald Smith, qui deviendra plus tard Lord Strathcona [nº 128]».

Il favorisa également de son aide financière la Verdun Protestant Hospital for the Insane de façon particulière. En 1892, malgré plusieurs dons antérieurs, il fournit les fonds nécessaires à la construction du pavillon Molson et du gymnase. Un certain docteur Maurice Buck, de London (Ontario), avait été le premier au monde à préconiser l'utilisation d'exercices physiques et de jeux

Mr. Denison suggests, "was probably one of the first made anywhere for that purpose." As well as to other institutions Molson's generosity was extended to the Montreal General Hospital and Bishop's College School, Lennoxville.

In his will he left $10,000 to the Trustees of the Mount Royal Cemetery Company for the erection of the first crematorium in Canada. "Unlike most of the Molson family, John Henry Robinson was a Unitarian and his direction that his body be cremated made it necessary for his remains to be taken to Boston, Massachusetts."

MCGILL UNIVERSITY, MONTREAL

dans le traitement des maladies mentales. Le don de M. Molson, selon Denison, «fut probablement le premier à être fait à cette fin». M. Molson dota également d'autres institutions dont l'Hôpital général de Montréal et Bishop's College à Lennoxville.

Il légua, à sa mort, ($10 000. aux administrateurs de la Mount Royal Cemetery Company pour permettre la construction du premier four crématoire au Canada. «Contrairement aux autres membres de sa famille, John Henry Robinson Molson était unitarien; on dut transporter son corps à Boston (Massachusetts) pour l'incinérer et ainsi satisfaire ses dernières volontés.»

UNIVERSITÉ MCGILL, MONTRÉAL

151 *Sampson Robbins* 1907
29-1/2 x 23-1/2 in. (74.9 x 59.7 cm) (s)
INSCRIPTION: signed l.l., *Robert Harris.*

Dr. Sampson Paul Robbins was Principal of McGill Normal School from 1883 to 1907. The portrait commission was arranged by Mr. Nicholson, Registrar of McGill, and as Harris notes, "there being no time to find out what sum exactly would be available, was left indefinite."

Robbins had been trained under Egerton Ryerson (1803–82) at Toronto Normal and had served as Headmaster of the Central School at Brantford, Upper Canada. He was one of the original staff of McGill Normal School in 1857.

MCGILL UNIVERSITY, MONTREAL

151 *Sampson Robbins* 1907
29-1/2 x 23-1/2 po (74.9 x 59.7 cm) (s.v.)
INSCRIPTION: signature, b.g.: *Robert Harris.*

M. Sampson Paul Robbins fut principal de la McGill Normal School de 1883 à 1907. C'est M. Nicholson, secrétaire et archiviste de McGill, qui commanda ce portrait à Harris et, comme celui-ci le note, «étant donné que nous n'avions pas le temps de déterminer quelle somme exactement serait disponible, elle n'a pas été établie».

Robbins fit ses études sous la direction d'Egerton Ryerson (1803–1882) à la Toronto Normal School et fut directeur de la Central School de Brantford, dans le Haut-Canada. Il fit partie de la première génération d'enseignants de la McGill Normal School, en 1857.

UNIVERSITÉ MCGILL, MONTRÉAL

152 *Sir Thomas Roddick* 1907
30 x 24 in. (76.2 x 60.9 cm) (s)
INSCRIPTION: signed u.r., *Robert Harris –.*
HARRIS PAPERS: "I have just finished a portrait of Dr. Roddick in scarlet robes which gives great satisfaction." (Letter from Harris to his mother, dated 31 January 1908)

Sir Thomas George Roddick, the surgeon, was born in Newfoundland at Harbour Grace in 1846, and educated at Truro, Nova Scotia, after which he entered McGill and obtained his M.D. in 1868. He practiced as a surgeon in Montreal and in 1875 was appointed Professor of Clinical Surgery at McGill. From 1901 to 1908 he was Dean of the Faculty of Medicine. From 1896 to 1898 he was President of the British Medical Association, and in 1900 was made an Honourary F.R.C.S. (Eng.).

As well as gaining distinction as a surgeon, Thomas Roddick served with the militia during the Fenian raids and with the North West Expeditionary of 1885 when he held the rank of surgeon-general. As a Conserva-

152 *Sir Thomas Roddick* 1907
30 x 24 po (76.2 x 60.9 cm) (s.v.)
INSCRIPTION: signature, h.d.: *Robert Harris–.*
DOCUMENTS HARRIS: «Je viens d'achever un portrait du docteur Roddick, en robe écarlate, qui plaît beaucoup.» (Lettre de Harris à sa mère, 31 janvier 1908).

L'éminent chirurgien Sir Thomas Roddick est né en 1846 à Harbour Grace (Terre-Neuve). Il fit ses études à Truro (Nouvelle-Écosse), puis à McGill où il obtint son doctorat en médecine en 1868. Il pratiqua la chirurgie à Montréal et, en 1875, il fut nommé professeur de chirurgie clinique à McGill. Il fut doyen de la faculté de médecine de 1901 à 1908. De 1896 à 1898, il fut président de la British Medical Association et devint, en 1900, F.R.C.S. honoraire (Angleterre).

En plus d'être chirurgien éminent, Thomas Roddick servit dans la Garde nationale durant le soulèvement des Fenians et participa, en 1885, à l'Expédition du Nord-Ouest à titre de chirurgien-major. Conservateur représentant le comté de Montréal-Ouest, il

tive he sat in the House of Commons from 1896 to 1904 representing Montreal West. He died at Montreal in 1923.

This work is on permanent loan to the Royal College of Physicians and Surgeons, Ottawa.

EXHIBITIONS: *1908 Montreal Spring Exhibition*, no. 84; *1915 Montreal Spring Exhibition*, no. 104, repr. p. 21; *1919 Montreal*, no. 45.

THE MONTREAL GENERAL HOSPITAL

siéga à la Chambre des communes de 1896 à 1904. Il mourut à Montréal en 1923.

Ce portrait est prêté en permanence au Collège royal des médecins du Canada, Ottawa.

EXPOSITIONS: *1908 Montréal, Printemps*, nᵒ 84; *1915 Montréal, Printemps*, nᵒ 104 et reprod. p. 21; *1919 Montréal*, nᵒ 45.

HÔPITAL GÉNÉRAL DE MONTRÉAL

---

153 *Mrs. James Ross* 1907
38 x 29-1/2 in. (96.5 x 74.9 cm)
INSCRIPTION: signed l.l., *Robert Harris.*

Anne Ross (née Kerr) was born in New York in 1848. Always deeply concerned with the welfare of others it would appear that before her marriage, in 1872, to the contractor, James Ross, of Montreal she possibly intended to become a nurse. Certainly she took a course as a Nurse's Aid. After her marriage she devoted much of her time and interest to the old Montreal Maternity Hospital and was actively engaged on its Board.

James Ross was one of the Chief contractors for the construction of the C.P.R., and as his wife she traveled about the country with him. While living in Lindsay, Ontario, largely through her influence, James Ross built the Lindsay Ross Memorial Hospital.

Their son, J.K.L. Ross (for a study of Mrs. J.K.L. Ross, see cat. no. 154) built the Ross Memorial Pavilion at the Royal Victoria Hospital, Montreal, in memory of his parents. A fine companion portrait of James Ross, by Robert Harris, also hangs in the Ross Pavilion.

Mrs. Ross died in 1915.

EXHIBITION: *1919 Montreal*, no. 47.

THE ROYAL VICTORIA HOSPITAL, MONTREAL

153 *Mᵐᵉ James Ross* 1907
38 x 29-1/2 po (96.5 x 74.9 cm)
INSCRIPTION: signature, b.g.: *Robert Harris.*

Anne Ross (née Kerr) est née à New York en 1848. Profondément préoccupée du bien-être de ses semblables, elle aurait, avant d'épouser en 1872 James Ross, un entrepreneur de Montréal, eu l'intention de devenir infirmière. Chose certaine, elle suivit un cours d'aide-infirmière. Mariée, elle consacra une bonne partie de son temps libre à l'ancien Montréal Maternity Hospital et devint membre actif du conseil de direction.

James Ross fut l'un des principaux entrepreneurs lors de la construction du chemin de fer du Canadien Pacifique. Son épouse l'accompagna dans ses voyages à travers le Canada. Lors du séjour du couple à Lindsay (Ontario), James Ross fit construire, principalement sur le conseil de sa femme, le Lindsay Ross Memorial Hospital. Mᵐᵉ Ross mourut en 1915.

Leur fils, J.K.L. Ross (voir l'étude pour un portrait de Mᵐᵉ J.K.L. Ross, nᵒ 154) fit construire, à la mémoire de ses parents, le pavillon Ross Memorial de l'hôpital Royal Victoria à Montréal. Un portrait de James Ross par Robert Harris, qui fait bien pendant à celui-ci, est également suspendu dans le pavillon Ross Memorial.

EXPOSITION: *1919 Montréal*, nᵒ 47.

HÔPITAL ROYAL VICTORIA, MONTRÉAL

---

154 *Study for "Mrs. J.K.L. Ross and Children* 1907
Oil on board
11 x 9 in. (27.9 x 22.8 cm) (s)

This is one of two studies for a large, untraced portrait group (exhibited *1908 Toronto R.C.A.* as *Mrs. J.K.L. Ross and Children*). See note on cat. no. 153.

CONFEDERATION ART GALLERY AND MUSEUM, CHARLOTTETOWN

154 *Étude pour Mᵐᵉ J.K.L. Ross et les enfants* 1907
Huile sur bois
11 x 9 po (27.9 x 22.8 cm) (s.v.)

Une de deux études pour un grand portrait de groupe perdu (présenté lors de l'exposition *1908 Toronto, A.R.A.C.*, sous le titre *Mrs. J.K.L. Ross and Children*). Voir également le commentaire du nᵒ 153.

CONFEDERATION ART GALLERY AND MUSEUM, CHARLOTTETOWN

155 *Thomas Fyshe* 1908
30 x 24 in. (76.2 x 60.9 cm)
INSCRIPTION: signed u.l., *Robert Harris –.*

Thomas Fyshe was born in Prestonpans, East Lothian, Scotland, on 3 October 1845. As a youth he served as a clerk with the Bank of Scotland. After emigrating to Canada he entered the Bank of North America at Kingston, Ontario. He was transferred to Montreal in 1868 and later moved to New York in 1869. He was then appointed as Agent for the Bank of Nova Scotia at their office in Saint John, New Brunswick.

At the Annual Meeting held in Halifax in 1876, Thomas Fyshe was appointed Cashier of the Bank (the titles of General Manager and Manager were substituted for those of Cashier and Agent respectively in 1898). Fyshe held this position as Cashier until June 1897 when he resigned to accept the position of joint General Manager of the Merchants Bank of Canada.

Thomas Fyshe published various pamphlets relating to banking and served as a Civil Service Commissioner from 1907 to 1908. His mother-in-law was Mrs. Thomas Leigh Leonowens, the famous Anna, Governess to a king of Siam (cat. no. 143).

EXHIBITION: *1908 Montreal Spring Exhibition*, no. 86.

THE BANK OF NOVA SCOTIA

155 *Thomas Fyshe* 1908
30 x 24 po (76.2 x 60.9 cm)
INSCRIPTION: signature, h.g.: *Robert Harris –.*

Thomas Fyshe est né à Prestonpans (East Lothian, Écosse) en 1845. Dans sa jeunesse, il fut commis à la Bank of Scotland. Émigré au Canada, il entra au service de la Bank of North America à Kingston (Ontario). Il fut muté à Montréal en 1868, puis, en 1869, à New York. Il fut ensuite nommé agent de la succursale de la Banque de Nouvelle-Écosse à Saint-Jean (Nouveau-Brunswick).

À l'assemblée annuelle tenue à Halifax en 1876, Thomas Fyshe fut nommé caissier de la Banque (les titres de directeur général et de gérant ne remplacèrent qu'en 1898 ceux de caissier et d'agent). Fyshe occupa ce poste jusqu'en juin 1897, date à laquelle il démissionna pour devenir co-directeur général de la Merchants Bank of Canada.

Thomas Fyshe publia diverses brochures concernant les opérations bancaires et il fut commissaire de la Fonction publique en 1907 et en 1908. Il fut le gendre de Mᵐᵉ Thomas Leigh, la célèbre Anna Leonowens, gouvernante de l'héritier présomptif du royaume de Siam (n° 143).

EXPOSITION: *1908 Montréal, Printemps*, n° 86.
LA BANQUE DE NOUVELLE-ÉCOSSE, HALIFAX

156 *Bernard Harrington* 1908
45-3/4 x 35-3/4 in. (116.2 x 90.8 cm) (s)
INSCRIPTION: signed l.r., *Robert Harris.*

"The portrait of Dr. Harrington is by Robert Harris C.M.G. and represents the subject in scarlet gown and hood as Doctor of Laws. The presentation of this portrait was made by Dr. Adams who referred to Dr. Harrington's long connection with McGill.... There probably never had been, said the Dean, anyone connected to the University who was more beloved by all or who had exerted a greater influence for good. The portrait was presented by certain graduates in Chemistry and Mining, extracts from whose letters were read." (*Montreal Gazette*, 23 November 1908)

Harrington (1848–1907) was born at St. Andrews, Lower Canada, and educated at McGill and also at the Sheffield Scientific School at Yale where he obtained his PH.D. in 1871.

He was on the staff of McGill from 1872 till 1907 his first appointment being Lecturer in Assaying, Mining and Chemistry. From 1883 to 1907 he was David J. Greenshields Professor of Chemistry and Mineralogy, and from 1898 Director of the Chemistry and Mining Building and during the final six

156 *Bernard Harrington* 1908
45-3/4 x 35-3/4 po (116.2 x 90.8 cm) (s.v.)
INSCRIPTION: signature, b.d.: *Robert Harris.*

«Le portrait, de la main de Robert Harris, C.M.G., représente M. Harrington en toge et coiffe écarlates de docteur en droit. Au cours de sa présentation, M. Adams parla des liens de longue date qui unissent M. Harrington à McGill . . . Selon le doyen, il n'y a probablement eu personne à l'Université qui fût plus aimé de tous ou qui ait exercé une meilleure influence. Le portrait a été offert par des diplômés en chimie et en mines, dont on a lu des extraits de lettres.» (*The Montreal Gazette*, livraison du 23 novembre 1908).

Bernard Harrington est né en 1848 à Saint-André, dans le Bas-Canada. Il fit ses études à McGill et à la Sheffield Scientific School de Yale où il obtint son doctorat en 1871.

Il fit partie du personnel enseignant de McGill de 1872 à 1907, d'abord comme chargé de cours d'analyse du minerai, de mines et de chimie, puis, de 1883 à 1907, comme professeur de chimie et de minéralogie à David J. Greenshields et, à partir de 1898, directeur de l'immeuble de chimie et des mines; au cours de ses six dernières

years of office, was MacDonald Professor of Chemistry and Mineralogy.
EXHIBITION: *1919 Montreal*, no. 6.
MCGILL UNIVERSITY, MONTREAL

années de fonctions, il fut professeur de chimie et de minéralogie à MacDonald. Il mourut en 1907.
EXPOSITION: *1919 Montréal*, nº 6.
UNIVERSITÉ MCGILL, MONTRÉAL

---

157 *My Old Montreal Model* 1908
18-1/2 x 15-1/2 in. (47 x 39.4 cm)
INSCRIPTION: signed l.r., *R. Harris.*

The original drawing for this painting was found in Charlottetown in 1972, thus establishing the date of the work, which was hitherto unknown.
EXHIBITIONS: *1917 Montreal Spring Exhibition*, no. 162; 1939, Toronto, Canadian National Exhibition, [exhibition by the Department of Fine Art], no. 98; *1967 Charlottetown*, no. 88.
THE NATIONAL GALLERY OF CANADA, OTTAWA (1450)

157 *Mon vieux modèle de Montréal* 1908
18-1/2 x 15-1/2 po (47 x 39.4 cm)
INSCRIPTION: signature, b.d.: *R. Harris.*

L'esquisse préliminaire de ce tableau, découverte à Charlottetown en 1972, établit la date d'exécution du tableau, demeurée jusqu'alors inconnue.
EXPOSITIONS: *1917 Montréal, Printemps*, nº 162; 1939, Toronto, [organisée par le Department of Fine Art], *Canadian National Exhibition*, nº 98; *1967 Charlottetown*, nº 88.
GALERIE NATIONALE DU CANADA, OTTAWA (1450)

---

158 *Self-portrait* 1908
Oil on board
10-1/2 x 9-1/4 in. (26.7 x 23.5 cm)
INSCRIPTION: signed l.r., *R.H.;* dated l.l., *6 May/1908.*
PROVENANCE: Miss Mary Beth Harris, Charlottetown; Klinkhoff Gallery.
AGNES ETHERINGTON ART CENTRE QUEEN'S UNIVERSITY AT KINGSTON

158 *Autoportrait* 1908
Huile sur bois
10-1/2 x 9-1/4 po (26.7 x 23.5 cm)
INSCRIPTION: signature, b.d.: *R.H.;* date, b.g.: *6 mai 1908.*
HISTORIQUE: Mlle Mary Beth Harris, Charlottetown; Klinkhoff Gallery.
AGNES ETHERINGTON ART CENTRE QUEEN'S UNIVERSITY AT KINGSTON

159 *Study for "Sir Walter Cassels"* 1909
Charcoal
24-3/4 x 17-1/2 in. (62.9 x 44.4 cm)

Study for a portrait not in the exhibition.
CONFEDERATION ART GALLERY AND
MUSEUM, CHARLOTTETOWN

159 *Étude pour Sir Walter Cassels* 1909
Fusain
24-3/4 x 17-1/2 po (62.9 x 44.4 cm)

Le portrait exécuté à la suite de cette
étude n'est pas présenté dans le cadre de
de cette exposition. Voir également le n° 160.
CONFEDERATION ART GALLERY AND
MUSEUM, CHARLOTTETOWN

160 *Study for "Sir Walter Cassels"* 1909
13-3/4 x 8-1/4 in. (34.9 x 20.9 cm) (s)
HARRIS PAPERS: "The general tone of the
hair and board were not far removed from
the face and . . . the light blue eyes were a
marked feature. The whole effect of head,
including hair, a good deal below the white
of the collar and though the whole effect of
flesh is clean and ruddy still there is a vi-
bration of tender greys nearly all through.
In his smiling the eyes rather close up the
outer light in lower muscles below the eye,
and this comes out brighter, also the raising
of the corner of the mouth and the dis-
appearance of the effect is so marked when
his face is serious." (Sketchbook entry, dated
8–9 October 1908)

Study for a portrait not in the exhibition.
Judge Cassels (1845–1923) was born in
Quebec, and educated at the Quebec High
School, then at the University of Toronto
where he obtained his B.A. in 1865. His
father-in-law was Robert Hamilton, Chancellor of Bishop's College, Lennoxville, and
also barrister. Mr. Justice Cassels practised
law privately for several years in Toronto
and obtained one of the Briefs as Council for
the C.P.R. in the Onderdonk Arbitration. He
was one of the leaders of the Ontario Bar
Association, and in 1908 was appointed
Judge of the Exchequer Court of Ontario. A
keen golfer, he was President of the Toron-

160 *Étude pour Sir Walter Cassels* 1909
13-3/4 x 8-1/4 po (34.9 x 20.9 cm) (s.v.)
DOCUMENTS HARRIS: «La teinte générale des
cheveux et de la barbe était très proche de
celle du visage . . . sur lequel se détachaient
les yeux d'un bleu clair. Les cheveux, des-
cendent bien au-dessous du collet blanc de
sa toge et, quoique la chair donne une impression générale de propreté et de santé,
un gris tendre vibre néanmoins et envahit
l'ensemble du portrait. Lorsqu'il sourit, la
lumière extérieure, retenue par les muscles
situés au-dessous des yeux, donne encore
plus d'éclat au regard tandis que les commis-
sures des lèvres se relèvent. La disparition
de l'effet est très sensible lorsque le visage
est sérieux.» (Cahier de croquis, 8–9 octobre
1908).

Le portrait exécuté à la suite de cette
étude n'est pas présenté dans le cadre de
cette exposition. Voir également le n° 159.
Le juge Cassels est né à Québec en 1845.
Il fit ses études à la Quebec High School,
puis à l'université de Toronto où il obtint
son B.A. en 1865. Son beau-père, Robert
Hamilton, fut chancelier du Bishop's College
à Lennoxville, et membre du barreau. Cassels exerça le droit à son compte durant
plusieurs années à Toronto et, en tant que
conseiller des chemins de fer du Canadien
Pacifique, il obtint une des causes de l'arbi-
trage Onderdonk. Il fut un des chefs de
l'Ontario Bar Association et, en 1908, il fut

to Golf Club, and Mrs. Cassels presented his portrait by Harris to the club in 1909.

The painting on display here is the sketch for the large portrait which has since been, in part, destroyed. The portrait itself was over seven feet in height, and it is interesting to note that this was one of the few occasions when Harris made detailed colour-guides in his sketchbooks.

CONFEDERATION ART GALLERY AND
MUSEUM, CHARLOTTETOWN

nommé juge de la Cour de l'Échiquier de l'Ontario. Golfeur passionné, il fut président du Toronto Golf Club et c'est à ce club que Mme Cassels offrit en 1909 ce portrait exécuté par Harris. Sir Walter Cassels mourut en 1923.

La toile exposée ici est l'esquisse qui a servi à l'exécution de l'œuvre définitive. Celle-ci, qui a été en partie détruite depuis, mesurait plus de sept pieds de haut, et il est intéressant de remarquer que c'est un des rares tableaux pour lesquels Harris a noté des indications détaillées des couleurs dans son cahier de croquis.

CONFEDERATION ART GALLERY AND
MUSEUM, CHARLOTTETOWN

---

161 *Sarah Harris* 1909
Oil on panel
16 x 12 in. (40.7 x 30.5 cm)
INSCRIPTION: signed l.l., *Robert Harris*; dated and signed on reverse, *Sarah Harris/Painted 15 & 16 Aug./1909/in Victoria B.C./by her brother/Robert Harris.*
PROVENANCE: Mrs. Freda Harris, Charlottetown.
EXHIBITION: *1967 Charlottetown* (not in cat.)
PRINCE STREET SCHOOL, CHARLOTTETOWN

161 *Sarah Harris* 1909
Huile sur bois
16 x 12 po (40.7 x 30.5 cm)
INSCRIPTION: signature, b.g.: *Robert Harris*; inscription (trad.), date et signature au verso: *Sarah Harris/Peint les 15 & 16 août/1909/à Victoria (C.B.)/par son frère/Robert Harris.*
HISTORIQUE: Mme Freda Harris, Charlottetown.
EXPOSITION: *1967 Charlottetown* (ne fait pas partie du catalogue).
PRINCE STREET SCHOOL, CHARLOTTETOWN

---

162 *The Misses Lois, Sara, and Mary Hill*
c. 1909
60-1/2 x 44-1/2 in. (153.7 x 113 cm)
INSCRIPTION: signed l.r., *Robert Harris.*

A pencil sketch for this portrait group, dated 12 May 1909, in the Charlottetown Art Gallery and Museum.
EXHIBITION: *1910 Montreal Spring Exhibition*, no. 161 (as *Daughters of Rev. Principal Hill, D.D.*).
THE ART GALLERY OF ONTARIO, TORONTO
GIFT OF THE GRANDCHILDREN OF
S.H.C. MINER IN MEMORY OF THEIR PARENTS,
DR. AND MRS. E. MUNSON HILL, 1970

162 *Mlles Lois, Sarah et Mary Hill* c. 1909
60-1/2 x 44-1/2 po (153.7 x 113 cm)
INSCRIPTION: signature, b.d.: *Robert Harris.*

Un croquis au crayon pour ce portrait de groupe, en date du 12 mai 1909, est à la Confederation Art Gallery and Museum.
EXPOSITION: *1910 Montréal, Printemps*, n° 161 (*Daughters of Rev. Principal Hill, D.D.*).
THE ART GALLERY OF ONTARIO, TORONTO
DON DES PETITS-ENFANTS DE S.H.C. MINER
À LA MÉMOIRE DE LEURS PARENTS,
LE DOCTEUR ET MME E. MUNSON HILL, 1970

163 *Lemuel Tweedie* 1911
50 x 40 in. (127 x 101.6 cm)
INSCRIPTION: signed l.l., *Robert Harris.*

From 1910 onwards, portrait commissions for Harris were not as abundant as they had been earlier, and there are only occasional references to them in letters and in the sitter-book.

One of the better commissions was made on 13 December 1911 when arrangements were made for him to paint the Lieutenant Governor of New Brunswick for $750, plus frame ($59.75) and packing ($7.70). There is no indication of how long the commission took to complete but Robert Harris was paid in full on 11 December the following year.

Mr. Tweedie, who had been Prime Minister of New Brunswick from 1900 to 1907 and from 1907 to 1912, Lieutenant Governor, was born in Chatham, New Brunswick, in 1848, where he was educated. Called to the Bar in 1871, three years later he was elected to the Legislative Assembly, from 1874 to 1878 and from 1886 to 1907.

PROVINCE OF NEW BRUNSWICK
DEPARTMENT OF SUPPLY AND SERVICES

163 *Lemuel Tweedie* 1911
50 x 40 po (127 x 101.6 cm)
INSCRIPTION: signature, b.g.: *Robert Harris.*

À partir de 1910 Harris ne reçoit pas autant de commandes de portraits qu'auparavant. Il n'en mentionne d'ailleurs que quelques-unes dans ses lettres et son journal de travail.

Une des ses meilleures commandes date du 13 décembre 1911, où on lui offre $750 (plus $59.75 pour l'encadrement et $7.70 pour l'emballage) pour le portrait du lieutenant-gouverneur du Nouveau-Brunswick. On ne dit pas combien de temps il a fallu à Harris pour exécuter le portrait, mais il fut payé le 11 décembre de l'année suivante.

M. Tweedie, qui fut premier ministre du Nouveau-Brunswick de 1900 à 1907 et lieutenant-gouverneur de 1907 à 1912, est né à Chatham (Nouveau-Brunswick) en 1848. C'est à Chatham, également, qu'il fit ses études. Inscrit au barreau en 1871, il fut élu député et siégea à l'Assemblée législative de 1874 à 1878 et de 1886 à 1907.

PROVINCE DU NOUVEAU-BRUNSWICK
MINISTÈRE DES APPROVISIONNEMENTS ET
SERVICES

164 *Replica of "Dr. George W. Campbell"*
1913
42-1/2 x 34-1/4 in. (108 x 87 cm) (s)
INSCRIPTION: signed l.l., *Robert Harris.*
HARRIS PAPERS: "Agreed with Dr. Shepherd to do a portrait of Dr. Campbell for £200. Frame to be paid for by me. He being authorized he said to do this by the family of Dr. C. under the Executors of his son's will and this amount having been set apart in the will of one of them and the executors having desired him to make arrangement for it which he has accepted. Picture for McGill. Hang hall of Medical hall of Medical faculty." (Sitter-book, entry dated 25 June 1913) "Delivered portrait framed July 13. exch. $968.88. 10th November 1913. Paid by Draft to Dr. S. endorsed to me." (Sitter-book, entry dated 11 April 1913 [sic])

This painting is a replica by Harris of his portrait destroyed in the 1907 fire at McGill School of Medicine.

Dr. George W. Campbell was born in 1810 in Roseneath, Dumbartonshire, Scotland, where his father was Factor to the Duke of Argyle, a Justice of the Peace and Deputy-Lieutenant for the County of Dumbarton.

In his early years George Campbell had as his tutor the Reverend Dr. Mathieson,

164 *Réplique du Docteur George W. Campbell*
1913
42-1/2 x 34-1/4 po (108 x 87 cm) (s.v.)
INSCRIPTION: signature, b.g.: *Robert Harris.*
DOCUMENTS HARRIS: «Je me suis entendu avec le docteur Shepherd pour exécuter un portrait du docteur Campbell pour 200 livres sterling. Cadre à être fourni par moi. Il s'est dit autorisé à le faire par la famille du docteur C. d'après les exécuteurs testamentaires de son fils et que cette somme avait été réservée par l'un d'eux et que les exécuteurs lui avaient demandé de faire les arrangements nécessaires, ce qu'il avait accepté. Portrait pour McGill. À suspendre dans le corridor du Medical Hall de la Faculté de médecine.» (Journal de travail de l'artiste, 25 juin 1913).

«Ai livré le portrait encadré le 13 juillet. $968.88 en échange. 10 novembre 1913. Payé par traite au docteur S. endossé pour moi.» (Journal de travail de l'artiste, 11 avril 1913 [sic].)

Ce tableau est une réplique par Harris de son portrait détruit en 1907 lors de l'incendie de l'École de médecine de McGill.

Le docteur George W. Campbell est né à Roseneath (Dumbartonshire, Écosse) en 1810. Son père y était régisseur du duc d'Argyle, juge de paix et lieutenant adjoint du Comté de Dumbarton.

Au cours de ses jeunes années George Campbell eut pour tuteur le révérend

and then, during his undergraduate course at Glasgow University, went on to win the Brisbane Bursary of £50 a year for four years which enabled him to attend the medical classes. Then, having passed one session in Dublin he obtained his doctorate in Medicine from Glasgow University. He was awarded his L.R.C.S. at Edinburgh University in 1832, the same year when he emigrated to Canada.

At the age of twenty-five, Campbell was given the chairs of Surgery and Midwifery at McGill, and was also elected attending physician and surgeon of the Montreal General Hospital. After eighteen years service in the hospital he resigned, though remained active as a consultant. In 1842 he resigned his lectureship in Midwifery at McGill and from then on lectured at the University, teaching his favourite subject, the principles and practice of surgery. During his forty years of active work at McGill, including his eighteen years as attending physician at the Montreal General Hospital, George Campbell had a very large general practice and also served on the boards of management of several public institutions. In 1860, Dr. George W. Campbell, was appointed Dean of the Medical Faculty of McGill University, and held this office with distinction till ill-health forced him to resign in 1875.

MCGILL UNIVERSITY, MONTREAL

Mathieson, puis, durant ses études à l'université de Glasgow, il se vit décerner la bourse Brishame de 50 livres sterling par année pour quatre ans, ce qui lui permit d'étudier la médecine. Par la suite, après un an à Dublin, il obtint son doctorat en médecine de l'université de Glasgow. En 1832, l'année où il émigra au Canada, il reçut son L.R.C.S. de l'université d'Édimbourg.

À vingt-cinq ans, il devint professeur de chirurgie et d'obstétrique à McGill et médecin et chirurgien à l'Hôpital général de Montréal. Après dix-huit années de profession médicale dans cet hôpital, il quitta son poste pour devenir consultant. En 1842, il quitta son poste du département d'obstétrique pour se consacrer davantage à l'enseignement des principes et de la pratique chirurgicales, son sujet favori. Au cours de ses quarante ans à McGill (dont dix-huit alors qu'il occupait également un poste à l'Hôpital général), George Campbell fit beaucoup de pratique générale et fut membre de plusieurs conseils d'administration d'institutions publiques. En 1860, le docteur Campbell fut nommé doyen de la Faculté de médecine de McGill. Il occupa de façon remarquable ce poste jusqu'en 1875, lorsqu'il dut démissionner pour des raison de santé.

UNIVERSITÉ MCGILL, MONTRÉAL

---

165 *Sir Frederick Barker* 1914
46 x 23 in. (116.8 x 58.4 cm)
INSCRIPTION: signed u.r., *Robert Harris –*.

Sir Frederick Barker was born at Sheffield, New Brunswick, in 1838 and educated at the University of New Brunswick, Fredericton. After being called to the Bar in 1861 he practiced law in Saint John and from 1885 to 1887 represented Saint John as a Conservative, in Ottawa. In 1893 he was appointed puisne judge of the Supreme Court of New Brunswick, and Chief Justice in 1908. He died at Saint John in 1915.

BARRISTERS' SOCIETY OF NEW BRUNSWICK

165 *Sir Frederick Barker* 1914
46 x 23 po (116.8 x 58.4 cm)
INSCRIPTION: signature, h.d.: *Robert Harris –*.

Sir Frederick Barker est né à Sheffield (Nouveau-Brunswick) en 1838. Il fit ses études à l'Université du Nouveau-Brunswick de Fredericton. Admis au barreau en 1861, il exerça le droit à Saint-Jean et de 1885 à 1887, il fut député conservateur de Saint-Jean aux Communes. En 1893, il fut nommé juge-conseiller de la Cour suprême du Nouveau-Brunswick, dont il devint juge en chef en 1908. Il mourut à Saint-Jean en 1915.

BARRISTER'S SOCIETY OF NEW BRUNSWICK, FREDERICTON

166 *The Right Reverend Bishop Andrew Hunter Dunn* 1914
30-1/4 x 24-1/4 in. (76.8 x 61.6 cm)
INSCRIPTION: signed u.l., *Robert Harris.*
HARRIS PAPERS: "I went to Quebec the other day. I am painting Bishop Dunn, who has resigned and is going to England next month." (Letter from Harris to his mother, dated 26 October 1914) "The portrait of old Bishop Dunn I have been painting was finished about the time he died on shipboard as he reached England." (Letter from Harris to his mother, dated 3 December 1914)

Andrew Hunter Dunn was born at Saffron Walden, Essex, England in 1839. He received his early education in England and Germany, and graduated from Cambridge in 1866 with an M.A. He was then ordained by the Bishop of London, and served in that diocese for several years, becoming Vicar of All Saints Church, South Acton in 1873.

In 1892 he was elected to the See of Quebec by the Quebec Diocesan Synod, as successor to the Right Reverend James Williams. He came to Canada, and was consecrated Bishop in Christ Church Cathedral, Montreal, on 18 September 1892.

Bishop Dunn served the diocese of Quebec until 1914, when he resigned, and died aboard the H.M.S. *Hesperian* en route to Liverpool, in his seventy-sixth year. He was buried in Benhilton, Sutton Surrey in England.

He was a man of many interests and was much beloved by the members of the clergy and laity alike. He took a great interest in the field of education, notably at Bishop's University, Lennoxville and its school, along with King's Hall, Compton. Bishop Dunn was also a member of the Provincial Board of Education.

The *Quebec Diocesan Gazette*, which still flourishes, was founded by Bishop Dunn in 1894. He was also instrumental in obtaining for the diocese a permanent episcopal residence, "Bishopthorpe," for himself and his successors.

THE CHURCH SOCIETY, DIOCESE OF QUEBEC

166 *Le très révérend évêque Andrew Hunter Dunn* 1914
30-1/4 x 24-1/4 po (76.8 x 61.6 cm)
INSCRIPTION: signature, h.g.: *Robert Harris.*
DOCUMENTS HARRIS: «Je suis allé à Québec l'autre jour. Je suis à peindre le portrait de l'évêque Dunn qui a démissionné et part pour l'Angleterre le mois prochain.» (Lettre de Harris à sa mère, 26 octobre 1914).
«J'ai terminé le portrait du vieil évêque Dunn juste avant qu'il ne meure sur le bateau, comme il atteignait l'Angleterre.» (Lettre de Harris à sa mère, 3 décembre 1914).

Andrew Hunter Dunn est né à Saffron Walden (Essex, Angleterre) en 1839. Il fit ses études en Angleterre et en Allemagne et obtint une maîtrise ès arts de Cambridge en 1886. Il fut alors ordonné par l'évêque de Londres et fit son ministère dans ce diocèse durant plusieurs années avant de se voir confier, en 1873, la paroisse d'All Saints Church, à South Acton.

En 1892, le synode diocésain de Québec l'élut évêque de Québec pour succéder au très révérend James Williams. Il vint au Canada et fut consacré évêque à la Christ Church Cathedral de Montréal, le 18 septembre 1892.

L'évêque Dunn administra le diocèse de Québec jusqu'à sa démission en 1914. Il mourut à bord du *H.M.S. Hesperian*, en route pour Liverpool, à l'âge de soixante-seize ans. Il fut inhumé à Benhilton (Sutton Surrey, Angleterre).

Esprit souple et ouvert, il jouit d'une grande popularité tant auprès des membres du clergé que des laics. Il s'intéressa vivement au domaine de l'enseignement, notamment à la Bishop's University de Lennoxville et à son école, ainsi qu'au King's Hall de Compton. L'évêque Dunn fut également membre du Conseil provincial de l'instruction publique.

En 1894, l'évêque Dunn fonda la *Quebec Diocesan Gazette*, qui existe encore aujourd'hui. C'est en grande partie grâce à ses efforts, d'autre part, que le diocèse obtint une résidence épiscopale permanente, le «*Bishopthorpe*».

THE CHURCH SOCIETY, DIOCESE OF QUEBEC

167 *Charles Hays* 1915
48-1/8 x 39-1/8 in. (122.2 x 99.4 cm)
INSCRIPTION: signed u.r., *Robert Harris.*
HARRIS PAPERS: "Mrs. C. M. Hays. Pine Avenue. To paint portrait of her late husband about 40 x 50. $1,100." (Sitter-book, entry dated January 1915)

Charles Melville Hays, an American by birth, was President of the Grand Trunk Railway. Born in Illinois in 1856 he was educated at the local schools in Rock Island till the age of seventeen, when he entered the service of the Atlantic and Pacific Railway. By 1889 he had been appointed General Manager of the Wabash System and then came to Canada to take up appointment as General Manager of the G.T.R. in 1896. He was also President of the G.T.R. Hays was drowned at sea in the s.s. *Titanic* in 1912.
EXHIBITION: *1915 Montreal Spring Exhibition,* no. 162.
THE NATIONAL GALLERY OF CANADA, OTTAWA (6399)
GIFT OF MRS. LOUISE H. GRIER, MONTREAL, 1956

167 *Charles Hays* 1915
48-1/8 x 39-1/8 po (122.2 x 99.4 cm)
INSCRIPTION: signature, h.d.: *Robert Harris.*
DOCUMENTS HARRIS: «Mme C.M. Hays. Avenue des Pins. Pour peindre le portrait de son défunt mari, environ 40 x 50 po, $1 100.» (Journal de travail de l'artiste, janvier 1915).

Charles Melville Hays, américain de naissance, fut président du Grand Tronc. Né dans l'Illinois en 1856, il fréquenta les écoles locales de Rock Island jusqu'à l'âge de dix-sept ans, puis entra au service de l'Atlantic and Pacific Railway. En 1889, il fut nommé directeur général du réseau de Wabash. Il vint en 1896 au Canada où il devint directeur général du Grand Tronc. Il fut aussi président du Grand Tronc du Pacifique. Charles Hays périt dans le naufrage du *S.S. Titanic* en 1912.
EXPOSITION: *1915 Montréal, Printemps,* n° 162.
GALERIE NATIONALE DU CANADA, OTTAWA (6399)
DON DE MME LOUISE H. GRIER, MONTRÉAL, 1956

168 *Sir Ezekiel McLeod* 1916
44-1/2 x 32 in. (113 x 81.3 cm)
INSCRIPTION: signed l.l., *Robert Harris;* signed and dated on reserve, *Chief Justice Hon. Ezekiel McLeod – N.B./painted by Robert Harris C.N.G.* [sic], *in Montreal, in 1916.*

In April 1916, Robert Harris was commissioned by the Bar Association of New Brunswick to paint Chief Justice McLeod for the Court House at Fredericton.
Born at Cardwell, New Brunswick in 1840, Ezekiel McLeod was educated at Harvard University, obtaining his LL.B. in 1867. The following year he was called to the Bar of New Brunswick, and in 1882, appointed Q.C. He represented Saint John in the Legislative Council between 1882–86 and in the House of Commons, Ottawa from 1891 to 1896. He was Attorney General and appointed puisne judge in 1896, rising to Chief Justice in 1914. He died at Hampton, New Brunswick, in 1920.
BARRISTERS' SOCIETY OF NEW BRUNSWICK

168 *Sir Ezekiel McLeod* 1916
44-1/2 x 32 po (113 x 81.3 cm)
INSCRIPTION: signature, b.g.: *Robert Harris;* inscription (trad.), signature et date, au verso: l'honorable juge en chef *Ezekiel McLeod – N.-B./peint par Robert Harris C.N.G.* [sic], à Montréal, en *1916.*

En avril 1916, le barreau du Nouveau-Brunswick demandait à Robert Harris de peindre le portrait du juge en chef McLeod pour le Palais de justice de Fredericton.
Né à Cardwell (Nouveau-Brunswick) en 1840, Ezekiel McLeod fit ses études à l'université Harvard où il obtint son LL.B. en 1867. L'année suivante, il fut admis au barreau du Nouveau-Brunswick; il fut nommé conseiller de la reine en 1882. De 1882 à 1886, il représenta Saint-Jean au Conseil législatif et de 1891 à 1896 il fut député du même comté aux Communes. Il fut nommé procureur général et juge-conseiller en 1896, puis juge en chef en 1914. Il mourut à Hampton (Nouveau-Brunswick) en 1920.
BARRISTERS' SOCIETY OF NEW BRUNSWICK, FREDERICTON

169 *Self-portrait* 1916
29 x 24 in. (73.7 x 60.9 cm)
INSCRIPTION: signed l.r., *Robert Harris*–.
THE MONTREAL MUSEUM OF FINE ARTS
GIFT OF MRS. ROBERT HARRIS IN MEMORY
OF HER HUSBAND

169 *Autoportrait* 1916
29 x 24 po (73.7 x 60.9 cm)
INSCRIPTION: signature, b.d.: *Robert Harris*–.
MUSÉE DES BEAUX-ARTS DE MONTRÉAL
DON DE MME ROBERT HARRIS À LA
MÉMOIRE DE SON MARI

Chronology

Chronologie

1849	Born in Cydd, Brymn-a-In, Vale of Conway, North Wales, on 17 September.	Naissance de Robert Harris à Cydd (Brymn-a-In, Vale of Conway, Galles du Nord), le 17 septembre.
1856	Emigrated with his family to Charlottetown, P.E.I.	Émigre, avec sa famille, à Charlottetown (Î.-P.-É.).
1863	Completed education at Prince of Wales College, Charlottetown. Worked for Henry Cundall (cat. no. 5), a surveyor.	Termine ses études au Prince of Wales College de Charlottetown. Travaille pour l'arpenteur-géomètre Henry Cundall (nº 5).
1867	First visit to England. Visited Brown's Museum, Liverpool, and London and Wales.	Premier voyage en Angleterre. Se rend à Liverpool, où il visite le Brown's Museum, à Londres et au pays de Galles.
1868	Returned to Charlottetown.	Retour à Charlottetown.
1871	Commissioned to paint speakers of the P.E.I. House of Assembly.	Chargé de peindre les orateurs de la Chambre d'assemblée de l'Île-du-Prince-Édouard.
1872–1873	Moved to Boston after visiting Halifax. Attended the "Anatomical Classes" of W.C. Rimmer (1816–79) and other art courses. Commissioned to do book and newspaper illustrations.	S'installe à Boston, après un séjour à Halifax. Fréquente les «cours d'anatomie» de W.C. Rimmer (1816–1879) ainsi que d'autres cours d'art. Est chargé de faire des illustrations pour des livres et des journaux.
1874	Returned to Charlottetown for rest and treatment of eye condition.	Retour à Charlottetown pour prendre du repos et faire soigner ses yeux.
1876	Second visit to England.	Second voyage en Angleterre.
1877	Enrolled in Slade School, University of London, for one term studying with Alphonse Legros (1837–1911). Copied at the National Gallery and the South Kensington Museum. Moved to Paris and enrolled at the studio (see cat. no. 35) of Léon Bonnat (1834–1923).	S'inscrit à la Slade School de l'université de Londres pour un trimestre où il étudie sous la direction d'Alphonse Legros (1837–1911). Copie des œuvres de la National Gallery et du South Kensington Museum. Gagne Paris où il fréquente l'atelier (voir nº 35) de Léon Bonnat (1834–1923).
1878	Visited London, Liverpool, and Wales before returning to Charlottetown.	Visite Londres, Liverpool et le pays de Galles avant de rentrer à Charlottetown.
1879	Moved to Toronto. Exhibited with the Ontario Society of Artists.	S'installe à Toronto. Fait une exposition avec l'Ontario Society of Artists.
1880	Became Vice-President of the O.S.A. Invited by the Marquess of Lorne (later ninth Duke of Argyll; 1845–1914), Governor General of Canada (1878–83), to accept nomination as an Academician in the newly-formed Royal Canadian Academy of Arts.	Devient vice-président de l'O.S.A. Est invité par le marquis de Lorne (qui deviendra plus tard duc d'Argyll, 1845–1914) alors gouverneur général du Canada, à devenir membre de l'Académie royale des arts du Canada nouvellement créée.

1881	Made illustrations for George Grant's (cat. no. 70) *Picturesque Canada* (published c. 1882) under the supervision of Sir Lucius O'Brien (1832–99). Resigned from O.S.A. and sailed for Paris where he again enrolled in the studio of Bonnat.	Fait des illustrations pour le *Picturesque Canada* (publié vers 1882) de George Grant (n° 70), sous la surveillance de Lucius O'Brien (1832–1899). Quitte son poste de vice-président de l'O.S.A. et retourne à Paris où il s'inscrit de nouveau à l'atelier Bonnat.
1882	Had paintings accepted for the Paris Salon and for an R.C.A. annual exhibition (in Montreal). Spent summer painting in Écouen.	Expose des tableaux au Salon de Paris et à l'exposition de l'A.R.A.C. à Montréal. Passe l'été à peindre à Écouen.
1883	After visiting Florence and Venice, returned to London and took a studio. Had work accepted for an R.A. exhibition. Returned to Canada, visited Ottawa, received commission to paint *The Fathers of Confederation* (see cat. nos. 40–42). Visited Toronto and summered in Charlottetown. Moved to Montreal and took studio. Taught art classes at the Art Association of Montreal. Works exhibited in Liverpool and Manchester.	Se rend à Florence et à Venise et retourne à Londres où il loue un atelier. On accepte une de ses œuvres pour une exposition de la Royal Academy. De retour au Canada, il visite Ottawa et reçoit la commande du portrait des *Pères de la Confédération* (voir les n°s 40–42). Visite Toronto, passe l'été à Charlottetown et gagne Montréal où il loue un atelier. Il donne des cours d'art à l'Art Association of Montreal. Expose à Liverpool et à Manchester.
1884	Delivered final canvas of *The Fathers of Confederation* to Ottawa.	Livre la toile terminée des *Pères de la Confédération* à Ottawa.
1885	Married Elizabeth Putnam (cat. nos. 45), daughter of Mrs. Lester N. Putnam (cat. no. 46), of Montreal. Honeymoon tour of England, Ireland, and Wales, and France, Holland, and Prussia. Took up residence in Montreal. Painted Sir Hugh Allan (cat. no. 44). Began painting *A Meeting of the School Trustees* (cat. no. 48).	Épouse Elizabeth Putman (n° 45), la fille de Mme Lester N. Putnam (n° 46), de Montréal. Voyage de noces en Angleterre, en Irlande, dans le pays de Galles, en France, en Hollande, en Allemagne. S'installe à Montréal. Fait le portrait de Sir Hugh Allan (n° 44). Commence son tableau *Une rencontre des commissaires d'école* (n° 48).
1886	He and Bessie sailed for England. Before settling in London, they lived for a time in Yorkshire, where he painted *Harmony* (cat. no. 50) exhibited that year in Liverpool.	Se rend en Angleterre avec Bessie. Avant de s'installer à Londres, ils restent quelque temps dans le Yorkshire, où il peint *Harmonie* (n° 50) qui sera exposé, la même année, à Liverpool.
1887	Left London in June and went to Paris where he took a studio. He and Bessie returned to Montreal via Charlottetown in September. Took a studio in Montreal.	Quitte Londres en juin et se rend à Paris où il loue un atelier. En septembre, rentre à Montréal avec Bessie, en passant par Charlottetown. Il loue un atelier à Montréal.
1888	Took a studio next to Otto Jacobi (cat. nos. 61, 80) at Fraser Institute. Several major portrait commissions. Summered at Sturgeon Point, Ont.	Loue l'atelier contigu à celui d'Otto Jacobi (n°s 61 et 80) au Fraser Institute. Reçoit plusieurs commandes importantes de portraits. Passe l'été à Sturgeon Point (Ontario).
1890	Refused presidency of R.C.A. Became founding member of the Pen and Pencil Club in Montreal.	Refuse la présidence de l'A.R.A.C. Devient membre fondateur du Pen and Pencil Club de Montréal.
1891	Took studio in new Y.M.C.A. building in Montreal. Summered at Cap à l'Aigle, Quebec, and at the Philosophy Summer Camp at Keene, N.Y.	Ouvre un atelier, à Montréal, dans le nouvel édifice du Y.M.C.A. Passe l'été à Cap-à-l'Aigle (Québec), et au Philosophy Summer Camp à Keene (New York).

1892	Elected President of the Pen and Pencil Club. Painted the well-known *Sands of Dee*.	Élu président du Pen and Pencil Club. Peint *Plage de Dee*.
1893	Elected President of the R.C.A. Awarded medal at the World's Columbian Exposition at Chicago. Summered at Kennebunkport, Maine.	Élu président de l'A.R.A.C. Reçoit une médaille à la *World's Columbian Exposition* de Chicago. Passe l'été à Kennebunkport (Maine).
1895	Commissioned to paint portrait of Lord Aberdeen (see cat. nos. 88, 89). Summered at Percé, Quebec.	Reçoit la commande du portrait de Lord Aberdeen (voir les nos 88 et 89). Passe l'été à Percé (Québec).
1896	Summered with his brother Edward (cat. no. 75) at Mahone Bay, N.S., and in P.E.I.	Passe l'été en compagnie de son frère, Edward (no 75), à Mahone Bay (N.-É.), ainsi qu'à l'Île-du-Prince-Édouard.
1897	Harris's mother (cat. no. 26) died. Began design for painting in her memory for All Souls Chapel, St. Peter's Cathedral, Charlottetown.	Décès de la mère de Harris (no 26). Commence l'ébauche d'un tableau à sa mémoire pour l'All Souls Chapel de St. Peter's Cathedral à Charlottetown.
1898	He and Bessie toured Prussia and Austria and Spain, visiting Munich, Berlin, Vienna, and Madrid. They returned to Montreal in November.	Se rend en Allemagne, en Autriche et en Espagne où il visite, avec Bessie, Munich, Berlin, Vienne et Madrid. Ils rentrent à Montréal en novembre.
1899	Harris's father died.	Décès du père de Harris.
1900	Publication of Try-Davies' *A Semi-Detached House and Other Stories*, illustrated by Harris. Won honorable mention at the Exposition universelle in Paris. Summered at Ogunquit, Maine.	Publication de *A Semi-Detached House and Other Stories* de Try-Davies, illustré par Harris. Reçoit une mention honorable à l'Exposition universelle à Paris. Passe l'été à Ogunquit (Maine).
1901	He and Bessie toured England and Scotland, returning to Montreal in October. Won Gold Medal at Pan-American Exhibition, Buffalo, N.Y.	Se rend en Angleterre et en Écosse avec Bessie. Ils rentrent à Montréal en octobre. Médaille d'or à la *Pan-American Exhibition*, tenue à Buffalo (New York).
1902	Painted Lord Strathcona (cat. no. 128) for Victoria College, Montreal.	Exécute le portrait de Lord Strathcona (no 128) pour le Victoria College de Montréal.
1903	Painted the Countess of Minto (cat. no. 131). He and Bessie once again visited Philosophy Summer Camp.	Fait le portrait de la comtesse de Minto (no 131). Se rend de nouveau, avec Bessie, au Philosophy Summer Camp.
1904	Created C.M.G. – the first Canadian artist to be so honoured. Awarded Gold Medal and Diploma at the Louisiana Purchase exposition in St. Louis.	Devient le premier artiste canadien nommé C.M.G. Médaille d'or et diplôme à la *Louisiana Purchase Exposition* de St. Louis.
1905	Among several portraits painted was that of the Honourable W. Weir (cat. no. 144), Speaker of the Quebec Legislative Assembly.	Peint plusieurs portraits dont celui de William Weir (no 144), orateur de l'Assemblée législative du Québec.
1906	Resided in Munich and then visited Rome, returning to Montreal at the end of the summer.	Habite Munich, puis visite Rome et rentre à Montréal à la fin de l'été.
1907	Summered at East Gloucester, Mass.	Passe l'été à East Gloucester (Massachusetts).

1909	Travelled to British Columbia.	Se rend en Colombie britannique.
1910	Exhibited portrait at an R.A. exhibition.	Expose un portrait à la Royal Academy de Londres.
1911	He and Bessie visited Paris, Berne, and Étaples-sur-Mer, returning to Montreal in November. Commissioned to paint Lemuel Tweedie, Lieutenant Governor of N.B. (cat. no. 163).	Visite, avec Bessie, Paris, Berne et Étaples-sur-Mer. Ils rentrent à Montréal en novembre. Reçoit la commande du portrait de Lemuel Tweedie (nº 163), lieutenant-gouverneur du Nouveau-Brunswick.
1912	Summered in Dalhousie, N.B., and Mahone Bay, N.S.; later visited Lake Placid, N.Y.	Passe l'été à Dalhousie (N.-B.), et à Mahone Bay (N.-É.), puis se rend à Lake Placid (New York).
1913	His brother, William Critchlow Harris, A.R.C.A., died suddenly.	Mort subite de son frère, William Critchlow Harris, A.R.A.C.
1914	Painted portrait of Sir Frederick Barker (cat. no. 165), Chief Justice of N.B., and Andrew Dunn (cat. no. 166), Anglican Bishop of the Diocese of Quebec.	Exécute le portrait de Sir Frederick Barker (nº 165), juge en chef de la Cour suprême du Nouveau-Brunswick, et d'Andrew Hunter Dunn (nº 166), évêque anglican du diocèse de Québec.
1915	Portrait of Lord Strathcona for Royal Victoria Hospital.	Fait le portrait de Lord Strathcona pour l'hôpital Royal Victoria.
1916	His large canvas *The Fathers of Confederation* burned in fire which destroyed the Parliament buildings, Ottawa.	Sa grande toile, *Les pères de la Confédération,* est détruite au cours de l'incendie des édifices du parlement, à Ottawa.
1917	Eyesight gave much trouble. Failing health generally.	Graves troubles de la vue; santé chancelante en général.
1918	Spent second successive summer in cottage at Holland Cove, P.E.I.	Passe un second été consécutif dans un chalet à Holland Cove (Î.-P.-É.).
1919	Died at 11 Durocher Street, Montreal, on 27 February. Buried in the cemetery of St. Peter's Church, Charlottetown, on 3 March.	Meurt chez lui, au 11, rue Durocher, à Montréal, le 27 février. Inhumé au cimetière de la St. Peter's Church de Charlottetown, le 3 mars.

Bibliography

Bibliographie

Documents: The Harris Papers

By the time the Robert Harris Memorial Gallery in Charlottetown was levelled to make way for the Confederation Centre in 1965, the surviving works of Harris had been transferred to one room in the basement of the city's Post Office. Along with these works – some 1,500 of them – went, among other things, several hundred letters, sixty-six as yet unnumbered sketchbooks, and, of course, Harris's sitter-book. The work of exploring, cataloguing, and restoring works of art has taken priority over a similar job of examining, ordering, and transcribing the documentary material – though a start has been recently made in the latter direction with the help of the Canada Council. It was, of course, upon these documents, confused and incomplete though they were, that I based my *Robert Harris 1849–1919: An Unconventional Biography*.

It is now known that the collection of letters alone is by no means complete; several Harris family members still have significant groups of correspondence. In one or two cases, during the writing of this catalogue, I have had to use printed transcriptions of such material. The task of transcription of those documents which are now in the Confederation Art Gallery has been made difficult by the old habit of cross-writing in order to save paper – and by Harris's habit, especially as he grew older, of scribbling anything anywhere with few, if any, indications of date. (Harris's sitter-book is, for example, a general account book, a diary, and a series of memoirs in no particular sequence – in short, a historian's nightmare.)

As far as autograph Harris material is concerned, I have done my best to determine such things as addressees and dates. More exact information, however, must await a more complete collection of material, a more professional examination, and of course an arbitrary system of classification and cross-reference.

Biographical Sources

For general biographical reference, recourse was had – after the standard histories of Canada and such works as Pierre Berton's brilliant *The Great Railway*, Toronto: McClelland and Stewart, 1971, and Peter Quennell's *Victorian Panorama*, London: Batsford, 1937 – to such dictionaries of biography as: *A Cyclopædia of Canadian Biography* (George Maclean Rose ed.), Toronto: Rose Publishing Co., 1888; *A Standard Dictionary of Canadian Biography* (Charles G.D. Roberts and Arthur L. Tunnell eds.),

Documents Harris

Lorsque la Robert Harris Memorial Gallery de Charlottetown fut rasée pour céder la place à la construction du Confederation Centre en 1965, les œuvres subsistantes de Robert Harris occupaient déjà une pièce au sous-sol du bureau de poste municipal. À ces quelque 1 500 œuvres venaient s'ajouter plusieurs centaines de lettres, 66 cahiers de croquis non numérotés et le journal de travail de l'artiste. La tâche de rechercher les œuvres d'art, de les classer et de les restaurer a dû précéder celle d'examiner, de mettre en ordre et de transcrire les documents. Bien que ce travail soit actuellement en voie de réalisation grâce à l'appui reçu du Conseil des arts, ce fut à la lumière de ces documents, aussi désordonnés et incomplets qu'ils étaient à l'époque, que nous avons rédigé notre *Robert Harris, 1849–1919. An Unconventional Biography*.

On sait maintenant que notre collection de lettres de Harris est loin d'être complète et que plusieurs membres de sa famille possèdent une partie importante de sa correspondance. À une ou deux reprises au cours de la rédaction de ce catalogue, nous avons dû recourir à la transcription imprimée de tels documents. L'habitude de Harris, courante à son époque, d'écrire en travers des lignes déjà écrites pour épargner du papier et celle qu'il avait, notamment vers la fin de sa vie, de griffonner un peu partout des notes sans préciser de date, ont rendu la lecture et la transcription des documents de la Confederation Art Gallery and Museum excessivement difficiles. (Pour ne citer qu'un exemple, ce que nous appelons continuellement dans ce catalogue son journal de travail est, en fait, un livre de comptes et un journal intime rempli de détails présentés sans ordre particulier – en un mot, un vrai cauchemar pour le chercheur.)

En ce qui a trait aux documents autographes de Harris, nous avons tenté de préciser, dans la mesure du possible, l'identité du destinataire et la date, par exemple. Pour disposer d'une documentation plus exacte toutefois, nous devrons posséder des documents plus complets qui seront étudiés plus rigoureusement et, évidemment, ordonnés selon un système quelconque de classification et de renvois.

Documents biographiques

Nous avons eu recours, dans nos notes biographiques – en plus des traités d'histoire couramment utilisés et d'ouvrages comme le remarquable *The Great Railway* de Pierre Berton publié chez McClelland and Stewart, Toronto, 1971, et le *Victorian Panorama* de Peter Quennell publié chez Batsford,

Toronto: Trans-Canada Press, 1934; *Dictionary of Canadian Biography* (Marc La Terreur ed.), Toronto: U. of T., 1972; *Chambers Biographical Dictionary* (J.O. Thorne ed.), Edinburgh: W.R. Chambers, 1968; *The Macmillan Dictionary of Canadian Biography* (W. Stewart Wallace ed.), Toronto: Macmillan, 1963; *The Canadian Men and Women of the Time; A Handbook of Canadian Biography of Living Characters* (Henry James Morgan ed.), Toronto: William Briggs, 1912.

Official and unofficial biographies such as the anonymous *Some Pages from an Artist's Life*, Charlottetown: Robert Harris Memorial Gallery, n.d.; Heather Gilbert's *Awakening Continent, The Life of Lord Mount Stephen*, Aberdeen: Aberdeen University Press, 1965; J.W. Lawrence's *The Judges of New Brunswick and their Times*, New Brunswick: 1907 (privately printed); W. Stewart MacNutt's *Days of Lorne*, Fredericton: University of New Brunswick Press, 1945; J.H. MacVicar's *Life and Work of Donald Harvey MacVicar, by his Son*, Toronto: Westminster Co., 1904; John McLennan, *The McLennan Family* (privately circulated, 1926); Moncrieff Williamson's *Robert Harris 1849–1919: An Unconventional Biography*, Toronto: McClelland and Stewart, 1972; and Augustus Bridle's article "Frederic Nicholls: Power Promoter," *The Busy Man's Magazine*, vol. XI, no. 5 (March 1906), pp. 5–15.

Regional and local histories such as Francis W.P. Bolger's *Prince Edward Island and Confederation, 1863–1873*, Charlottetown: St. Dunstan's University Press, 1964; B.F. Bowen's *Past and Present of Prince Edward Island*, Charlottetown: B.F. Bowen and Co., n.d.; Lorne C. Callbeck's *The Cradle of Confederation: a Brief History of Prince Edward Island*, Fredericton: Brunswick Press, 1964; W.L. Cotton's *Chapters in Our Island Story*, Charlottetown: Irwin Printing Co., 1927.

Corporate and institutional histories such as the anonymous *History of the Bank of Nova Scotia, 1832–1900*, Halifax: Bank of Nova Scotia, 1900; E.A. Collard's *Oldest McGill*, Toronto: Macmillan, 1964; Leo Cox's "Fifty Years of Brush and Pen" (a history of the Pen and Pencil Club of Montreal distributed in mimeograph in 1939); H.E. MacDermott's *History of Montreal General Hospital*, Montreal: Montreal General Hospital, 1950; Cyrus Macmillan's *McGill and Its Story 1821–1921*, Toronto: Oxford, 1921.

Selection of Other Works Cited or Consulted

Books such as Alan Gowans's *Looking at Architecture in Canada*, Toronto: Oxford, 1958; M.O. Hammond's *Painting and Sculpture in Canada*, Toronto: Ryerson, 1930; J. Russell Harper's *Painting in Canada; a history*, Toronto: U. of T., 1966 and his *Early Painters and Engravers in Canada*, Toronto: U. of T., 1970; R.H. Hubbard's *An Anthology of Canadian Art*, Toronto: Oxford, 1960 and *The Development of Canadian Art*, Ottawa: Trustees of the National

Londres, 1937 – aux dictionnaires biographiques suivants: *A Cyclopædia of Canadian Biography*. George Maclean Rose, édit., Rose Publishing, Toronto, 1888; *A Standard Dictionary of Canadian Biography*. Charles G. D. Roberts et Arthur L. Tunnell, édit., Trans-Canada Press, Toronto, 1934; *Dictionary of Canadian Biography*. Marc LaTerreur, édit., University of Toronto Press, Toronto, 1972; *Chambers Biographical Dictionary*. J. O. Thorne, édit., W. R. Chambers, Édimbourg, 1968; *The Macmillan Dictionary of Canadian Biography*. W. Stewart Wallace, édit., Macmillan, Toronto, 1963; *The Canadian Men and Women of the Time. A Handbook of Canadian Biography of Living Characters*. Henry James Morgan, édit., William Briggs, Toronto, 1912.

Biographies, officielles ou non: *Some Pages from an Artist's Life*, Robert Harris Memorial Gallery, Charlottetown, s.d.; Heather Gilbert: *Awakening Continent. The Life of Mount Stephen*, Aberdeen University Press, Aberdeen, 1965; J. W. Lawrence: *The Judges of New Brunswick and their Times*. Publié à compte d'auteur au Nouveau-Brunswick en 1907; W. Stewart MacNutt: *Days of Lorne*, University of New Brunswick Press, Fredericton, 1945; J. H. MacVicar: *Life and Work of Donald Harvey MacVicar, by his Son*, Westminster, Toronto, 1904; John McLennan: *The McLennan Family*. Distribué à compte d'auteur, 1926; Moncrieff Williamson: *Robert Harris, 1849–1919. An Unconventional Biography*, McClelland and Stewart, Toronto, 1972; et enfin, un article d'Augustus Bridle: *Frederic Nicholls: Power Promoter*, dans *The Busy Man's Magazine*, t. XI, n° 5 (mars 1906), p. 5–15.

Écrits sur l'histoire régionale et locale: Francis W. P. Bolger: *Prince Edward Island and Confederation, 1863–1873*, St. Dunstan's University Press, Charlottetown, 1964; B. F. Bowen: *Past and Present of Prince Edward Island*, B. F. Bowen, Charlottetown, s.d.; Lorne C. Callbeck: *The Cradle of Confederation: a Brief History of Prince Edward Island*, Brunswick Press, Fredericton, 1964; W. L. Cotton: *Chapters in our Island Story*, Irwin Printing, Charlottetown, 1927.

Écrits sur l'histoire de sociétés ou d'organismes: *History of the Bank of Nova Scotia, 1832–1900*, Bank of Nova Scotia, Halifax, 1900; E. A. Collard: *Oldest McGill*, Macmillan, Toronto, 1964; Leo Cox: *Fifty Years of Brush and Pen*. L'histoire du Pen and Pencil Club de Montréal, document publié par autocopie et distribué en 1939; H. E. MacDermott: *History of Montreal General Hospital*, Hôpital général de Montréal, Montréal, 1950; Cyrus Macmillan: *McGill and its Story, 1821–1921*, Oxford, Toronto, 1921.

Quelques autres ouvrages cités ou consultés

Livres: Alan Gowan: *Looking at Architecture in Canada*, Oxford, Toronto, 1958; M. O. Hammond: *Painting and Sculpture in Canada*, Ryerson, Toronto, 1930; J. Russell Harper: *La peinture au Canada, des origines à nos jours*, University of Toronto

Gallery of Canada, 1963, and Hubbard (ed.), *The National Gallery of Canada Catalogue of Paintings and Sculpture Volume Three: Canadian School*, Ottawa: Queen's Printer, 1960; Reed Kay's *The Painter's Guide to Studio Methods and Materials*, New York: Doubleday, 1972; R.S. Lambert's *The Adventure of Canadian Painting*, Toronto: McClelland and Stewart, 1947; G.C. McInnes's *Canadian Art*, Toronto: Macmillan, 1950; Newton Mac-Tavish's *The Fine Arts in Canada*, Toronto: Macmillan, 1925; and Paul Zucker's *Styles in Painting, A Comparative Study*, New York: Dover, 1963.

Articles such as R.F. Fleming's "The Royal Canadian Academy of Art," *The Yearbook of Canadian Art*, Toronto: Dent, 1913, pp. 205–09; W. Blackburn Harte's "Canadian Art and Artists," *New England Magazine*, vol. II, no. 2 (April 1891), p. 156; [J.G.]'s "Studio Talk: Canada," *The Studio*, vol. XIX, no. 83 (February 1900), p. 69; Frank MacKinnon's "Robert Harris and Canadian Art," *Dalhousie Review*, vol. XXVIII (July 1948), pp. 145–53; H. Mortimer-Lamb's "The Royal Canadian Academy of Arts," *The Studio*, vol. LXX, no. 287 (February 1917), p. 39; Robert M. Percival's "Art Department: The Robert Harris Portrait," [The New Brunswick Museum] *Museum Memo*, vol. 3, no. 1 (March 1971), pp. 4–6; B.K. Sandwell's "Most Famous Canadian Picture and its Painter: Robert Harris, R.C.A., and 'The Fathers of Confederation,' " *Saturday Night* (9 July 1927), p. 5; James Smith's "The Royal Canadian Academy. By its Secretary," *The Canadian Magazine*, vol. IX, no. 4 (August 1897), pp. 300–12; Moncrieff Williamson's "Robert Harris and the Fathers of Confederation," *The National Gallery of Canada Bulletin*, vol. 6, no. 2 (1968), pp. 8–21, and his "Charlottetown's Robert Harris 1849–1919," *artscanada*, Vol. XXIV, Nos. 6 and 7 (Issue No. 109/110; June/July 1967), 3/7.

Press et Presses de l'université Laval, Toronto et Québec, 1966, ainsi que son *Early Painters and Engravers in Canada*, University of Toronto Press, Toronto, 1970; R. H. Hubbard: *An Anthology of Canadian Art*, Oxford, Toronto, 1960, ainsi que *L'évolution de l'art au Canada*, Galerie nationale du Canada, Ottawa, 1963, et *The National Gallery of Canada Catalogue of Painting and Sculpture*, vol. III: *Canadian School*. R. H. Hubbard, édit., Imprimeur de la reine, Ottawa, 1960; Reed Kay: *The Painter's Guide to Studio Methods and Materials*, Doubleday, New York, 1972; R. S. Lambert: *The Adventure of Canadian Painting*, McClelland and Stewart, Toronto 1947; G. C. McInnes: *Canadian Art*, Macmillan, Toronto, 1950; Newton MacTavish: *The Fine Arts in Canada*, Macmillan, Toronto, 1925; Paul Zucker: *Styles in Painting. A comparative Study*, Dover, New York, 1963.

Articles: R.F. Fleming: *The Royal Canadian Academy of Art*, dans *The Yearbook of Canadian Art*, Dent, Toronto, 1913, p. 205–209; W. Blackburn Harte: *Canadian Art and Artists*, dans *New England Magazine*, t. II, no 2 (avril 1891), p. 156; [J.G.]: *Studio Talk: Canada*, dans *The Studio*, t. XIX, no 83 (février 1900), p. 69; Frank MacKinnon: *Robert Harris and Canadian Art*, dans *Dalhousie Review*, t. XXVIII, juillet 1948, p. 145–153; H. Mortimer Lamb: *The Royal Canadian Academy of Arts*, dans *The Studio*, t. LXX, no 287 (février 1917), p. 39; Robert M. Percival: *Art Department: The Robert Harris Portrait*, dans [The New Brunswick] *Museum Memo*, t. 3, no 1 (mars 1971), p. 4–6; B.K. Sandwell: *Most Famous Canadian Picture and its Painter: Robert Harris, R.C.A., and 'The Fathers of Confederation'*, dans *Saturday Night*, 9 juillet 1927, p. 5. James Smith: *The Royal Canadian Academy. By its Secretary*, dans *The Canadian Magazine*, t. IX, no 4 (août 1897), p. 300–312; Moncrieff Williamson: *Robert Harris and The Fathers of Confederation*, dans le *Bulletin*, Galerie nationale du Canada, no 12/1968 (1970), p. 8–21, ainsi que *Charlottetown's Robert Harris, 1848–1919*, dans *artscanada*, t. XXIV, nos 6 et 7 (nos 109/110, juin/juillet 1967), p. 3–7.

Index

Index

Credits

Coordination: Sherrill Moseley
Circulation: Richard Graburn
Framing: Gérald G. Pomainville
Packing: Denis J. DeCoste
Editing of English text: Peter Smith
Editing of French text: André LaRose
Photograph Editor: Alice Armstrong
Publications Production: Arnold Witty
Design: Eiko Emori
Printing: Southam-Murray

Photograph Credits

Colour: Confederation Art Gallery and Museum, Charlottetown: 34, 45; Brian Merrett, Montreal: 49 (cover), 128; The National Gallery of Canada, Ottawa: 50, 51, 112.

Black and white photographs are from the Confederation Art Gallery and Museum, Charlottetown, except as follows: Arnott Rogers Batten, Montreal: 146; The Beaverbrook Art Gallery, Fredericton: 142; Lloyd Bloom, Hamilton: 54, 116, 143; Mrs. R.J. Currie Gardner, Toronto: 120; Harvey Studios, Fredericton: 79, 82, 118, 163, 165, 168; Dr. Charlotte M. Horner, Cobourg: 37; Légaré & Kedl, Québec: 144; Gerry Lemay Studio, Sherbrooke: 114; McCord Museum, Montreal: 74, 105, 117, 121; Brian Merrett, Montreal: 43, 49, 60, 69, 84, 97, 102, 108, 119, 124, 128, 132, 133, 134, 141, 150, 152, 156, 164; The Montreal General Hospital, Montreal: 109, 111, 169; The Montreal Museum of Fine Arts, Montreal: 83, 131, 145; The National Gallery of Canada, Ottawa: 12, 27, 44, 48, 50, 53, 55, 77, 78, 80, 88, 89, 91, 96, 110, 112, 126, 127, 135, 140, 157, 166, 167; The New Brunswick Museum, Saint John: 51; L.E. Robinson, Charlottetown: 40, 41; The Royal Victoria Hospital, Montreal: 101, 153; Victor Sakuta, Kingston: 68, 70, 148, 158; Ron Vickers, Toronto: 24, 67, 81, 162; George Wotton, Charlottetown: 26, 34, 35, 39, 45.

Collaborateurs

Coordination de l'exposition: Sherrill Moseley
Préposé à la circulation: Richard Graburn
Encadrement: Gérald G. Pomainville
Emballage: Denis J. DeCoste
Révision du texte français: André LaRose
Révision du texte anglais: Peter Smith
Contrôle des photographies: Alice Armstrong
Préposé à la production: Arnold Witty
Présentation: Eiko Emori
Impression: Southam-Murray

Provenance des photographies

Photographies en couleurs (renvois aux nos de cat.): Confederation Art Gallery and Museum, Charlottetown: 34 et 45; Galerie nationale du Canada, Ottawa: 50, 51 et 112; Brian Merrett, Montréal: couverture, 49 et 128.

Photographies en noir et blanc (renvois aux nos de cat.): elles proviennent de la Confederation Art Gallery and Museum, Charlottetown, sauf les suivantes: Arnott Rogers Batten, Montréal: 146; The Beaverbrook Art Gallery, Fredericton: 142; Lloyd Bloom, Hamilton: 54, 116 et 143; Galerie nationale du Canada, Ottawa: 12, 27, 44, 48, 50, 53, 55, 77, 78, 80, 88, 89, 91, 96, 110, 112, 126, 127, 135, 140, 157, 166 et 167; Mme R.J. Currie Gardner, Toronto: 120; Gerry Lemay Studio, Sherbrooke: 114; Harvey Studios, Fredericton: 79, 82, 118, 163, 165 et 168; Hôpital général de Montréal, Montréal: 109, 111 et 169; Hôpital Royal Victoria, Montréal: 101 et 153; Dr Charlotte M. Horner, Cobourg: 37; Légaré & Kedl, Québec: 144; Brian Merrett, Montréal: 43, 49, 60, 69, 84, 97, 102, 108, 119, 124, 128, 132, 133, 134, 141, 150, 152, 156 et 164; Musée des beaux-arts de Montréal, Montréal: 83, 131 et 145; Musée McCord, Montréal: 74, 105, 117 et 121; The New Brunswick Museum, Saint-Jean: 51; L.E. Robinson, Charlottetown: 40 et 41; Victor Sakuta, Kingston: 68, 70, 148 et 158; Ron Vickers, Toronto: 24, 67, 81 et 162; George Wotton, Charlottetown: 26, 34, 35, 39 et 45.